IMPORTANT:

HERE IS YOUR REGISTRATION CODE TO ACCESS
YOUR PREMIUM McGRAW-HILL ONLINE RESOURCES.

For key premium online resources you need THIS CODE to gain access. Once the code is entered, you will be able to use the Web resources for the length of your course.

If your course is using **WebCT** or **Blackboard**, you'll be able to use this code to access the McGraw-Hill content within your instructor's online course.

Access is provided if you have purchased a new book. If the registration code is missing from this book, the registration screen on our Website, and within your WebCT or Blackboard course, will tell you how to obtain your new code.

Registering for McGraw-Hill Online Resources

REGISTRATION CODE

25gjy-7ybc-sce2-6shc

TO gain access to your McGraw-Hill web resources simply follow the steps below:

1. USE YOUR WEB BROWSER TO GO TO: **http://register.dushkin.com**
2. CLICK ON **FIRST TIME USER**.
3. ENTER THE REGISTRATION CODE* PRINTED ON THE TEAR-OFF BOOKMARK ON THE RIGHT.
4. AFTER YOU HAVE ENTERED YOUR REGISTRATION CODE, CLICK **REGISTER**.
5. FOLLOW THE INSTRUCTIONS TO SET-UP YOUR PERSONAL UserID AND PASSWORD.
6. WRITE YOUR UserID AND PASSWORD DOWN FOR FUTURE REFERENCE. KEEP IT IN A SAFE PLACE.

TO GAIN ACCESS to the McGraw-Hill content in your instructor's **WebCT** or **Blackboard** course simply log in to the course with the UserID and Password provided by your instructor. Enter the registration code exactly as it appears in the box to the right when prompted by the system. You will only need to use the code the first time you click on McGraw-Hill content.

Thank you, and welcome to your McGraw-Hill online Resources!

Mc Graw Hill Higher Education

0-07-297405-2 T/A SMITH: INCLUSIVE AND SPECIAL RECREATION, 5/E

INCLUSIVE AND SPECIAL RECREATION

Fifth Edition

INCLUSIVE AND SPECIAL RECREATION

Opportunities for Persons with Disabilities

Ralph W. Smith
The Pennsylvania State University

David R. Austin
Indiana University

Dan W. Kennedy
The Pennsylvania State University

Youngkhill Lee
Indiana University

Peggy Hutchison
Brock University

Boston   Burr Ridge, IL   Dubuque, IA   Madison, WI   New York   San Francisco   St. Louis
Bangkok   Bogotá   Caracas   Kuala Lumpur   Lisbon   London   Madrid   Mexico City
Milan   Montreal   New Delhi   Santiago   Seoul   Singapore   Sydney   Taipei   Toronto

Higher Education

INCLUSIVE AND SPECIAL RECREATION: OPPORTUNITIES FOR PERSONS WITH DISABILITIES

Published by McGraw-Hill, a business unit of The McGraw-Hill Companies, Inc., 1221 Avenue of the Americas, New York, NY, 10020. Copyright © 2005, 2001, 1998, 1994, 1989, 1985, 1981, 1977, 1973, 1969, 1965, 1961, 1956, 1951, 1948, by The McGraw-Hill Companies, Inc. All rights reserved. No part of this publication may be reproduced or distributed in any form or by any means, or stored in a database or retrieval system, without the prior written consent of The McGraw-Hill Companies, Inc., including, but not limited to, in any network or other electronic storage or transmission, or broadcast for distance learning.

Some ancillaries, including electronic and print components, may not be available to customers outside the United States.

This book is printed on acid-free paper.

1 2 3 4 5 6 7 8 9 0 FGR/FGR 0 9 8 7 6 5 4

ISBN   0 07 284387 X

Publisher: *Nicholas Barrett*
Sponsoring editor: *Nicholas Barrett*
Director of development: *Kate Engelberg*
Developmental editor: *Melissa Mashburn*
Senior marketing manager: *Pamela S. Cooper*
Media producer: *Lance Gerhart*
Project manager: *Jean R. Starr*
Senior production supervisor: *Carol A. Bielski*
Designer: *Marianna Kingakis*
Media project manager: *Kathleen Boylan*
Manager, Photo research: *Brian Pecko*
Cover image: *© Corbis*
Typeface: *10/12 Times Roman*
Compositor: *Interactive Composition Corporation*
Printer: *Quebecor World Fairfield Inc.*

Library of Congress Cataloging-in-Publication Data

Inclusive and special recreation : opportunities for persons with disabilities / Ralph W.
    Smith . . . [et al.]. — 5th ed.
        p. cm.
    Rev. ed. of: Inclusive and special recreation / Ralph W. Smith, David R. Austin, Dan W.
    Kennedy. 4th ed. c2001.
    Includes bibliographical references and index.
    ISBN 0–07–284387–X (alk. paper)
        1. People with disabilities—Recreation—United States.   2. People with disabilities—
    Recreation—United States—Planning.   3. Recreation—Law and legislation—United States.
    4. Inclusive education—United States. I. Smith, Ralph W. II. Smith, Ralph W. Inclusive and
    special recreation.
    GV183.5.S55 2005
    790.1'96—dc22   2004049359

www.mhhe.com

*This book is dedicated
to the ones we love.*

CONTENT OVERVIEW

PART

I   Introduction and Overview 2

1 Introduction to Inclusive and Special Recreation 4

2 Concepts and Attitudes Underlying Inclusive and Special Recreation Services 19

3 Legislation Affecting Recreation Services 37

4 Disabling Conditions 54

PART

II   Service and Facility Planning 74

5 Barriers to Recreation Participation 76

6 Design of Accessible and Usable Recreation Environments 96

7 The Planning Process 129

8 Selective Examples of Community Services 159

PART

III   Inclusive and Special Recreation Program Areas 178

9 Camping and Wilderness-Adventure Experiences 180

10 The Arts—for Everyone 199

11 Competitive Sports 223

PART

IV   Resources and Trends 250

12 Community Resources 252

13 Trends in Inclusive Recreation 270

Appendices 292

Index I1

CONTENTS

Preface xii

PART

I   Introduction and Overview 2

1 Introduction to Inclusive and Special Recreation 4

Why the Past Lack of Leisure Services for People with Disabilities? 5
A New Beginning: The ADA 7
What Is the Relationship of Therapeutic Recreation to Special Recreation? 10
Leadership with Persons Who Have Disabilities 12
Summary 16
Suggested Learning Activities 16
References 16

2 Concepts and Attitudes Underlying Inclusive and Special Recreation Services 19

Terms 20
Attitudes 26
The Theory of Planned Behavior 31
Changing Attitudes toward Serving Persons with Disabilities 32
Summary 34
Suggested Learning Activities 34
References 34

3 Legislation Affecting Recreation Services 37

Hopes and Limitations of Legislation 38
American Legislation 39
Canadian Legislation 49
Summary 50
Suggested Learning Activities 51
Sources of ADA Information 51
References 52

4 Disabling Conditions 54

Labeling 55
Conditions and Characteristics 57
Summary 71
Suggested Learning Activities 72
References 72

PART

II   Service and Facility Planning 74

5 Barriers to Recreation Participation 76

Types of Barriers 77
Overcoming Barriers 88
Summary 92
Suggested Learning Activities 92
References 93

6   **Design of Accessible and Usable Recreation Environments 96**

Terminology 97
The Expanding Role of Assistive
    Technology 97
Legislation 98
General Guidelines for Planning Recreation
    Facilities 98
Parks and Outdoor Recreation Areas 100
Water-Related Areas and Playfields 106
Playfields with Seating Areas 107
Recreation Buildings 108
Playgrounds 112
Applying Universal Design for the
    Optimal Recreation Environment 124
Summary 126
Suggested Learning Activities 126
References 127

7   **The Planning Process 129**

Needs Assessment 131
Planning Mandates, Policies, Goals,
    and Objectives 133
Implementation 135
Evaluation 144
Summary 152
Suggested Learning Activities 152
Sources of Information 153
References 153

8   **Selective Examples of Community Services 159**

Cincinnati Recreation Commission, Division
    of Therapeutic Recreation 160
City of Miami Department of Recreation,
    Programs for Persons with
    Disabilities 161
Northern Suburban Special Recreation
    Association Cooperative of the
    Park Districts 163
RCH, Inc., San Francisco, California 164
Active Living Alliance for Canadians
    with a Disability 166

Reach for the Rainbow 167
Recreation Integration Victoria 168
Individualized Funding and Brokerage:
    Imperial Counties Self-Determination
    Project, San Diego, California, and
    Vela Microboard Association, British
    Columbia 171
Summary 174
Suggested Learning Activities 175
References 175

PART

III   Inclusive and Special Recreation Program Areas 178

9   **Camping and Wilderness-Adventure Experiences 180**

Camping and People with Disabilities 181
Wilderness-Adventure Programs 189
Summary 195
Suggested Learning Activities 196
References 196

10   **The Arts—for Everyone 199**

What Constitutes "The Arts"? 200
Benefits of Arts Participation 201
The Arts and Disability Culture 207
Leadership in the Arts 209
Arts Participation—Examples 210
Summary 220
Suggested Learning Activities 220
References 221

11   **Competitive Sports 223**

Sports for Persons with Disabilities 224
Wheelchair Sports 230
Special Olympics 237
Barrie Integrated Baseball Association
    (Barrie, Ontario, Canada) 242
Bocce 244

Summary 246
Suggested Learning Activities 246
References 247

P A R T

IV   Resources and Trends 250

12 Community Resources 252

The Importance of Community
    Resources 253
Human Resources 253
Informational Resources 258
Financial Resources 259
Facility and Equipment Resources 261
Transportation Resources 264
Knowing the Community 264
Summary 267
Suggested Learning Activities 267
References 268

13 Trends in Inclusive Recreation 270

Program Trends 271
Approaches to Programs and Services 277
Approaches to Including Persons
    with Disabilities 279
Trends in Community Relations 283
Financial Trends 285
Professional Trends 286
Summary 288
Suggested Learning Activities 289
References 289

Appendices

*Appendix A   Selected Organizations Concerning
    Persons with Disabilities 292*

*Appendix B   Athletic and Recreation
    Organizations for Persons with
    Disabilities 295*

Index I1

PREFACE

Inclusion of persons with disabilities into all aspects of community life is becoming a reality throughout North America. In response to this societal change, recreation providers must offer programs and services that meet the needs of all consumers. The fifth edition of this textbook updates and expands our ongoing effort to help recreation personnel design and implement programs that provide optimal inclusion for persons with disabilities.

It is important to note that this textbook was written primarily for undergraduate students, especially those in their first two years of study. As such, it is appropriate for use in community or junior college courses, as well as within four-year baccalaureate programs. Throughout the preparation of this textbook, we have kept the needs, interests, and learning styles of undergraduate students foremost in our minds. Our goal has been to write in a style that is as appealing to undergraduate students as it is informative.

As with previous editions of this textbook, the fifth edition reflects the coordination of a team of specialists. Dr. Smith had primary responsibility for Chapters 4, 5, 9, 10, and 11. Drs. Austin and Lee were responsible for Chapters 1, 2, 6, 12, and 13; and Drs. Kennedy and Hutchison focused their attention on updating and revising Chapters 3, 7, and 8. Dr. Smith was responsible for the logistical coordination of the text and selected the photos for this edition.

ORGANIZATION OF THE FIFTH EDITION

The textbook is organized into four distinct parts and each part begins with a brief introduction. Part I, "Introduction and Overview," emphasizes the scope of inclusive and special recreation services and introduces students to important concepts and terminology. Part I also includes information on relevant legislation in the United States and Canada and provides useful facts and techniques related to selected disabling conditions. Part II, "Service and Facility Planning," focuses on planning services, program planning, and implementation. This section also includes detailed descriptions of exemplary inclusive and special recreation programs. Part III, "Inclusive and Special Recreation Program Areas," offers examples of program areas (or activities) that have proven effective in meeting the recreational needs of people with disabilities. The final section, Part IV, "Resources and Trends," provides valuable information on community resources related to inclusive and special recreation services. This section also outlines current trends in inclusive recreation. Two appendices conclude the text. Appendix A includes detailed contact information for a host of organizations concerned with people with disabilities. Appendix B lists the contact information for athletic and recreational organizations for persons with disabilities.

FEATURES OF THE FIFTH EDITION

The text maintains a strong research base as well as a practical usefulness. Key updates in the fifth edition include:

- Expanded coverage of inclusive and special recreation efforts in Canada. New and updated material includes information regarding Canadian legislation, exemplary programs, resources, and trends.
- Detailed coverage of the WHO ICF/ICIDH-2 classification system in Chapter 2, "Concepts and Attitudes Underlying Inclusive and Special Recreation Services."
- New sections on ADHD and Autism Spectrum Disorder in Chapter 4, "Disabling Conditions."
- A detailed discussion of Universal Design in a new section in Chapter 6, "Design of Accessible and Usable Recreation Environments," titled Applying Universal Design for the Optimal Recreation Environment.
- A broadened emphasis in Chapter 7, "The Planning Process," that encompasses planning services.
- The addition of more inclusive recreation program cases in Chapter 8, "Selective Examples of Community Services," as well as more inclusive recreation material throughout the text to place more emphasis on inclusion.
- New and updated discussions of actual recreation programs throughout Part III.
- New coverage of inclusive volunteering and expanded coverage of the importance of volunteerism to inclusive and special recreation programs in Chapter 12, "Community Resources." Chapter 12 also contains expanded coverage of fund-raising, including detailed information on grant writing.
- 2003 survey data regarding trends in inclusive recreation programs in Chapter 13, "Trends in Inclusive Recreation," which also includes new information on recent inclusive recreation advocacy efforts in the United States and Canada.

PEDAGOGY AND SUPPLEMENTS

To maximize its usefulness to students and instructors, *Inclusive and Special Recreation* provides these learning aids in every chapter:

- A chapter Summary reviews major chapter topics.
- Suggested Learning Activities provide students with relevant projects and activities—some of them Web-based—that foster independent learning. Instructors may choose to assign these projects to students singly or in groups.
- Illustrative material includes boxes, figures, tables, and photographs that enhance student interest and deepen their understanding of the material.
- Chapter References provide up-to-date resources for instructors and students alike.

A NEW text website (www.mhhe.com/Smith 5e) includes a host of useful resources. Every new copy of the text also contains a passcard that allows access to PowerWeb: Health and Human Performance. This password-protected website contains numerous articles relevant to inclusive recreation, as well as weekly updates and a daily news feed.

ACKNOWLEDGMENTS

We would like to express our sincere gratitude to the many people who have assisted in the preparation of all editions of this textbook. The reactions, insights, suggestions, and efforts of the following people were instrumental in the completion and revision of this book: Patricia Ardovino, University of Wisconsin—La Crosse; David Beaver, Challenge Publications; Robert Beland, University of Florida; Ray Bloomer, National Center for Accessibility; Boni Boswell, East Carolina University; Erin Broadbent, National Park Service; Barbara (Sam) Browne, formerly with the Cincinnati Recreation Commission; Tammy Buckley, The Pennsylvania State University; Josie Byzek and

Patti Fitzpatrick, *New Mobility Magazine;* Mary Cece and Lois Gill, formerly with the University of Maryland; John Chambers, City of Las Vegas, Parks and Leisure Activities; Ann Cody, formerly of *VSA arts;* Peg Connolly, formerly of National Council for Therapeutic Recreation Certification; Cliff Crase, Paralyzed Veterans of America; Michael Crawford, University of Nebraska Medical Center; Mary Crooks and Dorothy Lougee, Parks and Recreation Department, Lincoln, Nebraska; Susan Drenkhahn, Carmel Community, Inc., Chandler, Arizona; Rikki Epstein, formerly of National Recreation and Park Association; Jeanne (Hap) Feeley, formerly of the Pennsylvania Easter Seal Society; Colleen Fitzgerald, Boulder Parks and Recreation; Julie Forker, Maryland-National Capital Park and Planning Commission; Catherine Fowler, mother of Claudia Fowler; Deb Getz, Indiana University; Arnold Grossman, New York University; Alex Gieser, formerly of The League, Baltimore, Maryland; Gene Hayes, University of Tennessee at Knoxville; James Herbert, The Pennsylvania State University; Helen Jo Hillman, formerly with the District of Columbia Department of Recreation; Wendy Ireland, Active Living Alliance for Canadians with a Disability; Jerry D. Kelley, International Alliance on Disability, Washington, D.C.; Michael Kendrick, Kendrick Consulting Services, Holyoke, Massachusetts; Terry Kinney, formerly of Temple University; C. Wayne Korinek, Parks, Recreation, and Library Department, Phoenix; Robin Kunstler, Lehman College, New York; Stan Labanowich, University of Kentucky; Greg Lais, Wilderness Inquiry; Steve LeConey, Cincinnati Recreation Commission; John Lord, John Lord Consulting, Kitchener, Ontario; Michal Ann Lord, Texas Recreation and Parks Society; David Morgan Lovis, Theatre Unlimited; Leo McAvoy, University of Minnesota; John McGovern and Darla Kuhs, Northern Suburban Special Recreation Association, Northfield, Illinois; Thomas McPike, Champaign (Illinois) Park District; Brett Millar, Barrie & District Association for People with Special Needs, Ontario; Anna Miller and Glori Steifler, formerly of The League, Baltimore; Valerie Miller, *Sports 'n Spokes* magazine; Bob Myers, formerly with the Montgomery County Health Department, Silver Spring, Maryland; Michael Naugle, Baltimore City Bureau of Recreation; Jed Nitzberg, The Hospital for Sick Children, Washington, D.C.; Sharon Norcio and Billie Wilson, Montgomery County Department of Recreation; Doug Nutting, Recreation Integration Victoria, Canada; David Park, National Park Service; Alison Pedlar, University of Waterloo; Lou Powell, University of New Hampshire; Lawrence Reiner, Northeast DuPage Special Recreation Association, Elmhurst, Illinois; Gary Robb, Bradford Woods, Indiana; Don Rogers, Indiana State University; Lyn Rourke, Courage Center, Golden Valley, Minnesota; Stuart Schleien, University of North Carolina at Greensboro; Jill Schoeniger, Pennsylvania Special Olympics; Tom Songster, Special Olympics, Inc.; Anne-Marie Spencer, GameTime®; Marcia Spevak, Department of Leisure Services, City of Miami; Carla Tabourne, University of Minnesota; Tanya Travers of *VSA arts*; Byron Welker, Hamilton Center, Indianapolis, Indiana; Christine Wilkinson, Georgian College; and many students from Indiana University, The Pennsylvania State University, Brock University, and the University of Maryland.

Special thanks are extended to our families for their understanding and support throughout the preparation and revision of this textbook. We sincerely hope that the finished product is worthy of the many sacrifices.

Ralph W. Smith
David R. Austin
Dan W. Kennedy
Youngkhill Lee
Peggy Hutchison

INCLUSIVE AND SPECIAL RECREATION

PART

I

Introduction and Overview

(Courtesy of *Sports 'n Spokes*/Paralyzed Veterans of America)

The public recreation and parks profession has long prided itself on its ability to contribute to the well-being and quality of life of the citizenry. Yet, as problems of persons with disabilities have become increasingly more visible in society, it has become apparent that this profession has had only a tenuous grasp on the nature of problems that citizens with disabilities face during their leisure and on the need for the full inclusion of persons with disabilities by leisure service providers. Fortunately, there is a vital movement among leisure service providers to establish services that meet the recreational needs of persons who have disabilities. The Americans with Disabilities Act has provided stimulus for this movement.

Although the provision of recreation services for persons with disabilities is a comparatively new area of interest for public recreation and parks, one can see origins of concern for people with special needs dating back to the beginnings of organized recreation in America. Chapter 1, Introduction to Inclusive and Special Recreation, reviews the historical and philosophical bases for the provision of leisure services for individuals with disabilities. Views of authorities such as Bullock, Carter, Kelley, Meyer, Robb, and Stein and Sessoms are presented, and conclusions are drawn that suggest that a harmonious arrangement for the cooperation of general leisure service professionals and therapeutic recreation specialists can become a reality.

Chapter 2, Concepts and Attitudes Underlying Inclusive and Special Recreation Services, presents concepts and attitudes basic to understanding the delivery of services for persons with disabilities. Concepts surrounding the terms *disability, handicap, special populations, special recreation, inclusive recreation, mainstreaming,* and *normalization* are discussed. Chapter 2 concludes with an in-depth approach to attitudes as they relate to serving persons with disabilities. A major segment of the section on attitudes is devoted to alternatives proposed by the National Easter Seal Society and Dattilo and Smith to avoid stigmatized language when referring to individuals with disabilities.

Chapter 3, Legislation Affecting Recreation Services, reviews legislation pertaining to equal access to educational and recreation services for those with disabilities. Particular attention is given to the Americans with Disabilities Act.

Although it is critical that we avoid the trap of labeling those with disabilities, we may find information concerning various disabling conditions to be useful. Chapter 4, Disabling Conditions, begins with a discussion of the potential pitfalls and hazards involved in labeling people who have disabilities. This is followed by helpful facts, tips, and techniques associated with specific types of disabilities.

1 INTRODUCTION TO INCLUSIVE AND SPECIAL RECREATION

(Courtesy of Courage Center, Golden Valley, MN)

Organized recreation in North America grew out of social concern for persons attempting to cope with a rapidly changing world created by the Industrial Revolution. Most authorities cite the establishment of a sand play area for disadvantaged children in Boston in 1885 as the beginning of the recreation movement in America. This play area became known as the Boston Sand Gardens. The provision of wholesome recreation was also a central part of the settlement-house movement established to ease the transition to urban living for thousands of persons immigrating to the cities of America during the Industrial Revolution. Settlement houses, such as Jane Addams's Hull House in Chicago, provided playgrounds for children and recreational opportunities for adults to help them adapt to an urban life characterized by overcrowding and poor living conditions.

The beginnings of organized recreation thus evolved from a humanistic concern for the welfare of those who found themselves with few resources in inhospitable circumstances. Wholesome recreation was viewed as necessary for those disadvantaged individuals who had special needs.

As community recreation grew, it began to lose its focus on meeting the needs of those who were disadvantaged. More affluent sections of cities began to demand and receive community recreation services. Community recreation steadily moved away from its historical roots of serving the disadvantaged to the cause of "recreation for all." Recreation began to be perceived not as a social instrument but as an end in itself, an experience all should enjoy.

Gray (1969), in a classic article titled "The Case for Compensatory Recreation," has written: "Gradually the social welfare mission weakened and a philosophy which sees recreation as an end in itself was adopted; this is the common view in public recreation agencies throughout the country" (p. 23).

In a similar vein, Sessoms and Stevenson (1981) have written that

> Adult education, recreation, and social group work all have a common heritage. Each is a product of the social welfare reforms that occurred in our cities and industries at the turn of the nineteenth century. Their founders shared a similar belief—they were concerned with the quality of life and believed that through the "proper" use of leisure, it could be achieved. (p. 2)

Like Gray, Sessoms and Stevenson (1981) observed that the organized parks and recreation movement has deviated from its original mission. They added,

> With both adult education and social work establishing their turf, recreation services did the same. Although some recreation specialists were concerned with the therapeutic or socially rehabilitative activities or with teaching and developing leisure skills and attitudes, the recreation profession set as its primary concerns the management of recreational environments and the offering of free-time activities. Outdoor recreation and sports programs became its program focus. (pp. 2, 3)

Although having its roots in socially purposeful programs for disadvantaged individuals, the recreation profession appears to have moved away from its initial focus. As community recreation has grown, it has broadened its scope to "recreation for all." However, as Carter and Kelley (1981) have suggested, the idea of recreation for all may have in reality become "recreation for the norm." As community recreation and parks departments have attempted to spread their resources to meet everyone's recreational needs, concern for people who have been socially disadvantaged by society has been lost as a central feature of public recreation and parks.

WHY THE PAST LACK OF LEISURE SERVICES FOR PEOPLE WITH DISABILITIES?

As might be anticipated, there have been pleas for a return to an extensive concern for leisure services to people who have been underserved. For example, early in the 1970s, Kraus (1971) wrote of the need for recreation and parks administrators to take leadership for socially purposeful programs, including those to serve elderly individuals and persons with physical and mental disabilities. From another perspective, in 1980 the International City Management Association in its publication *Managing Municipal Leisure Services* (Lutzin, 1980) called for the development of leisure services for people who have been disadvantaged. More recently, concerned leaders such as Anderson and Brown (1996); Anderson and Kress (2003); Bullock and Mahon (2000); Dattilo (2002); Schleien, Ray, and Green (1997); and others have emphasized the need for providing services that offer the greatest possible amount of physical and social integration of persons with disabilities.

Yet even today we find that persons with physical or mental disabilities often have been underserved by community public recreation and parks departments. Why is this? Why have many departments that owe their existence to the social welfare motive failed to respond to the needs of people with disabilities?

Perhaps the lack of services for people with disabilities has reflected the history of neglect of society in general for those who have not fit society's norms. During the first half of the 20th century, we systematically excluded indigent people and persons with physical or mental disabilities from community participation. Indigent old people were sent to "old folks homes" or "county poor farms." Individuals with mental retardation were placed in large institutions located in rural areas. Likewise, individuals with serious problems in mental health were taken away to "insane asylums." In short, those who deviated from society's norms were effectively removed from the mainstream of society. In light of this, it is not surprising that, as the recreation movement expanded across the United States and Canada, it lost its dedication to individuals from underserved groups.

Pragmatic Reasons for Lack of Service

Surveys of public recreation and parks departments have revealed several reasons for the past absence of services for people with disabilities. These reasons included insufficient budgets, lack of accessible facilities, lack of skills and knowledge necessary to establish a program, lack of adaptive equipment, lack of accessible community transportation, poor attitudes on the part of staff, community resistance, and a lack of awareness of the need for programs for people with disabilities (Austin, Peterson, & Peccarelli, 1978; Devine, 1998).

Probably the greatest blocks to services historically were the reported lack of awareness of the need for these programs and the perception that other agencies already provided such programs. These rationalizations allowed administrators of recreation and parks systems to entirely remove themselves from the responsibility of providing recreation for persons with disabilities. Perhaps the broadening of the concept of *therapeutic recreation,* discussed in the next section, prompted administrators to feel less responsible for the provision of recreation for people with disabilities.

A Broadening Concept of Therapeutic Recreation

In the United States during the 1940s and 1950s, there developed recreation services within hospitals and institutions serving persons with various physical and mental disabilities. In some instances, those who provided these services were known as "hospital recreation workers." They identified themselves primarily with the Hospital Recreation Section of the American Recreation Society. Their approach was that of "recreation for the sake of recreation." They believed that recreation existed within their hospitals to promote the general well-being of the patients. Another segment employed in hospitals and institutions identified themselves as "recreation therapists." They formed the National Association of Recreational Therapists. To them, recreation was more than a wholesome activity; it was a tool for treatment and rehabilitation.

These two contrasting groups joined in the 1960s under the banner of a then relatively new term, *therapeutic recreation*. Therapeutic recreation was used as an umbrella term to encompass the perspectives of both the American Recreation Society and the National Association of Recreational Therapists. Ultimately, therapeutic recreation came to be broadly interpreted as including any recreational service to individuals with mental or physical disabilities, in either the hospital or the community, whether for the purpose of providing treatment or for a recreative experience.

Carter and Kelley (1981) have made a persuasive case that the broadening of the concept of therapeutic recreation led to difficulty in establishing community-based recreation services for persons with disabilities. They have written,

> This expanded concept of therapeutic recreation that included community services has had two major consequences for disabled adults and children, consequences that are not necessarily regarded as positive. First, because most disabled and impaired individuals are now living in a noninstitutional setting or are in the process of being mainstreamed back into community life, they do not need, nor do they have any desire to have, "therapy." Furthermore, they have no wish to carry the stigma of being recipients of "therapeutic" recreation services. Therefore, the broadened service delivery perspective that has maintained a "treatment" image runs counter to the desires of many disabled adults and young people to seek a "normal" range of experiences like their nondisabled peers.
>
> Secondly, the therapeutic recreation field claims to be the primary professional group delegated the exclusive responsibility to serve disabled populations. The longer this image is promoted, the more difficult it becomes to convince the community recreation specialist that he must assume responsibility to provide recreation to all persons in his community regardless of the extent of their disabilities. (pp. 64, 65)

Carter and Kelley's points seem to be well-founded. Most persons with disabilities who live in the community do not require the therapy usually associated with therapeutic recreation, nor do they

wish to be stigmatized as being recipients of therapeutic recreation services. Like other citizens, the vast majority of people with disabilities and their families simply want the opportunity to take part in recreation experiences.

The twin concepts of mainstreaming and normalization call for helping people who have disabilities to take part in the mainstream of society within the most normative and least restrictive environment possible (Pedlar, 1990; Pedlar & Gilbert, 1997). Most persons in our society are not served by therapeutic recreation specialists but by community recreation personnel. It is, then, the responsibility of community recreation professionals to provide recreation services for those who have disabilities. Carter and Kelley feel that only when the therapeutic recreation profession steps aside and acknowledges that community recreation for persons with disabilities is the domain of public recreation and parks departments will the full responsibility be borne by those who have the obligation to meet the recreational needs of our citizens. It seems possible that by claiming to be primarily responsible for the entire spectrum of recreation for people with disabilities, therapeutic recreation specialists may in the past have allowed community recreation systems to relinquish their rightful duty to serve these individuals. Times, however, are changing. Federal legislation mandates that access to community recreation services must be offered to people who have disabilities.

A New Beginning: The ADA

With the passage of Public Law 101-336, the Americans with Disabilities Act (ADA), on July 26, 1990, the United States officially recognized the rights of people with disabilities to equal access to all services provided by local, state, and federal government, including recreational services. The ADA allows full and equal access by persons with disabilities to any place of public accommodation, governmental or private. Private recreation entities include restaurants, bars, theaters, stadiums, auditoriums, convention centers, museums, libraries, parks, amusement parks, zoos,

People with disabilities enjoy the same recreation activities as most other people in their communities.
(Courtesy of *Sports 'n Spokes*/Paralyzed Veterans of America)

TABLE 1.1	ADA Applies to:

- Public funded services (i.e., local, county, state, federal)
- Not-for-profit agencies (e.g., Easter Seals, Girl Scouts, YMCAs, camps)
- Private for-profit enterprises (e.g., theaters, amusement parks, bowling lanes)

Source: Anderson, L., & C.B. Kress. *Inclusion: Including People with Disabilities in Parks and Recreation Opportunities*. State College, PA: Venture Publishing, 2003.

golf courses, gymnasiums, or other places of recreation (*Federal Register,* 1991; Wehman, 1993). Thus, with the advent of the ADA, full accommodation for persons with disabilities is mandated by law. The ADA provides broad civil rights protections and equality of opportunity for Americans with disabilities in all aspects of their lives, including recreation.

While a number of recreation and leisure service providers in the United States recognized their moral obligation to serve persons with dis-

abilities prior to PL 101-336, many more did not. In this regard, it would probably be conceded that Canadians have been ahead of their American counterparts. The ADA marked a beginning for America—a beginning that included opportunity for full recreation participation for Americans with disabilities.

Because the ADA mandates the elimination of discrimination against people with disabilities in recreation, the nation's consciousness has begun to be altered, resulting in several particularly interesting outcomes. For instance, activists in Dade County, Florida, demanded the county's only nude public beach be made accessible so a 150-foot ramp was installed on the "clothing-optional" strip of Haulover Beach (Associated Press, 1995). At the urging of persons with hearing impairments, Walt Disney Company reached an agreement with the Department of Justice to provide interpreters and other assistance for people with hearing impairments at its theme parks in the United States. The National Collegiate Athletic Association (NCAA) also reached an agreement with the Department of Justice in which it relaxed its academic standards for athletes with learning disabilities (Selingo & Naughton, 1998). In what has been perhaps the most publicized happening related to the ADA, the U.S. District Court in Eugene, Oregon, ruled in favor of professional golfer Casey Martin in his quest to use a golf cart in Professional Golf Association (PGA) events because of a disability (i.e., congenital circulatory disorder) that prevents him from walking long distances. The use of golf carts is usually banned in PGA tournaments (Skyzinski, 1998; Tarde, 1998).

Yet, while strides have occurred due to the ADA, many Americans are not aware of the ADA. A Harris Poll revealed that even among persons with disabilities many do not know of the existence of the ADA. The National Organization on Disability and Louis Harris and Associates polled people with disabilities from the ages of 16 and older. Eight years after the passage of the ADA results showed that 54% of those who took part in the survey did not know that the ADA existed (Farrell, 1998).

The ADA defines persons with disabilities as anyone with a physical or mental impairment that substantially limits one or more major life activities, has a record of such an impairment, or is regarded as having such an impairment. Major life activities include: (a) walking, breathing, seeing, hearing, speaking, learning, and working; (b) activities of daily living (e.g., bathing, dressing, getting around the home); and (c) community and home management (e.g., household chores, shopping, getting around the community) (Disabilities Statistics Program, 1992).

Leisure and Persons with Disabilities in Canada

It has been mentioned that even before the passage of the ADA that Canadians had developed philosophical and practical notions of inclusive recreation that exceeded those in the United States. Back in the 1970s recreation providers in Canada were being challenged to provide recreation services for persons with disabilities. McGill (2000)

termed the 1970s "The Being Called to Account Period" for Canadian recreation providers. The unique perspective provided by the Canadians has been reflected in the Canadian publication *Journal of Leisurability*. This journal has positively influenced the delivery of inclusive recreation services in Canada and no doubt has motivated changes in the provision of inclusive recreation in America and throughout the world (Hutchison, 2000).

Numbers of Persons with Disabilities

In the United States, persons with disabilities constitute the largest minority group (Olkin, 1999). The most recent U.S. Bureau of the Census figures place the number of Americans with disabilities at 49.7 million. This represents 19.3% of the population or nearly one in five Americans (*United States Census 2000,* 2003). According to *Statistics Canada* (2003), 3.6 million Canadians report some level of disability. This is 12.4% of Canada's total population of over 31.5 million people. In both the United States and Canada, the vast majority of these individuals live in the community, as only a small fraction of individuals with disabilities live in institutions (LaPlante, 1992).

Both in the United States and in Canada, the prevalence of disability is highest among those who are older. Of those age 65 and older, over 40% of both Americans and Canadians have disabilities of some type (*Statistics Canada,* 2003; *United States Census 2000,* 2003). With the "baby boomer" generation leading the way, the number of Americans over the age of 65 will swell from about 12% of the population today to 20% by 2030 (*Census Brief,* 1997). Similar rapid growth is projected for Canada where the "population gain is fastest among the oldest" (*Statistics Canada,* 2003). Obviously, these projections for rapid growth in the retirement age population mean a large increase in the near future of the total numbers of persons with disabilities.

In sum, it is clear that there are significant and growing numbers of persons with disabilities in the United States and Canada. These citizens will require that they be provided equal access to recreation by public park and recreation agencies, as well as by private sector recreation providers.

What Is the Relationship of Therapeutic Recreation to Special Recreation?

The Purpose

The purpose of therapeutic recreation has long been debated. To clarify the situation, early in the 1980s the National Therapeutic Recreation Society (NTRS), a branch of the National Recreation and Park Association (NRPA), developed the philosophical position that "the purpose of therapeutic recreation is to facilitate the development, maintenance, and expression of an appropriate leisure lifestyle for individuals with physical, mental, emotional, and social limitations" (National Therapeutic Recreation Society, 1982).

In a more recent philosophical position statement, NTRS (1996) has continued to emphasize core values related to its traditional position of defining therapeutic recreation broadly as the provision of recreation and leisure opportunities for persons with disabilities. A core value expressed in the statement is the right to self-determined leisure for people with disabilities, which can lead to an enhanced quality of life. A further reflection of NTRS's concern for the provision of leisure opportunities for people with disabilities is NTRS's (1997) *Statement on Inclusion* that begins: "Diversity is a cornerstone of our society and culture and thus should be celebrated. Including people with disabilities in the fabric of society strengthens the community and its individual members" (p. 7). Thus, as an NRPA branch, NTRS has traditionally taken a broad perspective of therapeutic recreation as being a field concerned with the rights of persons with disabilities to participate in life-enhancing recreation and leisure experiences.

The NTRS position has remained strikingly similar to that taken by the Hospital Recreation Section of the American Recreation Society (ARS) in the 1950s and early 1960s. At the time, ARS championed the cause of recreation as a need and right of all individuals, including persons with illnesses and disabilities. Those affiliated with the Hospital Recreation Section of ARS were tied to the recreation movement that stood for "recreation for all" and, therefore, viewed therapeutic recreation as the provision of wholesome recreation experiences for ill and disabled persons.

In contrast, throughout the 1950s and early 1960s, the National Association of Recreational Therapists (NART) held a treatment-oriented philosophy. NART members viewed therapeutic recreation as the provision of recreation as a means to treatment. Those affiliating with NART had little association with organized recreation but were more closely aligned with the health and rehabilitation community. Their cause was not recreation; it was health restoration.

Contemporary professional associations have replaced the old ARS and the NART, yet the philosophical division between those with a "recreation" orientation and those with a "treatment" orientation continues. Although the National Recreation and Park Association has long since replaced the American Recreation Society, those supporting the NRPA/NTRS position still retain the "recreation for all" philosophy of ARS. The American Therapeutic Recreation Association (ATRA) seems to have picked up where NART left off.

The forming of ATRA in 1984 may be perceived as an attempt by clinically oriented therapeutic recreation specialists to break away from NRPA/NTRS to form a professional association that would foster the delivery of treatment services. The expressed concern of ATRA is with the application of intervention strategies using recreation to promote independent functioning and to enhance the optimal health and well-being of clients (American Therapeutic Recreation Association, 1993). This position is shared by a number of therapeutic recreation specialists (e.g., Austin, 1997; Bullock & Mahon, 2000; Carter, Van Andel, & Robb, 2003; Meyer, 1980, 1981) who have argued that the purpose of therapeutic recreation is to use recreation as a purposeful clinical intervention to help clients relieve or prevent problems and to assist them in personal growth in an effort to allow achievement of as high a level of health as possible. Although they realize the tremendous benefits to be achieved in recreation, these authors see recreation (as applied in therapeutic recreation) as a means to an end, not an end in itself.

A Clinical Perspective of Therapeutic Recreation

Carter and Kelley (1981) have warned that any philosophical approach must establish clear boundaries for the field. They draw a distinction between recreation and therapeutic recreation by stating that the primary purpose of *recreation services* is the provision of recreation experiences for participants. In contrast, it is the view of these experts that the primary purpose of *therapeutic recreation* is to help individuals achieve optimal health and independence through a desired change.

Likewise, Bullock and Mahon (2000) favor an approach to therapeutic recreation (TR) focused on using recreation experiences to promote independent functioning and enhance optimal health and well-being. Further, they stipulate that such therapeutic services need to be delivered by Certified Therapeutic Recreation Specialists (CTRSs). They have articulated their philosophy in the following statement:

> Therapeutic recreation is not any and all recreation services for people who have disabilities. Just having a disability does not qualify a person to receive *therapeutic* recreation services. The person with a disability may receive therapeutic recreation services, or she simply may receive recreation services (usually called special or adapted recreation—which usually occurs in a segregated community-based setting). The determination between recreation and therapeutic recreation is made on the basis of need and mandate for treatment rather than on disability. To call recreation services *therapeutic* because they are in a hospital setting is not only inaccurate but also patronizing and stigmatizing to a person who happens to have a disability. (p. 126)

Bullock and Mahon go on to state:

> As such, it is not accurate to call a municipal or county recreation program or a girls club program for people with disabilities *therapeutic recreation*. Such programs are not therapeutic recreation (treatment) programs— at least not by virtue of their service mandate. They are recreation programs for people with disabilities. . . . (p. 126)

Austin (1999) has similarly stated that the term "therapeutic recreation" should be reserved to describe the actions of therapeutic recreation specialists who intervene in their clients' lives using purposeful interventions directed through the application of the *therapeutic recreation process*. The therapeutic recreation process involves (1) individual client assessment, (2) individual program planning, (3) implementation of the program, and (4) evaluation of the effect of the program.

Robb (1980) has expressed a comparable view. He has written,

> The position (defining therapeutic recreation as the application of the therapeutic recreation process) seems to be the best approach . . . to enhance organizational understanding, eliminate encroachment, and spell out jurisdictional boundaries. In my discussion with leaders of the park and recreation field, I believe many would welcome this delimitation. Acceptance of this position would eliminate conflicts within the TR field. Persons currently working with special populations in a service capacity through recreation experiences . . . could identify with the general recreation field. Perhaps this identification would provide the impetus and leadership needed for the broader field to accept the responsibility of serving all people. (p. 46)

Thus, Robb believes therapeutic recreation should maintain a singularity of purpose by employing the therapeutic recreation process as a means to helping clients. By so restricting therapeutic recreation, he expects the general field of parks and recreation would react by assuming its rightful responsibility for the provision of recreation for people who have disabilities.

Therapeutic Recreation and Inclusive Recreation: A Polarity

In the field of therapeutic recreation, two philosophical points of view have emerged. One defines therapeutic recreation primarily as the provision of leisure services for those people who have some type of limitation. This position has been adopted by the National Therapeutic Recreation Society, a branch of the National Recreation and Park Association. The other view holds that therapeutic recreation should restrict itself to the application of purposeful interventions employing the therapeutic recreation process, and should, therefore, relinquish the provision of community recreation for people with disabilities to community recreation and parks personnel.

At this point, we take the position that a polarity does exist. We believe that inclusive recreation (i.e., recreation including persons with disabilities) and therapeutic recreation (i.e., recreation as a clinical intervention directed toward treatment or rehabilitation aims) stand as two separate entities. This book examines inclusive recreation services, *not* therapeutic recreation. Further, we believe the time has come to embrace new wording to describe the full inclusion of persons with disabilities into the recreation mainstream. We propose *inclusive recreation* be used because it is a broader term than special recreation and it better reflects equal and joint participation of persons with and without disabilities. The term *special recreation* can continue to be employed to describe special or adapted activities, such as the Special Olympics and wheelchair sports, through which specific needs are met.

It is our intent to bring about an appreciation of the importance of inclusive recreation services for persons with disabilities, as well as a knowledge of how to develop and deliver such services. We have made a concerted effort to provide a nonclinical textbook that deals with the provision of inclusive recreation and special recreation services to persons with disabilities.

LEADERSHIP WITH PERSONS WHO HAVE DISABILITIES

Stein and Sessoms' (1977) *Recreation and Special Populations* has been an important book in the movement to bring recreation services to persons with disabilities. In the view of Stein and Sessoms, professionals from the general recreation and parks field should provide community-based recreation services for people with special needs. They have written,

> If such concern (for special populations) is to be converted into new and expanded community service, it must be accompanied by a growing cadre of professional recreation leaders and volunteers who have gained some awareness and understanding of the leisure problems of these disadvantaged people and who are oriented to the possibilities of providing leisure opportunities aimed at resolving their needs. Here, it is important to understand, our focus is on present and future recreators who are trained for general community service rather than on those leaders who might be considered specialists in working with a specific population. (pp. 15, 16)

Stein and Sessoms go on to state:

> Experience has demonstrated that a professional recreator who is effective in working with people in general can be equally effective in working with people from a special population. The only provisions beyond his professional skills and understanding are 1) that he be properly oriented to any unique psychological, social, or physical difficulties and possible limitations that may sometimes be faced by persons within a given population; and 2) that he be endowed with the attitudinal capacity to work with such people. Remember, we are discussing the ability to work with *people*—nothing more! Therefore, we should recognize that such orientation and attitudinal capacity are essential in working with *any* segment of a general population, whether considered special or not. (p. 16)

Devine (1998) has suggested that existing general recreation staff can be given training to enable them to work with participants who have disabilities. She identified training needs of park and recreation staff related to inclusion through a national survey. These include:

1. Disability awareness;
2. Attitude and sensitivity toward people with disabilities;
3. Program modification strategies, policy and procedure revision strategies, and updates on ADA regulations. (p. 9)

Thus, authorities have proposed that general community recreation professionals can and should assume responsibility for inclusive recreation opportunities. But what specific skills and knowledge are needed to work in community recreation with people who have special needs? Perhaps a study covered in the next section will help to answer this important question.

Competencies Needed to Work with Persons Who Have Disabilities

Austin and Powell (1980) conducted an investigation to determine what competencies entry-level general community recreation professionals should possess to enable them to serve participants with disabilities. They first found 142 colleges and universities in the United States and Canada that offered a course in recreation for special populations for general recreation and parks students. Instructors of the relevant course at 62 of the institutions of higher education, along with 27 administrators of community-based recreation programs for persons with special needs, participated in a competency identification study. These instructors and administrators identified 86 competencies they felt were necessary for entry-level recreation personnel to work with people who have disabilities.

The 86 competencies identified by Austin and Powell were organized according to clusters of similar competencies. The highest-ranked cluster dealt with competencies related to attitudes (rated 4.26 on a 5-point scale). Other high-ranking areas of competence were facility design and accessibil-

TABLE 1.2	Areas of Competency
Cluster	**Mean Score**
Attitudes	4.26
Facility design and accessibility	4.17
Orientation to recreation for persons with disabilities	4.15
Leadership and supervision	4.09
Mainstreaming	3.94
Program design	3.92
Aids, appliances, safety procedures	3.89
Trends and issues	3.84
Leisure education	3.80
Professionalism	3.79
Resources and services	3.75
Advocacy and legislation	3.75
Training	3.73
Equipment and supplies	3.69
Characteristics of persons with disabilities	3.50
Funding sources	3.26

Source: D. R. Austin and L. G. Powell. Competencies needed by community recreators to serve special populations. In D. R. Austin, Ed., *Directions in Health, Physical Education, and Recreation; Therapeutic Recreation Curriculum: Philosophy, Strategy, and Concerns* (Bloomington: Indiana University School of Health, Physical Education and Recreation, 1980), p. 34.

ity (4.17), orientation to recreation for persons with disabilities (4.15), leadership and supervision (4.09), and mainstreaming (3.94). The rankings for all 16 clusters of competencies are shown in Table 1.2.

To present the nature of specific competencies, a representative sample was listed under each of the highest ranked clusters. First, under the *attitudes* cluster are competencies such as the following:

- Understands how positive attitudes toward persons with disabilities may be developed within recreational programs
- Demonstrates awareness of personal attitudes toward persons with disabilities
- Understands various societal attitudes toward persons with disabilities

Under the cluster on *facility design and accessibility* are competencies such as the following:

- Understands the frustrations experienced in an inaccessible environment
- Describes physical barriers to accessibility and how they can be eliminated
- Identifies resources available on the design of barrier-free recreational environments

Representative of the cluster on *orientation to recreation for persons with disabilities* are competencies dealing with philosophical understandings, including the following:

- Develops a personal/professional philosophy of recreation for persons with disabilities in community settings
- States a rationale for the provision of community recreation for persons with disabilities
- Knows role of recreation services for persons with disabilities in the community recreation department

The *leadership and supervision* cluster contains competencies such as the following:

- Recognizes the importance of considering individual needs and interests during program leadership
- Knows principles of instruction useful for executing recreation activities for special populations
- Knows how to facilitate integrated recreational groups (create an atmosphere conducive to mainstreaming)

The *mainstreaming* cluster contains the following competencies, among others:

- Understands concepts of mainstreaming
- Understands concepts of normalization
- Describes approaches to mainstreaming in community recreation

The competencies identified by Austin and Powell's (1980) experts constitute a listing of

TABLE 1.3	Abbreviations Related to Inclusive and Special Recreation
Abbreviation	**Stands for:**
ABs	Able-bodied people
ADA	Americans with Disabilities Act
ADL	Activities of daily living
AT	Assistive technology
CPRA	Canadian Park and Recreation Association
IDEA	Individuals with Disabilities Education Act
NCA	National Center on Accessibility
NRPA	National Recreation and Park Association
NTRS	National Therapeutic Recreation Society
Reg Neg	U.S. Access Board Regulatory Negotiation advisory committee
TABs	Temporarily able-bodied
TDD or TTY	Telecommunications device for individuals with hearing impairments

basic skills and knowledge necessary for entry-level professionals assuming positions in recreation and parks departments. This information, coupled with that provided by others such as Anderson and Brown (1996); Anderson and Kress (2003); Dattilo (1994); Project INCLUDE (1998); and Schleien, et al. (1997) could serve as a basic foundation for preservice and in-service training of community recreation professionals.

Comment on Leadership Responsibility in Community Recreation

Public recreation and parks agencies must return to their professional heritage of concern with recreation for persons who have been underserved. As the suppliers of public recreation and parks services, they have the responsibility to offer recreation services for persons with disabilities, since it

Right to Leisure

- The pursuit of leisure is a condition necessary for human dignity and well-being.
- Leisure is a part of a healthy lifestyle and a productive life.
- Every individual is entitled to the opportunity to express unique interests and pursue, develop and improve talents and abilities.
- People are entitled to opportunities and services in the most inclusive setting.
- The right to choose from the full array of recreation opportunities offered in diverse settings and environments and requiring different levels of competency should be provided.

Taken from the NTRS Position Statement on Inclusion, approved by the NTRS Board of Directors, October 29, 1997.

is their duty to serve the recreational needs of their jurisdictions at large. But it is particularly important that public recreation and parks agencies reach out to underserved segments of the population, including persons with physical or mental disabilities and older persons.

Further, we believe that inclusive and special recreation programs should be largely organized and led by general recreation professionals. If such programs are to be an integral part of the organization's offerings, they should be provided by the regular professional staff. The exception to this would be in programs with therapeutic intent. These are programs directed toward facilitating change through meeting specific objectives. Use of the therapeutic recreation process to effect specific outcomes calls for the knowledge and skills possessed by a professional prepared as a therapeutic recreation specialist. Therefore, we envision therapeutic recreation specialists working in recreation and parks agencies in programs aimed at therapeutic objectives, with general recreation professionals delivering opportunities for leisure experiences. There appears to be no reason why general recreation professionals and therapeutic recreation specialists should not function together in the cause of providing necessary services for persons with disabilities.

With the passage of the ADA, it is also the law of the land in the United States that recreation providers allow access to their services by persons with disabilities. The ADA, however, goes beyond governmental recreation agencies to also cover all public recreation accommodations including sport, resort, and commercial recreation enterprises. Therefore, we urge students preparing for careers in any aspect of public or private recreation to ready themselves for the important task of serving persons with disabilities.

Finally, we strongly endorse the concept of inclusive recreation. Both public and private recreation providers must offer inclusive services so that persons with disabilities have access to enjoy recreation experiences as others do. We recognize that special recreation programs designed specifically for persons with disabilities (e.g., wheelchair sports) are at times preferred by some participants. Yet, we believe that every person with a disability has the right to be fully included with others enjoying existing recreation programs and facilities as long as he or she meets the basic requirements (e.g., age, height, and skill) to participate. Persons with disabilities should never be excluded by any recreation provider simply because they are disabled. All recreation providers must remove physical and social barriers and make reasonable accommodations so that people with disabilities may have free and equal access to recreation. Means must be provided for persons with disabilities and without disabilities to recreate together.

SUMMARY

The organized recreation movement in the United States grew out of a social welfare concern reflected by the establishment of the Boston Sand Gardens and recreation programs in settlement houses. Eventually, however, public recreation lost its focus on individuals with special needs as a new philosophy developed that viewed recreation as an end in itself, rather than as a means to reach social ends. A similar change occurred in Canada.

It has been suggested that a broadened concept of therapeutic recreation (TR), which viewed TR as encompassing all recreation for persons with disabilities, further contributed to a perception that public recreation and parks did not have a responsibility for providing services for persons with disabilities, because these services were being provided by those identified as therapeutic recreation specialists. This broad view of therapeutic recreation has been challenged by several authors who have taken the position that inclusive and special recreation services rightfully fall within the domain of general recreation and parks. The Americans with Disabilities Act makes it mandatory that all recreation providers (both public and private) make their facilities and programs accessible to persons with disabilities. The final segment of the chapter discussed in-service training needs and necessary competencies for recreation professionals to offer leisure opportunities for those persons who have disabilities.

SUGGESTED LEARNING ACTIVITIES

1. Prepare a two- to four-page paper in which you provide support for the idea that organized recreation evolved out of humanistic concerns.

2. In a discussion group, list reasons why communities fail to offer leisure services to people with disabilities. Which reason or reasons do most of the group members consider most prominent?

3. Interview a parks and recreation administrator in your hometown on the subject of community recreation for people with disabilities. Ask why the community offers (or fails to offer) leisure services for people with disabilities. Prepare a two- to three-page report on your interview.

4. Prepare a two- to three-page paper on the relationship between therapeutic recreation and inclusive recreation services. Arrive at your own position regarding the relationship.

5. Prepare a two-page paper in which you agree or disagree with this statement: "Existing general recreation staff can be given training to enable them to work with participants with disabilities."

6. Examine the 16 critical competencies listed in the chapter. Then do a three- to five-page self-assessment paper based on the critical competencies.

7. In class, discuss how you believe general recreation professionals and therapeutic recreation specialists can function together in the provision of community recreation for persons with disabilities.

8. Go to the ADA home page on the Web. Evaluate it for usefulness to students studying inclusive recreation. Report your findings in class.

9. Locate the home page for the *Journal of Leisurability* on the Web. Review past issues for articles of interest to you. Of the articles you select, choose one to report on in class.

REFERENCES

American Therapeutic Recreation Association. *Recreational Therapy: An Integral Aspect of Comprehensive Healthcare.* Hattisburg, MS: American Therapeutic Recreation Association, 1993.

Anderson, L., & C. Brown. *Inclusion: Strategies for Including People with Disabilities in Parks and Recreation Opportunities.* Bismarck, ND: North Dakota Parks and Recreation Department, 1996.

Anderson, L., & C. C. Kress. *Inclusion: Including People with Disabilities in Parks and Recreation Opportunities.* State College, PA: Venture Publishing, Inc., 2003.

Associated Press. Nude beach unveils its first wheelchair ramp. *The Herald-Times,* Bloomington, IN, March 4, 1995, p. A5.

Austin, D. R. *Therapeutic Recreation Processes and Techniques* (4th ed.). Champaign, IL: Sagamore Publishing, 1999.

Austin, D. R., J. A. Peterson, & L. M. Peccarelli. The status of services for special populations in park and recreation departments in the state of Indiana. *Therapeutic Recreation Journal, 12*(1), 50–56, 1978.

Austin, D. R., & L. G. Powell. Competencies needed by community recreators to serve special populations. In D. R. Austin, Ed. *Directions in Health, Physical Education, and Recreation, Therapeutic-Recreation Curriculum: Philosophy, Strategy, and Concepts.* Bloomington, IN: Indiana University School of Health, Physical Education, and Recreation, 1980, pp. 33, 34.

Bullock, C. C., & M. J. Mahon. *Introduction to Recreation Services for Persons with Disabilities: A Person Centered Approach* (2nd ed.). Champaign, IL: Sagamore Publishing, 2000.

Carter, M. J., & J. D. Kelley. Recreation programming for visually impaired children. In J. D. Kelley, Ed. *Recreation Programming for Visually Impaired Children and Youth.* New York: American Foundation for the Blind, 1981, pp. 63–79.

Carter, M. J., G. E. Van Andel, & G. M. Robb. *Therapeutic Recreation: A Practical Approach* (3rd ed.). Prospect Heights, IL: Waveland Press, Inc., 2003.

Census Brief, U.S. Department of Commerce, Economics and Statistics Administration, Bureau of the Census. Washington, DC: 1997.

Colton, D. Longevity is global sleeping giant. *USA Today, 17*(129), March 17, 1999, pp. 1, 2.

Dattilo, J. *Inclusive Leisure Services: Responding to the Rights of People with Disabilities* (2nd ed.). State College, PA: Venture Publishing, Inc., 2002.

Devine, M. A. Inclusion . . . An update: Results of a national survey. *NTRS Report, 23*(3), 8, 9, 1998.

Disability Statistics Program. *Disability Statistics Abstract: People with Functional Limitations in the U.S.* San Francisco: Disability Statistics Program, University of California, 1992.

Farrell, M. A. Many with disabilities unaware of the ADA. *Venice Gondolier,* Venice, FL, September 19, 1998, p. 4.

Federal Register, 54(144), July 26, 1991.

Gray, D. E. The case of compensatory recreation. *Parks and Recreation, 4*(4), 23, 24ff, 1969.

Hutchinson, P. The evolution of integration research: Celebrating 25 years of the Journal of Leisurability. *Journal of Leisurability, 27*(4), 32–43, 2000.

Kraus, R. *Recreation and Leisure in Modern Society.* New York: Appleton-Century-Croft, 1971.

LaPlante, M. P. *Disability Statistics Abstract: How Many Americans Have a Disability?* San Francisco: Disability Statistics Programs, University of California, 1992.

Lutzin, P. B. Serving the handicapped and elderly. In S. G. Lutzin, Ed. *Managing Municipal Leisure Services.* Washington, DC: International City Management Association, 1980, p. 152.

McGill, J. A retrospective: Twenty-five years of practice in the field of leisure and persons with disabilities, Journal of Leisurability. *Journal of Leisurability, 27*(4), 9–31, 2000.

Meyer, L. E. Three philosophical positions of therapeutic recreation and their implications for professionalization and NTRS. In *Proceedings of the First Annual Post-Doctorate Institute.* Bloomington: Indiana University Department of Recreation and Park Administration, 1980, pp. 28–42.

Meyer, L. E. Three philosophical positions of therapeutic recreation and their implication for professionalism and NTRS/NRPA. *Therapeutic Recreation Journal, 15*(2), 7–16, 1981.

National Therapeutic Recreation Society. Philosophical position statement of the National Therapeutic Recreation Society, 1982.

NTRS. *Philosophical Position Statement.* [Online]. Available: http://www.nrpa.org/branches/ntrs/philos.htm, 1996.

NTRS. NTRS Position Statement on Inclusion. *NTRS Report, 23*(1), 7, 1997.

Olkin, R. *What Psychotherapists Should Know about Disability.* New York: The Guilford Press, 1999.

Pedlar, A. Normalization and integration: A look at the Swedish experience. *Mental Retardation, 28*(5), 275–282, 1990.

Pedlar, A., & A. Gilbert. Normalization and integration: The Canadian experience. In D. M. Compton, Ed. *Issues in Therapeutic Recreation: Toward the New Millennium* (2nd ed.). Champaign, IL: Sagamore Publishing, 1997, pp. 489–506.

Pegels, C. C. *Health Care and the Older Citizen.* Rockville, MD: Aspen, 1988.

Project INCLUDE. *Project INCLUDE Manual and Training Materials.* Evanston, IL: National Lekotek Center, 1998.

Robb, G. M. A practitioner's reaction to three philosophical positions of therapeutic recreation and their implications for professionalization and NTRS. In *Proceedings of the First Annual Post-Doctorate Institute.* Bloomington: Indiana University Department of Recreation and Park Administration, 1980, pp. 43–52.

Schleien, S. J., M. T. Ray, & F. P. Green. *Community Recreation and People with Disabilities: Strategies for Inclusion* (2nd ed.). Baltimore: Paul H. Brookes Publishing Co., 1997.

Selingo, J., & J. Naughton. NCAA agrees to loosen its rules for athletes with learning disabilities: *The Chronicle of Higher Education,* A47, June 5, 1998.

Sessoms, H. G., & J. L. Stevenson. *Leadership & Group Dynamics in Recreation Services.* Boston: Allyn and Bacon, 1981.

Skyzinski, R. Through the green. *Golf Journal, 51*(2), 4, March/April, 1998.

Statistics Canada. [Online]. Available: http://www.statcan.ca/start.html and http://www.statcan.ca/english/freepub/89-577-XIE/canada.htm, July 9, 2003.

Statistics Canada. *Population Aged 15 and Over with a Disability, by Nature of Disability.* [Online]. Available: http://www.statcan.ca/english/Pgdb/People/Health/health12a.htm, 1991.

Statistics Canada. *Population by Age Group.* [Online]. Available: http://www.statcan.ca/english/Pgdb/People/Population/demo31a.htm, 1998.

Stein, T. A., & H. D. Sessoms. *Recreation and Special Populations* (2nd ed.). Boston: Holbrook Press, 1977.

Tarde, J. After Casey Martin, what? *Golf Digest, 49*(4), 46–48, April, 1998.

United States Census 2000, U.S. Department of Commerce, Economics and Statistics Administration, U.S. Census Bureau. Washington, DC: 2003.

Wehman, P. *The ADA Mandate for Social Change.* Baltimore: Paul H. Brookes, 1993.

Worsnop, R. L. Despite business grumbling, disabilities act here to stay. *Sunday Herald-Times,* Bloomington, IN, January 19, 1997, p. 61.

2

CONCEPTS AND ATTITUDES UNDERLYING INCLUSIVE AND SPECIAL RECREATION SERVICES

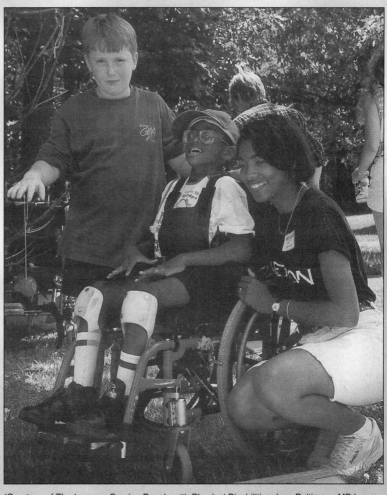

(Courtesy of The League: Serving People with Physical Disabilities, Inc., Baltimore, MD.)

This chapter deals with concepts and attitudes basic to understanding the delivery of inclusive and special recreation services. The chapter begins with a review of terminology related to inclusive and special recreation services. Terms often used without precise definition in the parks and recreation literature are reviewed. This discussion is offered with the hope that it will make clear the terms that appear not only in this textbook, but throughout literature dealing with recreation services for individuals with disabilities.

Also contained in this chapter is a discussion of attitudes toward the provision of recreation programs and services for individuals with disabilities. Attitudes are important to our understandings, because our attitudes influence our behavior toward providing programs and services for persons with disabilities.

TERMS

It is not surprising that students are often confused by the terms *impaired, disabled,* and *handicapped.* These terms are regularly used without definition in the parks and recreation literature. Many authors use the terms interchangeably; others distinguish between them.

Impairment

Impairment is defined by the World Health Organization (1980) as "any loss or abnormality of the psychological, physiological, or anatomic structure or function" (p. 47). Therefore, the term *impairment* refers to any residual effects of disease, injury, or genetic disorder that disrupts physical, cognitive, or affective functioning. Impairments are prolonged conditions, but they are not necessarily permanent (Livneh & Antonak, 1997). An impairment leads to disability, which *may* lead to a handicap.

Disability/Handicap

A useful distinction between the terms *disability* and *handicap* is that the word *disability* refers

to a specific impairment or disorder, whereas a *handicap* results from actions of the person with the disability or by society. That is, persons with a specific disability can handicap themselves by believing that they cannot do something when, in fact, they could function under the right conditions. Society can also handicap persons with disabilities by refusing them opportunities.

According to the Americans with Disabilities Act, a disability is defined as (a) a physical or mental impairment that substantially limits one or more of an individual's life activities (e.g., specific physical or developmental disabilities); (b) a record of such impairment; and (c) being regarded as having such an impairment (Wehman, 1993, p. xxii).

Society can cause persons with disabilities to be handicapped, as indicated by Lord (1981). He has stated,

> Being handicapped is a social phenomenon. Our society handicaps many people. Examples include individuals with physical disabilities because of lack of accessibility to community facilities; persons with mental retardation or learning disabilities because of poor teaching or low expectations; single parents because of limited child support and narrow definitions of what constitutes a family; older adults because of stereotyped and inappropriate programming; and all of the above because of negative attitudes, economic deprivation, segregation, and denial of human rights. (p. 4)

Thus, the terms *impaired, disabled,* and *handicapped* have singular meanings. At the same time, however, the reader must remain aware that in popular use the terms are often employed to mean the same thing.

New WHO Terminology

The World Health Organization (WHO) adopted the classifications of impairment, disability, and handicap in 1980. However, dissatisfaction arose over the years as the terms *disability* and *handicap* were often confused and their meanings became unclear. The term *handicap* was also becoming less favorably viewed (*Disability Data Briefing,* 1997). Additionally, the 1980 terminology reflected a medical viewpoint that did not include the effect on functioning of either society or the abilities of the individual (*The Definition of Disability,* 2003).

As a result there were calls from activists for more consistency in disability definitions and the adoption of new terminology that reflected a biopsychosocial model of human functioning. New language came into being when the International Classification of Functioning, Disability, and Health was put in place by the WHO in 2001. The new classification system (termed both ICF and ICIDH-2) replaced the terms *disability* and *handicap.* Within the new system the terms *impairments, activities,* and *participation* were adopted to reflect (a) body functions or structures, (b) personal activities, and (c) participation in society.

The terminology used to describe people with disabilities is very important because words can affect the way people think about persons with disabilities and the way people treat persons with disabilities. Thus, the new terminology was made to be more positive by using "activities" instead of disability and "participation" instead of handicap. In addition the new system addressed the effect of the environment (i.e., physical, social, and attitudinal world) and personal factors (e.g., gender, age, fitness, other health conditions, lifestyle, education, social background, past experiences) on the individual's health condition (Tate, 2003; WHO, 2000).

Under the new system, *impairments* are defined as problems in body function (i.e., physiological or psychological functions) or body structure (i.e., organs, limbs, and their components) such as significant deviation or loss. The term *activities* is the name for the dimension that concerns the tasks or actions the person may do. The expression "activity limitation" then is used to replace the term *disability.* Instead of the impairment leading to a disability it leads to an activity limitation. The final dimension is *participation,* which replaces "handicap." Participation is doing a task or an action in a life situation in the individual's

environment. "Participation restrictions" are problems a person may have in doing the task or action or the experience in the actual context in which he or she lives. That is, participation involves the relationship between the individual's health condition, personal factors, and factors in the person's environment. For example, an environment with barriers will restrict participation while a favorable environment may facilitate participation (*Disability Data Briefing,* 1997; WHO, 2000; 2002).

Because of the new terminology suggested by the WHO, perhaps someday in the future in this book and in other literature the expression "persons with activity limitations" will replace "persons with disabilities." For the near future, however, it is likely that the term *disability* will continue to be used as an umbrella term to refer to individuals whose impairments lead to activity limitations.

Perhaps the most important lesson to be taken from the new WHO terminology is that persons with disabilities (or activity limitations) should be viewed from biological, individual, and social perspectives. As the WHO (2002) has stated:

> Disability is a complex phenomena that is both a problem at the level of a person's body, and a complex and primarily social phenomena. Disability is always an interaction between features of the person and features of the overall context in which the person lives, but some aspects of disability are almost entirely internal to the person, while another aspect is almost entirely external. (p. 9)

Disabilities or activity limitations are thus viewed as resulting from interactions between impairments and contextual factors. Contextual factors deal with both environmental factors and personal factors. Environmental factors such as societal attitudes, social structures, and accessibility to facilities may likely influence the individual's ability to function, as will personal factors such as gender, age, coping mechanisms, fitness, social background, and past experiences (WHO, 2002). When disability is perceived in this way, it is clear that recreation and leisure professionals may play a significant role as facilitators who can improve the functioning of the individual with a disability by providing a positive environment and, perhaps, enhance the person as an individual.

Special Populations

The term *special populations* has been used consistently in the literature to cover a broad range of persons, including those with disabilities. We can say the term describes those who have special needs because of some social, physical, mental, or psychological difficulty. Because of its encompassing nature and the implication that people from "special populations" are somehow similar in most aspects, we have avoided using this term except when citing the works of others. We consider it a dated term and would hope that it will not continue to be used.

Special Recreation

The term *special recreation* has emerged to describe recreation and leisure provisions that accommodate recreation participation by persons with special needs and particularly by persons with disabilities. Special recreation services allow participation by individuals who have disabilities that necessitate special accommodations (modifications of activities, altered environments, personal assistance, etc.) above and beyond the kinds of accommodations generally provided. The word *special* is not being used to refer to individuals; rather, the term *special recreation* is intended to deemphasize categorizing people by placing primary emphasis on the unique (special) nature of the accommodations required (Meyer, 1984).

The term *special recreation* has come to be used to describe special or adapted activities, such as the Special Olympics or wheelchair sports, typically segregated programs provided exclusively for people with disabilities (Austin & Crawford, 2001; Bullock & Mahon, 2000). Other special recreation activities are offered as steppingstones whereby persons with disabilities can gain recre-

ational and social skills in order to move to integrated programs (Schleien, Ray, & Green, 1997). However, with the recent focus on inclusion, many believe there should be less focus on special recreation.

Inclusive Recreation

Inclusive recreation is a phrase used to capture the full acceptance and integration of persons with disabilities into the recreation mainstream. It reflects free and equal access to recreation participation by persons with disabilities. In the future, we envision that people who are disabled will, as a matter of course, be welcomed and accommodated by public and private recreation entities so even the term inclusive recreation will no longer be necessary. Indicative of a trend toward this is the finding that 98% of Americans believe that all persons, regardless of ability, should have the opportunity to participate in the mainstream of society (Wehman, 1993). We agree completely with Rynders and Schleien (1991) who have stated: "We must develop ways to enable people with disabilities to exercise their right to be fully participating members of communities in which they live" (p. 5). The basis of the term inclusive recreation may have come from work by Smith (1980) who employed the term *inclusive programming* to mean providing recreation opportunities for everyone. The term *inclusive recreation* has been extensively used in Canada since the 1970s.

Anderson, Brown, and Soli (1996) have emphasized that inclusive recreation involves the community not only allowing persons with disabilities to be present but completely involving them. They have written:

> It is important to understand that inclusion means not only *physical* inclusion, but *social* inclusion as well. People with disabilities, like all people, want to meet new friends, have opportunities for social interaction, and be a functional participant in a recreation activity. Physical *and* social inclusion must be fostered for these needs to be met. (p. 19)

Inclusion Is:

- Having the same choices and opportunities in recreation activities that other people have.
- Being accepted and appreciated for who you are.
- Being with friends who share your interests, not your disability.
- Being a valued customer and a welcomed participant in community recreation programs, regardless of ability levels.
- Having recreation facilities and areas that are accessible and easy to use by everyone.
- Providing the necessary individual adaptations, accommodations, and supports so every person can benefit equally from a recreation experience in the community with friends.

Anderson, L., C. Brown, & P. Soli. *Inclusion: Strategies for Including People with Disabilities in Parks and Recreation Opportunities.* Bismarck, ND: Rural Recreation Integration Project, 1996, pp. 19, 20.

Some programs are difficult to categorize. They are not special recreation because they are not segregated, and they are not truly inclusive recreation because they are designed as an interim step toward inclusion that mix persons with and without disabilities. These programs bring people of "mixed abilities" together and in so doing must emphasize systematic planning and support that recognizes the unique characteristics of individual participants, rather than providing for one population as is the case of special recreation programs. Such programs have been referred to as *integrated options* by Schleien, et al. (1997). An example would be "reverse mainstreaming" (Schleien & Green, 1992) in which programs traditionally designed for persons with disabilities are expanded to allow participation by persons without disabilities.

Mainstreaming

With the advent of the concept of inclusion, the term *mainstreaming* has become less prevalent in the literature. Mainstreaming has typically been used to refer to providing persons with disabilities opportunities to learn, work, and recreate in settings that have traditionally served the general public (Stein, 1985).

Mainstreaming, then, concerns the provision of opportunities for persons with disabilities to join

in the mainstream of society. All of society's services, including parks and recreation, are a part of the mainstream that should be accessible to every citizen.

It has been said that mainstreaming is both a goal and a process (Austin & Powell, 1980). As a goal, mainstreaming involves integrating people with special needs into the mainstream of society. It is based on the concept that all persons deserve to participate in the *least restrictive environment* possible so that they can function at their optimal level of independence. A least restrictive environment is a recreational setting where persons with disabilities have opportunity to recreate with persons without disabilities in a natural recreation environment to the maximum extent possible.

The term *mainstreaming* has also been used to indicate the process by which alternatives are created so that persons with disabilities can experience the least restrictive environment possible. It is the process by which individuals move from a segregated program toward an inclusive one. This process may involve a *continuum of services* that allows individuals to move progressively toward their optimal level of functioning. Schleien et al. (1997) have proposed such a continuum of services for persons with disabilities. This continuum ranges from: *noninvolvement,* where society fails to provide for the needs of people with disabilities;

to *special recreation,* where segregated programs are provided; to *integrated* opportunities that mix persons with and without disabilities; to, finally, *inclusive recreation,* where people with disabilities are entitled to the same respect and attention as others receiving recreation services in the community.

Many people have begun to use the term inclusion, rather than mainstreaming, because of a level of dissatisfaction with the extent of social integration of persons with disabilities into communities under the concept of mainstreaming. Bullock and Mahon (2000) have written:

> The introduction of the term inclusion served notice that there is dissatisfaction with the extent to which people with disabilities have become a part of their communities. Inclusion gives people equal opportunity to grow and develop to their fullest potential. The fundamental principle of inclusion is the valuing of diversity within the human community. When inclusion is fully embraced, we abandon the idea that children or adults have to become "normal" in order to contribute to the world. We begin to look beyond typical ways of becoming valued members of the community, and in so doing begin to realize the achievable goal of providing all people with an authentic sense of belonging. (p. 58)

Those strongly endorsing the concept of inclusion deeply hold that all individuals possess intrinsic value and that differences should be embraced as people learn to live with one another. Further, Bullock and Mahon (2000) have stipulated that movement toward the use of the term inclusion places additional focus on the development of important ideals that have not yet been regularly reflected in existing community recreation environments. These include the development of acceptance, friendships, and natural supports in the community.

Unfortunately, models for the cultivation of successful inclusive environments are only beginning to emerge. Research by Wilhite, Devine, and Goldenberg (1999) has offered encouraging signs that elements such as the prior preparation of participants, frequent contact between those with and without disabilities, cooperative activities, minimal and natural accommodations, and the equal status of participants may lead to positive inclusion experiences.

Normalization

Another important term is *normalization.* This term refers to the provision of relatively normal experiences so that individuals with disabilities can maintain or develop traits and behaviors that are as culturally normative as possible (Wolfensberger, 1972). In Wolfensberger's words, normalization is ". . . the utilization of means which are as culturally normative as possible, in order to establish and/or maintain personal behaviours and characteristics which are as culturally normative as possible" (p. 28).

The term normalization does imply that recreation services for people with disabilities should be as close to the cultural norm as possible. This means that people with disabilities should have opportunities for access to the same settings as others who are not disabled. Additionally, programs should not be led by therapeutic recreation specialists but by the service staff who provide services to nondisabled citizens because this is the cultural norm.

Professionals who believe in strictly following the principle of normalization oppose the provision of any segregated special recreation programs because such activities are not "normal." Special recreation programs, however, do exist for many reasons. Within such segregated special programs the principle of normalization calls for these programs to be as normal as possible. As a general rule, the least possible modification of activities is seen as being best. For example, segregated athletic participation should be as close as possible to the way the sport is normally played. Modifications need to be minimal so that as normal an athletic experience as possible can be gained by participants. Another example involves planning activities to fit the age range of participants. Activities should be age appropriate. Adults who have mental retardation should not be expected to take part in childish games. They should be able to enjoy normal adult activities suited to their skills rather than be forced into activities designed for children.

The concept of normalization has lead to deinstitutionalization throughout the United States and Canada. *Deinstitutionalization* refers to the movement to return persons with disabilities from institutions to the community so that they may live in normal settings. This movement has resulted in more people with disabilities living in the communities and, therefore, additional demand by persons with disabilities for community-based recreational services.

Normalization has been listed as a major principle in recreation inclusion, according to Sylvester, Voelkl, and Ellis (2001). These authors have stated: "Services should reflect such *positive* cultural norms as choice, autonomy, dignity, independence, the right to work and leisure, and living according to the typical rhythms and patterns of life" (p. 226). Other principles of recreation inclusion listed by Sylvester, Voelkl, and Ellis (2001) include providing persons with disabilities with self-determination, socially valued roles, and environments that are conducive to personal growth.

Accessibility

The term *accessibility* is sometimes misunderstood because many people employ the term primarily as it relates to wheelchair users gaining access to a building or area (Gorham & Brasile, 1998). However, the term accessibility involves more than this. Two types of accessibility are discussed in the literature, *physical accessibility* and *program accessibility.*

Physical accessibility, as defined by Anderson, et al. (1996), ". . . means recreation facilities and areas are barrier-free and people with disabilities can approach, enter, and use them unimpeded" (p. 31). For example, accessible parking and curb cuts are provided so the area or facility can be reached without encountering obstacles. Entry doors must be wide enough and have low thresholds to permit entrance. Once inside, people with disabilities must be able to use the area or facility. The term *universal accessibility* has been employed to signify design features that allow use of areas and facilities by everyone in society, including groups such as mothers with strollers, bicyclists, older persons with visual or mobility impairments, and wheelchair users.

A term heard more in recent years is *program accessibility.* As defined by Anderson et al. (1996), "Program accessibility is designing recreation programs and activities so that people with disabilities can actively and socially participate in them. It involves providing necessary supports and services, so people with disabilities can pursue the activities of their choice" (p. 53). Accommodations to make a program accessible may include: (a) removing architectural barriers (e.g., steps); (b) removing communication barriers (e.g., installing visual fire alarms); (c) providing aids or services (e.g., providing a sign language interpreter); (d) removing transportation barriers (e.g., providing transportation); and (e) changing policies, practices, or procedures (e.g., changing a rule to allow a guide dog) (McGovern, 1992, pp. 12–14).

Advocacy

During the 1970s, a movement developed that emphasized the rights of persons with disabilities. This movement to some degree resembled the civil rights movement of the 1960s. However, its concern was with the rights of persons with disabilities, rather than with the rights of African Americans. It was during the period of the 1970s that the term *advocacy* came into the vocabulary of many concerned helping professionals and parents of children with disabilities. At the time Hillman (1972) explained that advocacy involved arguing for and defending a cause.

Those advocating for their own rights are said to engage in *self-advocacy.* Today the role of people with disabilities has grown to the point that they assume much of the leadership for advocacy by engaging in self-advocacy. Nevertheless, it remains the role of therapeutic recreation specialists and inclusive recreation specialists to advocate for the right of persons with disabilities to receive services from general recreation professionals in both the public and commercial sectors.

ATTITUDES

What Are Attitudes?

Attitude theorists almost inevitably include an affective component in defining the term *attitude*. That is, they see attitudes as reflecting the degree of favorableness, or unfavorableness, an individual feels toward an attitude object. In other words, our attitudes are a gauge of our liking for someone or something. We "admire" or "detest" someone. We "love" or "hate" something (Mannell & Kleiber, 1997; Weber, 1992).

Attitudes are thought to have a cognitive component in that they are based on beliefs, thoughts, or ideas held toward attitude objects, whether the objects are persons, groups, places, or things. While attitudes may certainly influence behavior, they deal primarily with how individuals *feel* toward an object, not with how they act.

Thus, in summary, we may say that attitudes rest on learned beliefs and reflect an individual's degree of liking for the attitude object. While attitudes may have a strong effect on behavior, there does not appear to be a one-to-one correspondence between attitudes and behaviors. Attitudes deal with the degree of liking for an object. Behaviors deal with our actions.

Language and Attitudes toward Persons with Disabilities

The words we use in our everyday language tend to reflect our attitudes. Use of the terms *the disabled* or *the handicapped* are offensive to many persons because their use implies that the individuals placed in these categories are not unique human beings but are the same as all others so categorized. It is as misleading to categorize people with disabilities as "the disabled" as it would be to categorize those enrolled in elementary schools,

high schools, vocational schools, and colleges as "the students." They are all students, but there the similarity ends. Their only similarity is that they are studying in educational institutions. Yet once labeled one of "the students," a young adult may be perceived differently when encountered by university personnel or the local police, or when attempting to cash a check at a place of business or obtaining housing in the community.

Likewise, the only similarity among those with disabilities is that they differ from most others in having a disability. Even in regard to their disabilities, there is a tremendous degree of variability among those who have disabilities. Orthopedic disabilities are different from learning disabilities or mental impairments. Hearing impairments differ from emotional disturbances, and so on. However, once we label a person as handicapped, there is a tendency not to think of him or her as an individual with unique potentials. Instead we restrict our thinking about the individual to the labeled condition. Our stereotyped thinking minimizes our perceptions of the person's uniqueness as a human being. We focus our perceptions on categorical differences, rather than on the individual. It was in recognition of this problem that former President Reagan's May 10, 1988, Executive Order 12640 changed the name of the 41-year-old President's Committee on Employment of the Handicapped to the President's Committee on Employment of People with Disabilities.

Because labeling a person does tend to restrict everyone's thinking, in this book we have attempted to avoid using the terms *the handicapped* or *the disabled*. Instead, we have used the phrase "persons with disabilities." In so doing we hope to remind ourselves and the reader that those who have a disability are, above all, individual human beings much more similar to us than different. Appropriate use of terminology regarding persons who have disabilities should not be minimized. It is of fundamental importance in establishing the inherent worth and dignity of *all* human beings. Emphasizing this point, Mary Johnson, editor of the often-controversial publication *The Disability Rag* has identified language and words as probably the biggest limitation facing persons with disabilities (Rag Time, 1989).

Guidelines concerning appropriate terminology in portraying persons with disabilities have been provided by the National Easter Seal Society (NESS) (1981), Dattilo and Smith (1990), and Dattilo (2002). Based on these works, the following principles are offered:

1. Emphasize the uniqueness and worth of each individual by considering the person first. When generic references to a disabling condition are necessary, the word *disability* is more appropriate than the word *handicapped.*

Following this guideline, phrases such as *person with a disability* or *individual who has a disability* are appropriate, because these place the person or individual first. It would be inappropriate to refer to persons with disabilities as the *disabled,* since this places the emphasis on the noun *disabled* and implies that the person's identity is tied to his or her disability. Also, this guideline suggests avoiding the use of the term *disabled* as an adjective, such as in *disabled persons.*

2. Because the person is not the condition, reference to the person in terms of the condition he or she has is inaccurate as well as demeaning. (NESS, 1981, p. 284)

We should never refer to someone as an *epileptic* or a *CP.* Instead, we should refer to him or her as "a person who has epilepsy" or "a person who has cerebral palsy." The individual is much more than a person who happens to have epilepsy or cerebral palsy or any other disorder. Moreover, the use of acronyms (e.g., CP, MR) should be avoided whenever possible because they emphasize the condition rather than the person. Also, for some who are unaware of their meaning, acronyms

It is sometimes necessary to use the person's disability as an adjective; however, such terminology should be avoided, if possible.
(Photo by Lawrence M. Levy)

TABLE 2.1	Empowering Language	
Use Affirmative Language		**Instead of Negative Language**
• Persons who have disabilities.		• Disabled people.
• Person who has multiple sclerosis.		• Afflicted by MS.
• Person with cerebral palsy.		• CP victim.
• Person with Down syndrome.		• Mongoloid.
• Person with a seizure disorder.		• Epileptic.
• People with visual impairments.		• The blind.
• Uses a wheelchair.		• Confined to a wheelchair.
• Child without a disability.		• Normal child.

Adapted from Davis, C. M. *Patient Practitioner Interaction: An Experiential Manual for Developing the Art of Health Care* (3rd ed.). Thorofare, NJ: SLACK Incorporated, 1998; and *Re-creating Recreation for Inclusion.* Evanston, IL: National Lekotek Center, 1998.

may add negative connotations to a disabling condition (see Table 2.1).

3. Some categorical terms are used correctly only when communicating technical information—for example, hard of hearing, deaf, partially sighted, and blind. (NESS, 1981, p. 284)

Rather than using expressions such as *partially sighted* or *deaf,* it is more appropriate to use the expressions *persons who have partial vision* or *individuals who have a partial hearing loss.* Such expressions not only place the emphasis on the person but more accurately reflect the disabilities.

Avoid using words or terms that are negative, judgmental, or paternalistic (including use of otherwise acceptable terms in an appropriate context). Instead, use objective descriptions to emphasize each individual's abilities. Terms such as *afflicted with, crippled, invalid,* and *victim* should be avoided. Instead of saying *afflicted with,* say "the individual has an affliction." Rather than using the negative term *crippled,* use an expression such as *the person with a physical disability,* and so on (see Table 2.1). Also, it is more empathetic and accurate to use the phrase *a woman who uses a wheelchair* instead of such terms as *confined to* or *wheelchair-bound.* Words such as *defect* or *defective* reinforce negative ideas about persons with disabilities. As the Easter Seal Society guidelines stipulate, it is permissible for us to use the terms

defect or *defective* in describing an object—but not in describing human beings. Instead of *birth defect,* we can say *disability present at birth* or *born with.* Other terms that cause difficulty if used incorrectly are *diagnose, disease,* and *patient.*

Paternalistic terms may belittle individuals, such as referring to adults as *kids,* or they may overemphasize routine achievements by using terms like *brave* or *courageous.*

4. When it is necessary to make a distinction, use the phrase *people without disabilities.*

Particularly offensive to many people with disabilities is the use of the term *normal* to apply to individuals without apparent disabilities. As Dattilo and Smith (1990) stated, such use implies that a disability is the single distinguishing factor that divides people into two primary categories: "normal" and "disabled." The preferred phrase is *people without disabilities;* however, the term *nondisabled* may also be acceptable and is used periodically within this book. Another term for a person without a disability is *TAB.* This term is an acronym for "temporarily able-bodied" and is intended to make persons without disabilities aware they may experience a disabling condition at some point in their lives. TAB, however, is not a widely known expression and should be avoided unless it is specifically used to illustrate the point that anyone may experience a disability.

Appropriate terminology related to disability is constantly changing. A term considered appropriate at one time may later be considered inappropriate or even offensive. Conversely, as Dattilo (2002) has written:

> Words that are currently creating controversy, and have yet to receive a general consensus, may be the words of choice in the future. In all situations, listen to your constituents to determine the terms and phrases they most prefer and attempt to understand their reasons for these choices. (p. 104)

Negative Attitudes

Schleien et al. (1997) have termed negative attitudes, "One of the most powerful obstacles faced by individuals with disabilities who are attempting to be included in community recreation programs . . ." (p. 61). Negative attitudes held by recreation professionals and coparticipants in recreation can be large barriers to inclusive recreation experiences. Unfortunately, people often hold the most negative attitudes toward those individuals who have the most severe disabilities and those whose disabilities may seem the most threatening, such as persons who are mentally ill. A part of negative attitudes may be placing persons with disabilities in "sick roles" in which those with disabilities are perceived to be dependent on others to gain participation in society and, therefore, in need of help from persons who are not disabled. Even persons who have disabilities may fall into the trap of adopting negative self-attitudes in which they see themselves as being sick or dependent and different from others (Schleien et al.). Such negative attitudes toward persons with disabilities may negatively influence attitudes toward fully including persons with disabilities in public and commercial recreation experiences.

It is critical that efforts be taken to change these attitudes because negative attitudes can be pervasive obstacles to inclusive recreation. Laws, such as the ADA, mark a giant step forward toward inclusion but recreation and leisure provides and the public must begin to adopt positive attitudes toward inclusive recreation in order for persons with disabilities to truly be included in their community recreation environments (Schleien et al., 1997).

Means to Attitude Change

Attitude change is perceived to be brought about through two means. One is through the use of *persuasive communication.* The second is through *exposure.*

Persuasive Communication

Authorities agree that attitudes are changed by means of one of two routes to persuasion. These are the *central route* and the *peripheral route.* When people carefully scrutinize presentations, they are using the central route. People concern themselves with carefully considering the arguments contained in the message and how strong they are. Attitudes usually change to the extent that arguments are strong. People tend to follow the central route in instances when they care about a particular issue. When the topic is less important, people are more likely to follow the peripheral route. Using the peripheral route, individuals are more affected by the mood they are in and tend to pay more attention to factors such as the communicator's attractiveness and likability. Celebrities are often used to persuade via the peripheral route (Aronson, Wilson, & Akert, 1999; Cooper & Aronson, 1992).

Therefore, to alter attitudes toward serving persons with disabilities, certain principles should be followed. If the audience sees the issue as important, strong arguments need to be put forth to ensure a persuasive communication. On the other hand, if the audience does not perceive the topic as being important, the presenter should be chosen carefully, because the attributes of the communicator (e.g., attractiveness) may have a significant effect, and care should be taken to put audience members in a good mood.

A related strategy is to ask audience members to *role-play.* If persons are asked to play the role of someone who holds a position differing from theirs, they often will alter their beliefs to correspond with the role assumed. Some research has found that role playing produces greater attitude changes than receiving a presentation (Worchel, Cooper, & Goethals, 1991). Although there is a lack of empirical evidence in the literature indicating the use of role playing in changing attitudes toward serving individuals with disabilities, it would appear to be an effective method.

Altering Attitudes toward Persons with Disabilities

Both role playing and presentations have been successfully employed to alter general attitudes toward individuals with disabilities. Researchers at the University of Illinois (Clore & Jeffery, 1972) found that role-playing a wheelchair user by traveling on campus for an hour brought about more positive attitudes toward persons with disabilities. Such realistic experiences should not be confused, however, with simulations in which individuals without disabilities take part in recreational activities while simulating disabilities. Donaldson (1980), after reviewing the research, has stated, "the present fad of game-type disability simulations may have little effect in helping participants see [persons with disabilities] in less stereotypic ways" (p. 511).

Presentations have sometimes been effective in changing global attitudes toward persons with disabilities. One study (Austin, Powell, & Martin, 1981) involved the use of a class presentation that positively influenced the attitudes recreation and leisure studies students held toward individuals with disabilities. Results of studies involving such presentations, however, have been equivocal. To date, the exact factors that contribute to positive changes have not been identified. Further research is needed to determine more precisely the factors that facilitate positive changes resulting from presentations directed toward altering attitudes about persons with disabilities.

Exposure

Zajonc (1968) conducted the now-classic "black bag" social psychology study. Zajonc exposed university students in a speech class to an unknown person hidden inside a large black bag. The person in the black bag sat quietly on a table in the rear of the classroom during the entire semester. At the beginning, students were hostile toward the black bag but grew to like it by the end of the term. It was reasoned that mere exposure to an object (in this case, the black bag) was sufficient to bring about attitude enhancement. In other words, attitudes are enhanced by mere exposure to, or contact with, an attitude object.

Exposure as a Means to Alter Attitudes toward Persons with Disabilities

Research has revealed that mere contact with individuals who have disabilities, unlike contact with black bags, does not necessarily produce more positive attitudes toward these individuals. In fact, negative attitudes may result if nondisabled persons experience tension or anxiety, or perceive information that reinforces existing stereotypes (Donaldson, 1980). It is of utmost importance to structure the situation so that nondisabled persons experience pleasant feelings during their exposure to persons with disabilities because uninitiated people may feel uncomfortable with persons who have disabilities. It is likewise important that old stereotypes are not reinforced but instead are changed as a result of the contact. Recreational situations should provide an ideal setting for altering attitudes through exposure to persons with disabilities. A pleasant recreation environment offers an ideal situation in which persons without disabilities can interact with individuals who provide healthy, positive images of persons with disabilities. An example of this is college students working in recreational sports programs with skilled athletes who are disabled.

In addition to contact occurring in a friendly recreational setting in which people can get to know one another, other conditions that can enhance attitudes have been identified through research. These include mutual interdependence in achieving a common goal, equal status and power, and social norms that support acceptance and tolerance. Mutual interdependence involves a cooperative situation where individuals must depend on each other to accomplish a goal that is important to them, such as might occur in many recreational activities. Equal status and power are important because when status is unequal, interactions can easily follow stereotypical patterns. This defeats the purpose of contact, which is to break down those stereotyped beliefs. Finally, social norms that support acceptance and tolerance can help change attitudes. For example, if the leader of a recreation activity in a community center reinforces a norm of acceptance and tolerance, those in the group will be more likely to conform to fit the norm (Aronson et al., 1999).

In retrospect, while the mere contact hypothesis was perhaps naive, it has led us to more research that has revealed that, under certain conditions, contact with persons who have disabilities can lead to more positive attitudes. Nevertheless, even though exposure may produce a positive effect on general attitudes toward people with disabilities, global attitudes have not been found to correlate with specific behaviors, such as providing recreation services for people with disabilities. The following section covers work that questions our traditional thinking regarding attitudes and behavior.

A Myth?

Several authors in the field of leisure and recreation (e.g., Howe-Murphy & Charboneau, 1987; Schleien & Ray, 1988) have proclaimed that negative attitudes toward persons with disabilities cause barriers to the provision of recreation services for these persons. However, Ajzen (1988) has argued convincingly that attitudes toward any given object (e.g., persons with disabilities) can predict only a *general pattern* of behavior, and not a *specific* behavior. Thus a general measure of attitude (i.e., a score on a scale measuring attitudes toward persons with disabilities) would not be useful in predicting a specific behavior, such as providing recreation services for persons with disabilities.

Following the conceptual framework provided by Ajzen (1988), we would be unwise to believe that if we alter attitudes toward persons with disabilities in a positive way, we can expect those

holding more favorable attitudes to be more likely to provide inclusive recreation services. Ajzen stipulates that, to predict a *specific behavior,* one needs to know the *specific attitude* related to that behavior. To predict whether a community parks and recreation professional would provide services designed for persons with disabilities, we would need to know his or her specific attitude toward serving them, not what general attitude he or she holds toward individuals who have disabilities.

There are factors other than attitudes that could influence whether persons with disabilities would be served by community parks and recreation specialists. Factors such as social norms, influences from other people, consequences of the behaviors, and personality traits have been used in predicting behavior (Ajzen, 1988; Ajzen & Fishbein, 1980). Another factor influencing behavior is the amount of experience a person has had with the attitude object (Fazio & Zanna, 1978; Regan & Fazio, 1977). Findings suggest that behaviors can be predicted from attitudes when the person has had previous experience with the attitude object. For example, an individual who has had experience in the provision of recreation for persons with disabilities would be more apt to act in accord with his or her attitudes toward serving persons with disabilities than would a person without previous experience.

Thus, the traditional model in which it was supposed that improvement in general attitudes toward persons with disabilities would result in increased provision of recreation services to persons who have disabilities has not found support in modern attitude literature. The level of specificity of the attitude and other factors (e.g., social norms, previous experiences) need to be taken into consideration when attempting to predict any behavior, including the provision of recreation services to persons who have disabilities.

THE THEORY OF PLANNED BEHAVIOR

Ajzen (1988, 1991) has developed an attitude model to extend theoretical understandings of the relationship between attitudes and behavior. It is

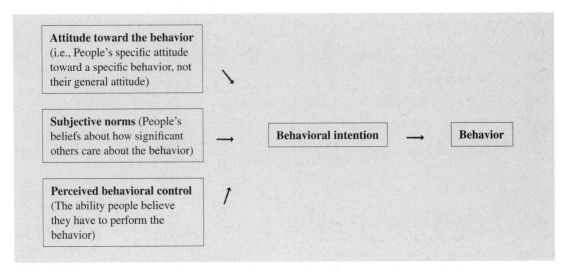

Figure 2-1   The Theory of Planned Behavior
Adapted from Ajzen, I. The theory of planned behavior. *Organizational Behavior and Human Decision Processes,* 50, 179–211, 1991.

named "The Theory of Planned Behavior" (see Figure 2-1). Ajzen's theory holds that the *attitude toward the specific behavior* and the *subjective norm* (the influence of significant others and the person's motivation to comply with their desires), along with *perceived behavioral control* (the amount of control the person feels), combine to bring about a *behavioral intention.* Knowledge of the behavioral intention can then be used to predict *actual behavior.* There is no direct correspondence between the behavioral intention and behavior, because other factors may interfere with the intention being carried out (e.g., resources available or experience with the attitude object).

For example, even though an administrator may intend to initiate inclusive recreation services, an emergency may occur that could divert resources from being used to begin the program. While the administrator may wish to initiate a plan, outside interferences may prevent that behavior. The behavioral intention may not be carried out.

Nevertheless, without a positive attitude toward establishing the service and social norms that support the action (such as support from the board and staff), there would be no behavioral intention to initiate the service. Thus, the critical nature of

developing positive attitudes toward *serving* citizens with disabilities is apparent. While it may be meritorious to attempt to create more positive general attitudes toward persons with disabilities, there is apparently no reason to believe that this will bring about increased services for these individuals. Therefore, the focus of the discussion will be on the specific attitude of service to persons with disabilities, rather than on general attitudes toward persons who have disabilities.

CHANGING ATTITUDES TOWARD SERVING PERSONS WITH DISABILITIES

How then do we bring about changes in attitudes toward serving persons with disabilities using the Theory of Planned Behavior? Because our attitudes rest on learned beliefs, our efforts should be aimed toward altering the most prominent, or salient, beliefs related directly to the behavior of serving persons with disabilities. There are four means to altering beliefs on which an attitude is based. We can (1) discard old beliefs, (2) add new salient ones, (3) alter their strength (how much we believe them), or (4) change their evaluation (how negative or positive we are) (Austin & Austin, 1983).

To alter beliefs, we must first identify them. Once identified, we may develop strategies to persuade the individuals to alter their belief system. For example, it might be discovered that the person holding a negative attitude toward serving individuals who have disabilities believed that carrying out the service would cause a great deal of inconvenience on his or her part. Information could be provided to show that a minimum amount of inconvenience would be involved for the comparatively large rewards to be received. Another example would be adding beliefs related to the enjoyment the person might receive in setting up a new service. If it is found that the person is not aware of positive benefits, such as getting to travel to other parks and recreation departments to meet with colleagues already offering a program, or the good will created in the community as a result of establishing a program, these might be pointed out to him or her (Austin & Austin, 1983).

Subjective Norms

Subjective norms are similarly based on beliefs, therefore they too are subject to change. Beliefs in regard to perceived social norms can be added, deleted, or changed in strength. Motivation to comply to the norm can also be changed.

For example, beliefs toward serving persons with disabilities might be made more positive if the individual learns that a highly regarded administrator in a neighboring community is initiating an inclusive and special recreation program. The impact of this knowledge could be multiplied if it were learned that several influential citizens had recently made public statements favoring the establishing of recreation services for people with disabilities and that the mayor, who once opposed any parks and recreation program expansion, came out for inclusive and special recreation programming. The motivation to comply with what significant others desire would likely be increased if the individual saw that his or her compliance might be viewed in a positive way by influential citizens on whom the department relies for support. Thus, by altering beliefs and providing the motivation to

comply with significant others, a subsequent increase in the overall subjective norm would be anticipated.

Perceived Behavioral Control

Like attitudes and social norms, the weighing of perceived control is apt to influence behavioral intention. When abilities to take action are seen to be inadequate, motivation to act will be lacking. On the other hand, if people believe they have what it takes to succeed, they will be willing to take action. For example, if staff members feel they have the opportunity and resources to deliver services for persons with disabilities, they will, given they hold positive attitudes and believe they have the support of significant others.

Summary to Attitudes Discussion

It has been suggested that any change in attitude toward the behavior, in subjective norms, or in perceived control can facilitate change in behavioral intentions. In turn, this may bring about changes in behavior. The application of this model in parks and recreation has been discussed in regard to the specific behavior of establishing services for persons with disabilities. Once beliefs toward serving persons with disabilities have been identified, it is possible to design strategies to alter the information base underlying the attitudes and social norms of policymakers.

The popular notion that general attitudes (such as attitudes toward persons who have disabilities) can be used to predict specific behaviors (such as the provision of inclusive recreation services) has been seriously questioned. Ajzen's (1991) Theory of Planned Behavior has been presented as an alternative to traditional thinking about attitudes. Three key components (attitudes, subjective norms, and perceived control) purportedly influence behavioral intentions, and ultimately, behavior. Furthermore, attitudes and subjective norms are based on salient beliefs held by individuals. Therefore, attitudes and subjective norms may be changed by altering beliefs.

SUMMARY

Critical to understanding the provision of services for people with disabilities is a knowledge of concepts and attitudes that underlie inclusive recreation services. Within this chapter, terms were covered that relate to inclusive and special recreation. To comprehend these terms is to begin to form a foundation for grasping concepts related to inclusive recreation services. Also integral to this understanding is the application of modern attitudes theory to the relationship between attitudes and behavior in serving persons with disabilities. Knowing how attitudes are formed and changed provides parks and recreation professionals with the means to bring about positive attitudes toward serving individuals who have disabilities.

SUGGESTED LEARNING ACTIVITIES

1. Define the following terms in your own words: *disabled, handicapped, impaired, inclusive recreation, special recreation.* Then compare your definitions with those of other students.

2. On the Web, locate information on the International Classification of Functioning, Disability and Health published by the World Health Organization (WHO). Review the material. Report in class if this activity was helpful to understanding the WHO classification system.

3. In a small group, discuss how you can be an advocate for persons with disabilities. Do you see any conflict of interest on your part as a recreation professional, as opposed to parents of children with disabilities or those who have disabilities?

4. In a one- or two-page paper, discuss distinctions between normalization, mainstreaming, and least restrictive environment.

5. In a small group, discuss the term *attitudes.* Then discuss what you feel to be the attitudes of recreation students on your campus toward the provision of leisure services for persons with disabilities.

6. List practical strategies you might use as a recreation professional to alter attitudes toward serving persons with disabilities. Bring your list to class to compare it with those of other students.

7. Spend a day with a person who has a disability. Discuss misconceptions that you had about life with a disability, and state how this experience has affected your attitude toward persons with disabilities.

REFERENCES

Ajzen, I. *Attitudes, Personality and Behavior.* Chicago: Dorsey Press, 1988.

Ajzen, I. The theory of planned behavior. *Organizational Behavior and Human Decision Processes, 50,* 179–211, 1991.

Ajzen, I., & M. Fishbein. *Understanding Attitudes and Predicting Social Behavior.* Englewood Cliffs, NJ: Prentice-Hall, 1980.

Anderson, L., C. Brown, & P. Soli. *Inclusion: Strategies for Including People with Disabilities in Parks and Recreation Opportunities.* Bismarck, ND: Rural Recreation Integration Project, 1996.

Aronson, E., T. D. Wilson, & R. M. Akert. *Social Psychology* (3rd ed.). New York: Longman, 1999.

Austin, D. R., & L. G. Powell. *Resource Guide: College Instruction in Recreation for Individuals with Handicapping Conditions.* Bloomington: Indiana University, 1980.

Austin, D. R., L. G. Powell, & D. W. Martin. Modifying attitudes toward handicapped individuals in a classroom setting. *The Journal for Special Educators, 17*(2), 135–141, 1981.

Austin, D. R., & M. E. Crawford, Eds. *Therapeutic Recreation: An Introduction* (3rd ed.). Boston: Allyn and Bacon, 2001.

Austin, J. K., & D. R. Austin. An attitude theory to enhance understanding of behavior related to mainstreaming blind and visually impaired persons in recreation activities. In J. D. Kelley, Ed. *Recreation Programming for Visually Impaired Children and Youth.* New York: American Foundation for the Blind, 1983, pp. 173–186.

Bullock, C. C., & M. J. Mahon. *Introduction to Recreation for People with Disabilities: A Person-Centered Approach* (2nd ed.). Champaign, IL: Sagamore Publishing, 2000.

Clore, G. L., & K. M. Jeffery. Emotional role playing, attitude change, and attraction toward a disabled person. *Journal of Personality and Social Psychology, 23,* 105–111, 1972.

Cooper, J., & J. M. Aronson. Attitudes and consistency theories: Implications for mental health. In D. N. Ruble, P. R. Costanzo, & M. E. Oliveri, Eds. *The Social Psychology of Mental Health.* New York: Guilford Press, 1992.

Dattilo, J. *Inclusive Recreation Services* (2nd ed.). State College, PA: Venture, 2002.

Dattilo, J., & R. W. Smith. Communicating positive attitudes toward people with disabilities through sensitive terminology. *Therapeutic Recreation Journal, 24*(1), 8–17, 1990.

Davis, C. M. *Patient Practitioner Interaction: An Experimental Manual for Developing the Art of Health Care* (3rd ed.). Thorofare, NJ: SLACK Incorporated, 1998.

Disability Data Briefing, Australian Institute of Health and Welfare. December 1997. [Online]. Available: http://216.239.53.104/search?q=cache: dqYEsm3g8kJ:www.workable.org.au/archive/aihw2. htm+icidh-2&hl=en&ie=UTF-8, August 15, 2003.

Donaldson, J. Changing attitudes toward handicapped persons: A review and analysis of research. *Exceptional Children, 46,* 504–514, 1980.

Fazio, R. H., & M. Zanna. Attitude qualities relating to the strength of the attitude-behavior relationship. *Journal of Experimental Social Psychology, 14,* 398–408, 1978.

Gorham, P., & F. Brasile. Accessibility: A bridge to a more inclusive community. In F. Brasile, T. K. Skalko, & J. Burlingame, Eds. *Perspectives in Recreational Therapy: Issues of a Dynamic Profession.* Ravensdale, WA: Idyll Arbor, Inc., 1998, pp. 323–342.

Hillman, W. A. Therapeutic recreation specialist as advocate. *Therapeutic Recreation Journal, 6*(2), 50, 1972.

Howe-Murphy, R., & B. G. Charboneau. *Therapeutic Recreation Intervention: An Ecological Approach.* Englewood Cliffs, NJ: Prentice-Hall, 1987.

Livneh, H., & R. F. Antonak. *Psychosocial Adaptation to Chronic Illness and Disability.* Gaithersburg, MD: Aspen Publishers, Inc., 1997.

Lord, J. Opening doors, opening minds! *Recreation Canada,* Special Issue, 4, 5, 1981.

Mannell, R. C., & D. A. Kleiber. *A Social Psychology of Leisure.* State College, PA: Venture Publishing, Inc., 1997.

McGrovern, J. *The ADA Self-Evaluation: A Handbook for Compliance with the Americans with Disabilities Act by Parks and Recreation Agencies.* Arlington, VA: National Recreation and Park Association, 1992.

Meyer, L. E. Personal communication. July 1984.

National Easter Seal Society. Guidelines. Portraying persons with disabilities in print. *Rehabilitation Literature, 42,* 284, 285, 1981.

Rag Time. *TASH Newsletter, 15,* 6, 8, February 1989.

Re-creating Recreation for Inclusion. Evanston, IL: National Lekotek Center, 1998.

Regan, D. T., & R. H. Fazio. On the consistency between attitudes and behavior: Look to the method of attitude formation. *Journal of Experimental Social Psychology, 13,* 28–45, 1977.

Rynders, J. E., & S. J. Schleien. *Together Successfully.* Arlington, TX: Association for Retarded Citizens of the United States, 1991.

Schleien, S. J., & F. P. Green. Three approaches for integrating persons with disabilities into community recreation. *Journal of Park and Recreation Administration, 10*(2), 51–66, 1992.

Schleien, S., M. Ray, & F. Green. *Community Recreation and People with Disabilities: Strategies for Inclusion* (2nd ed.). Baltimore: P. H. Brookes, 1997.

Schleien, S., & M. T. Ray. *Community Recreation and Persons with Disabilities: Strategies for Integration.* Baltimore, MD: Paul H. Brookes, 1988.

Smith, R. *Programming for Handicapped Individuals in Public Park and Recreation Settings.* Washington, DC: Hawkins and Associates, 1980.

Stein, J. U. Mainstreaming in recreational settings: It can be done. *Leisure Today.* In *Journal of Physical Education, Recreation and Dance, 56*(5), 3, 52, 1985.

Sylvester, C., J. E. Voelkl, & G. D. Ellis. *Therapeutic Recreation Programming: Theory and Practice*. State College, PA: Venture Publishing, Inc., 2001.

Tate, D. G. The ICIDH-2: A new classification of disablement. *The International Journal of Psychosocial Rehabilitation*. [Online]. Available: http://www.psychosocial.com/policy/icidh.html, August 12, 2003.

The Definition of Disability. [Online]. Available: http://www.dpa.org.sg/DPA/definition_disability.htm, August 16, 2003.

Weber, A. L. *Social Psychology*. New York: HarperCollins Publishers, 1992.

Wehman, P. *The ADA Mandate for Social Change*. Baltimore: Paul H. Brookes, 1993.

Wilhite, B., M. A. Devine, & L. Goldenberg. Perceptions of youth with and without disabilities: Implications for inclusive leisure programs and services. *Therapeutic Recreation Journal 33*(1), 15–28, 1999.

Wolfensberger, W. *Normalization*. Toronto: National Institute on Mental Retardation, 1972.

Worchel, S., J. Cooper, & G. R. Goethals. *Understanding Social Psychology* (5th ed.). New York: Brooks/Cole, 1991.

World Health Organization. *ICIDH-2 Prefinal Draft*. Madrid, Spain: November 2000. [Online]. Available: http://www.handinet.dk/prefinal.pdf, August 17, 2003.

World Health Organization. *International Classification of Functioning, Disability and Health,* May 2001. [Online]. Available: http://www.who.int/classification/icf/whares/whaen.pdf, August 16, 2003.

World Health Organization. *Towards a Common Language for Functioning, Disability and Health: ICF*. Geneva: 2002.

World Health Organization. *International Classification of Impairments, Disabilities, and Handicaps: A Manual of Classification Relating to the Consequences of Disease*. Geneva, Switzerland, 1980.

Zajonc, R. B. Attitudinal effects of mere exposure. *Journal of Personality and Social Psychology, 9*(2), 1–27, 1968.

3 LEGISLATION AFFECTING RECREATION SERVICES

(Courtesy of *New Mobility Magazine*)

In recent years, concern for equal rights for individuals who have disabilities has been developing and changing. Legislation pertaining to equal access, as well as rights to educational and recreational services, has evolved. In this chapter, reasons why legislation is such an important tool for change, as well as some of the limitations of legislation, are presented. This chapter then presents a selection of American and Canadian legislative acts that, to varying degrees, have affected the delivery of recreation services to persons with disabilities.

HOPES AND LIMITATIONS OF LEGISLATION

Historically, people with disabilities were seen as a burden to society, as nonpersons. Attention to persons with disabilities since World War II has led to better health care; the right to vote; and the right to free, appropriate public education. Legislation has been seen as one way of ensuring these opportunities were made available. Legislation can be a powerful vehicle for improving the lives of people with disabilities because the law names groups that have been ignored who will now be protected. Strong legislation indicates that people with disabilities have a right to access to a particular aspect of society. It also identifies the mechanisms by which the right will be accorded, including who must comply, by when, and with what standard. As Bullock and Mahon (2000) point out, lawmaking in the United States and Canada has some similarities. Anyone can bring forth an idea, but it must catch the attention of elected officials. It will go forth as a draft bill if there is sufficient evidence of need and support. Most bills go through many debates and revisions before the final vote. Over time, a bill will be reviewed, amended, and reissued, sometimes with title changes. Most importantly, legislation is put into policy when bureaucrats develop detailed regulations to guide implementation.

Although legislation was passed in the 1970s to prohibit discrimination on the basis of disability, discrimination continued in an array of areas, including employment, transportation, and *recreation*. There are several reasons why legislation may not be effective. First, legislation is only about laws and procedures, not other aspects of life. Certain things cannot be legislated; for example, accessibility legislation will ensure people get into a building, but cannot guarantee that once there, attitudes will change and they will be treated fairly or have the chance to make friends. The law cannot force political decisions, but rather the politicians must ensure dollars follow after a new law or judgment has been issued. Civil Rights legislation was enacted, but it took some time for attitudes to change in any substantial way; however, having a law precede attitude change is often necessary. Second, legislation can be weak because compromises are usually required to satisfy competing interests in order to get the legislation passed. Third, sometimes original legislation, such as PL 94-142 Education for All Handicapped Children Act of 1975, is stronger than later legislation or amendments. Fourth, even though a law is enacted, many citizens still feel their rights are not being accorded. Sometimes people use the courts to try to address their rights. However, in most countries, pursing litigation on an individual basis can be expensive, emotionally draining, and simply out of the range of possibility for an average citizen. Advocacy organizations are there to protect citizens with disabilities, but often lack the resources to pursue litigation on behalf of individuals or groups that are suffering (Hutchison & Mannell, 1980; Nesbitt, 1980).

Discrimination manifests itself in recreation programs and services in a variety of ways:

- It may occur when a person with a disability or family member of the person inquires about enrolling in a particular program and is referred inappropriately elsewhere.
- It occurs when parks, playgrounds, and other recreation facilities and equipment are not designed for accessibility and usability.
- It occurs when camp personnel refuse to accommodate a child with a mild impairment.

- It occurs when individuals with disabilities are not granted job interviews in a recreation service because they possess impairments.

Rights create conditions for community and inclusion, but do not ensure these will happen. Some organizations address disability issues through a human rights lens while others use a much broader framework. Any legislation and policy pertaining to individuals with disabilities should focus on issues of citizenship, inclusion, and barriers. Citizenship is important because it recognizes that approaches to disability have shifted from a traditional, rehabilitation model, where people are treated as clients and patients, to a community model, where people are afforded all the rights and responsibilities of citizenship. If we embrace a model of community and citizenship, then inclusion should be both a process and an outcome. Inclusion is important because it recognizes that people have the right to be in the community, accessing the same valued resources that other citizens use, in contrast to therapeutic or special programs. Barriers to citizenship and inclusion continue to plague people with disabilities and must be addressed in legislation and policy (Nelson, Lord, & Ochocka, 2001; Pedlar & Hutchison, 2000).

AMERICAN LEGISLATION

The Americans with Disabilities Act of 1990 is showcased in this first section, followed by accessibility legislation, rehabilitation acts, education legislation, and developmental disabilities efforts that have set the tone for many of the recent developments in the delivery of recreation and park programs and services to individuals with disabilities. When an act is passed by Congress, it is numbered such as PL (Public Law) 101-476. The first set of numbers, 101, refers to the session of Congress when it was passed and the second number, 476, refers to the sequence of passage and enactment of the act during that session. In other words, 101 is the 476th law passed by Congress and signed by the President during the 101st session (Bullock & Mahon, 2000).

The Americans with Disabilities Act of 1990, PL 101-336

Legislation providing a clear goal of eliminating discrimination against persons with disabilities was first introduced to the 100th Congress in 1988, and was known as the Americans with Disabilities Act (ADA). It was signed into law in July 1990.

What Is the Purpose of the Americans with Disabilities Act?

ADA is designed to increase significantly the opportunity for millions of Americans with disabilities to participate more fully in the activities and to benefit from the services available to all other Americans.

The bill represents a major expansion of the rights of individuals with disabilities. As have other civil rights measures, the requirements of the ADA apply to both public and private employers and to providers of public services. This encompasses a multitude of services including shopping, going to the movies, and participating in *recreation and park services*. As McGovern (1992) states:

> Make no mistake about it, the ADA IS a civil rights law. Congress intended that the ADA will extend the protections of the 1973 Rehabilitation Act to all 33,000 units of government, and all organizations and businesses in this country that affect the availability of goods, services, and facilities for the general public. (p. 7)

Recreation specialists need to be advocates for the civil rights of persons with disabilities and determine how the various aspects of the legislation affect programs and services. Nondiscriminatory practices are vital to the integration of persons with disabilities within the mainstream of American life. As noted by Schleien, Ray, and Green (1997), the community recreation professional must ensure that the philosophical position of the agency is nondiscriminatory in practice, policy, and attitudes.

Who Is Protected by the ADA?

All individuals with disabilities are protected. The ADA definition of *individual with a disability* is specific. A person with a disability is an individual who:

- has a physical or mental impairment that substantially limits one or more major life activities;
- has a record of such an impairment; or
- is regarded as having such an impairment.

For the requirements under the ADA to be applied, the disability has to result in a substantial limitation of one or more major life activities, such as caring for one's self, performing manual tasks, walking, seeing, hearing, speaking, breathing, learning, working, and *participating in community activities* (Enforcing the ADA: A Status Report from the Department of Justice, 1998). There has been some concern that the ADA might be more relevant and effective in protecting the rights of those with visible disabilities like cerebral palsy, who fought for the ADA, compared to the large numbers of people with "invisible" disabilities such as arthritis or cardiovascular conditions, who in general did not lobby for the ADA's passage (Johnson, 1997).

Who Must Comply with the ADA?

There are five titles within the ADA (see Table 3.1). Title V includes miscellaneous provisions and is not referenced in Table 3.1. Title I covers nondiscrimination in employment activities; Title II requires states and local government entities, programs, and transportation to be made accessible to and usable by persons with disabilities; Title III covers the accessibility and availability of programs, goods, and services provided to the public by private entities; and Title IV requires that telecommunications services be made accessible to persons with hearing and speech impairments.

For example, private employers, state and local governments, employment agencies, labor unions, and joint labor-management committees must comply with Title I of the ADA. An employer cannot discriminate against *qualified* applicants and employees on the basis of disability. Title III of the Act applies to privately operated entities including restaurants, public buildings, *parks,* and *other places of recreation.*

What Does the ADA Require of Businesses and Organizations?

The ADA requires businesses and organizations to afford individuals with disabilities a full and equal opportunity to enjoy the goods, services, facilities, privileges, and advantages of accommodations provided to their clientele. Businesses and organizations must provide these services to individuals with disabilities *in the most integrated setting appropriate to the needs of those individuals.* Therefore, all recreation programs, services, and activities must be available in the most integrated setting possible. To ensure the provision of services

TABLE 3.1	Americans with Disabilities Act Overview		
Title	Category	Effective Date	Enforcement
I	Employment	1/26/92	Equal Employment Opportunity Commission
IIA	Government services	1/26/92	U.S. Department of Justice*
IIB	Public transit	8/26/92	U.S. Department of Transportation
III	Public accommodations	1/26/92	U.S. Department of Transportation
IV	Telecommunications	7/26/93	Federal Communications Commission

*Complaints may be filed with the state, with the U.S. Department of Justice or a designated federal agency (e.g., for parks and recreation, the Department of Interior), or in federal court.

Four Rules for Compliance with the ADA

1. No medical questions on application forms.
2. Focus on individual ability, not disability.
3. Don't treat persons with disabilities differently from other people.
4. Provide reasonable accommodation where it is necessary so long as it doesn't pose an undue hardship.

in the most integrated setting, the ADA requires the following of covered businesses:

- that they make reasonable modifications in policies, practices, and procedures when necessary to afford services to individuals with disabilities, unless these modifications would fundamentally alter the nature of the services;
- that they provide auxiliary aids and services to ensure that individuals with disabilities are not excluded, denied services, segregated, or otherwise treated differently from other individuals, unless the auxiliary aid or service would fundamentally alter the nature of the service or would result in an undue burden;
- that they remove architectural and communication barriers that are structural, if the removal of these barriers is readily achievable;
- that they design new facilities so that they are readily accessible to individuals with disabilities unless accessibility is structurally impractical; and
- that, when undertaking an alteration of an existing structure, they design alterations in a manner that, to the maximum extent feasible, provides accessibility. The regulations specifically focus on accessibility in entrances, hallways, bathrooms, telephones, and drinking fountains.

In 1999, the Justice Department sued a major movie theater chain for not providing stadium-style seating to individuals who use wheelchairs. The lawsuit alleged that companies violated the Americans with Disabilities Act by denying movie goers who use wheelchairs or cannot climb stairs equal access to stadium-style seats. The ADA requires places of public accommodation, such as movie theaters, to provide equal access to persons with disabilities and prevents them from providing persons with disabilities a lower quality of goods and services than they provide other members of the general public (Department of Justice ADA Home Page, 1999).

Through a technical assistance grant from the U.S. Department of Justice, the Key Bridge Foundation accepts referrals of complaints under Titles II and III for mediation by professional mediators who have been trained in the legal requirements of the ADA. Many complaints deal with theaters, restaurants, and accessibility issues with office buildings. The following are two examples of results reached through mediation.

- In Kentucky, a person complained that the recreation building did not have accessible showers and doors. The respondent agreed to install a ramp to showers and to adjust the doors to make them accessible to persons with disabilities.
- A wheelchair user complained that a Pennsylvania theater was not accessible. The theater owner agreed to build ramps at the side entrance and to install a buzzer for anyone requiring assistance. The theater owner agreed to transfer films scheduled to be shown in inaccessible theaters to accessible theaters if requested by customers with disabilities. The owner also agreed to add sensitivity training to the staff training program.

What Does the ADA Mean to Providers of Recreation and Parks Services?

As indicated earlier, community-based recreation agencies must ensure that the philosophical position of their organization is nondiscriminatory in practice, policy, and attitudes. If this occurs in hiring practices and in the delivery of recreation and leisure services to persons with disabilities, then the intent of the law is met.

More specifically, when hiring individuals with disabilities, recreation and parks agencies must treat such persons the same as persons without disabilities and provide reasonable accommodation where it is necessary so long as it doesn't pose an undue hardship. For instance, the chairs in a recreation room may need to be reorganized to accommodate individuals in wheelchairs.

With regard to offering recreation and parks programs and services to persons with disabilities, these individuals cannot be excluded, denied, or otherwise treated differently from other individuals, unless the service or program would fundamentally alter the nature of the service or would result in an undue burden. For example, the recreation agency may have to provide or help provide transportation to and from a program site, or the parks and recreation agency may need to create a path in a park between playground apparatus to make the areas accessible and usable by children with disabilities (Dattilo, 2002; Strenstrud, 1993; Wehman, 1993).

The Title II requirements are of primary interest to recreation and leisure agencies. According to McGovern (1992), the key to the Title II requirements is the determination of whether an individual with a disability could meet *essential eligibility* requirements for the use or enjoyment of parks and recreation agency programs and services. For example, if an individual with a disability meets the essential eligibility requirements under the ADA, a parks and recreation department must consider revising requirements for registration and eligibility for participation in programs, removing architectural barriers, providing additional communications media to reach visual and hearing

impaired individuals, and providing additional services to accommodate special needs.

McGovern (1992) suggests that *essential eligibility* is likely to include capacity, charges, and conduct.

> Has this individual registered for the service, program, or activity before it was closed because it was at capacity?
> Will the individual pay the usual fees for the program?
> Will the individual follow reasonable rules of conduct? (p. 10)

Four additional factors that may modify eligibility are *residency, relative skill, safety,* and *age.* As McGovern points out, it is important that accommodations apply to all registrants.

According to McGovern (1995), safety can be a part of essential eligibility. Concerns about risk are part of every recreation program. Also, parks and recreation agencies are prohibited from providing substantial support to organizations that do discriminate. McGovern suggests that this is more offensive if the discrimination occurs on public property such as a park.

The ADA requires the considerations of three types of accommodations when an individual with a disability meets essential eligibility requirements:

1. The agency should modify rules, policies, or practices, as necessary, to enable an individual's participation.
2. The agency should remove architectural, transportation, and communication barriers to enable an individual's participation.
3. The agency should provide auxiliary aids or services as necessary (Epstein, McGovern, & Moon, 1994, pp. 90–91).

An early ADA-related court case dealt with making an accommodation to ensure safety. The Little League had a rule that prohibited coaches who used wheelchairs from being on the field (i.e., within coaching boxes along the baselines). It was the Little League's contention that this situation presented a safety risk to players. An Arizona court, however, decided that the rule was in violation of the ADA because it discriminated against an entire class of people with disabilities. To assess the safety risks involving persons with disabilities, it is necessary to conduct an "individualized assessment" specific to the situation.

As reported by the Associated Press by Golfweb (1998) [http://www.golfweb.com/ library/ martin/index.html], when Casey Martin sued the PGA Tour for a chance to ride a cart while playing the pro golf tour, he was thinking only of himself and his painful right leg. But after his federal court victory—the first time the Americans with Disabilities Act was invoked for competition in a major sport—Martin said he wants to be an inspiration for others with disabilities. Martin asked for a cart to accommodate his rare circulatory disorder that makes it painful and dangerous to walk. This case caused a national debate over the rights of persons with disabilities to compete in professional sports. The issue has to do with "undue burden." An undue burden exists when to make a reasonable accommodation for a program, service, or activity would impose a fundamental alteration in the nature of the program, service, or activity (McGovern, 1995). The Associated Press cited that big name players including Arnold Palmer and Jack Nicklaus testified for the PGA Tour, saying that fatigue can affect the game and that a cart could give a player an unfair advantage. But others like Eric Johnson, another golf pro, testified that carts can hinder good play and disrupt the feel of the course and rhythm that walking provides. Iowa Senator Tom Harkin indicated that ADA requires entities to make reasonable modifications to rules and argues that riding in a cart does not give a player an advantage in competing. The judge in the case acknowledged that the walking-only rule was "substantive," but said the PGA Tour failed to prove that waiving the rule for Martin would fundamentally alter competition. Since this time, his tour record and professional earnings would indicate that he has not had an unfair competitive advantage since using the cart (Kozlowski, 2001).

The following are examples of program requirements cited in a National Therapeutic Recreation Society Report (1998).

- Programs, services, and activities provided by community recreation agencies must be available in the most inclusive setting possible; ideally, this means people with and without disabilities participating side-by-side in the same program.
- Community recreation agencies can still offer separate, specialized recreation programs for individuals with disabilities, but these individuals also have the right to choose to participate in a general program.
- Community recreation agencies may not, under any circumstance, pass on the cost of ADA compliance to a participant with a disability.
- Community recreation agencies are responsible for examining their own programs, services, and facilities to determine whether they comply with the ADA.

In response to ADA requirements and a court ruling, the NRPA is offering an ADA Notice Kit to bolster ADA compliance efforts. The kit provides park and recreation agency patrons with required information on recreation program accessibility, reasonable accommodations, effective communication, employment, and ADA information resources (NTRS Report, 1998).

Finally, architectural and communication barriers must be removed so that persons with disabilities have access to programs and services. This can include providing access to buildings, restrooms, telephones, drinking fountains, and playgrounds. In October 2000, the U.S. Access Board issued the Final Rule for playgrounds, ensuring access to playgrounds, as well as the accessibility of the playground itself (ADAAG, 2000; Hendy, 2001). Recreation and parks agencies also need to make their programs accessible. This may involve modifying program materials. For example, a person with a visual impairment may want to play bridge. In this instance a special deck of cards with raised numbers may be necessary. If a person with a hearing impairment wants to view a movie, effort must be made to accommodate the person by doing such things as raising the volume, providing an amplifier, having an interpreter, or using closed captions. However, if one or more of these options puts an undue burden on the agency, then they do not have to comply. The ADA defines *undue hardship* as an accommodation that is unduly costly, extensive, substantial, or disruptive, or would fundamentally alter the nature or operation of the business or activity.

Rehabilitation Acts and Amendments

The original Vocational Rehabilitation Act was passed in 1954. The primary purpose of this act was to rehabilitate veterans with disabilities. Programs included direct medical assistance and vocational training. Nine years later, in 1963, the Rehabilitation Act Amendments included the phrase "recreation for ill and handicapped." Soon after this addition, several colleges and universities received federal monies from the Rehabilitation Services Administration (RSA) to initiate and/or develop master's degree programs to prepare recreators to work with persons with disabilities. Sessoms (1970) has stated that during the first five years of RSA support, 217 traineeships were awarded to 11 universities and colleges. Park (1980) suggested that more than 140 colleges and universities had received financial support by the end of the 1970s. Thus, hundreds of students received financial assistance through the RSA program. It is difficult to judge accurately the impact that the RSA traineeship program in recreation has had on either the profession of recreation or the number and quality of leisure services rendered to individuals with disabling conditions. However, it may be surmised that the impact has been significant. In addition, these academic programs laid the framework for the eventual development of therapeutic recreation options and emphases within recreation and parks curricula.

Rehabilitation Act of 1973, PL 93-112

The 1973 amendments (PL 93-112) added new directions to recreation services. The "Vocational Rehabilitation Act" was changed to the "Rehabilitation Act." Thus, the concept of rehabilitation was broadened. This act continued the authorization of recreation services in training and research but added new sections that have affected recreation services for persons with disabilities. Selected segments of the Rehabilitation Act follow.

1. Title II—*Research and Training*. This title continued to authorize funds for training recreation personnel to work with persons who have disabilities and for research monies for projects in recreation.
2. Title III, Section 304—*Special Projects and Demonstrations*. This section made monies available for grants for "operating programs to demonstrate methods of making recreational activities fully accessible" to individuals with disabilities. Several projects in recreation, such as the Parks and Recreation Commission in Wood County, West Virginia, which developed a recreation complex accessible to individuals with disabilities, have affected the delivery of recreation services.
3. Title V, Section 502—*Architectural and Transportation Barriers Compliance Board*. Section 502 created the Architectural and Transportation Barriers Compliance Board (A&TBCB) whose main function is to seek compliance with Public Law 90-480. Any citizen may file a complaint with this agency if a barrier is confronted in a public building or facility, particularly with respect to monuments, parks, and parklands covered by PL 90-480. Regulations entitled "Compliance with Standards for Access to and Use of Buildings by Handicapped Persons" were published by this agency in the Federal Register, Tuesday, November 25, 1980. Another function of the A&TBCB required by the Rehabilitation Act Amendments of 1978 (PL 95-602) was to establish minimum guidelines and requirements, published in the Federal Register on Friday, January 16, 1981, for the four federal standard-setting agencies. These four agencies designated by the

Architectural Barriers Act are the General Services Administration, Department of Housing and Urban Development, Department of Defense, and the United States Postal Service. These agencies had one year from the effective date of the regulations (January 6, 1981) to issue final revised standards that have as a minimum the guidelines that were published. Many of the A&TBCB provisions were adopted from ANSI (A 117.1-1980). The 1980 ANSI code was not adopted by the A&TBCB; therefore, each federal agency will be issuing new accessibility codes; different design standards are issued by the many diverse federal agencies.

4. Title V, Section 504—*Nondiscrimination Under Federal Grants.* Section 504 is acknowledged to be landmark legislation for Americans with disabilities. The Department of Health and Human Services (HHS) (formerly Department of Health, Education and Welfare) is the lead agency for Section 504 compliance. The Department of HHS published the first set of Section 504 regulations for recipients of HHS funds in the Federal Register, Wednesday, May 4, 1977, entitled "Nondiscrimination on Basis of Handicap: Programs and Activities Receiving or Benefiting from Federal Financial Assistance." This section states that "No otherwise qualified handicapped individual shall, solely by reason of his handicap, be excluded from the participation in, be denied the benefits of, or be subjected to discrimination under, any program or activity conducted by an executive agency or by the United States Postal Service." Failure to comply with the law can result in the withholding and/or withdrawal of federal financial assistance. Individuals with disabilities are defined as persons with a physical or mental impairment that substantially limits one or more major life activities. People who have a history of, or who are regarded as having, a physical or

mental impairment that substantially limits one or more major life activities are also covered. Major life activities include caring for one's self, walking, seeing, hearing, speaking, breathing, working, performing manual tasks, and learning. Some examples of impairments that may substantially limit major life activities, even with the help of medication or aids/devices, are AIDS, alcoholism, blindness or visual impairment, cancer, deafness or hearing impairment, diabetes, drug addiction, heart disease, and mental illness.

Rehabilitation Act Amendment of 1974, PL 93-516

The Rehabilitation Act Amendment of 1974 authorized the planning and implementation of the White House Conference on Handicapped Individuals, convened in May of 1977. Recreation was 1 of 16 major areas of concern at the White House Conference. The final report[1] noted the importance of recreation for individuals with disabilities and called for the expansion of recreation services and an increase in the number of professionally trained individuals employed in the field of recreation.

Recreation and leisure services, outdoor recreation for persons with disabilities, and recreational programs and facilities are mentioned in the report. The main points of the report included funding incentives, accessibility, community-based recreation programs, and employment and training of recreation professionals. In addition, under the heading of "Social Concerns," recreation was listed. The following is an abbreviated list of concerns dealing with the design of recreational services:

- accessibility
- program variety
- leisure skill
- development
- handicapped lobby
- transportation
- program integration
- funding for recreation
- public awareness

---

[1]*The White House Conference on Handicapped Individuals, Volume Two*: Final Report, Part C. Washington, D.C.: Superintendent of Documents, U.S. Government Printing Office, 1977.

Rehabilitation Act of 1978, PL 95-602

As with many federal programs, the 1973 Rehabilitation Act and the programs it authorized expired at the end of five years. In 1978 legislation was introduced to extend and amend the 1973 act. The 1978 act contained six separate sections that called for recreation and leisure services as part of the rehabilitation process. PL 95-602 authorized the continuation of training programs, although training funds for recreation were curtailed in several regions of the country. The act included recreation as a service to be provided in rehabilitation facilities and in special public projects and demonstration programs such as the Regional Activities and Recreation Center for the Handicapped in Wood County, West Virginia.

The Senate Committee on Human Resources, in introducing the Senate bill to amend and extend the 1973 Rehabilitation Act, stated:

- In recognition of the recreational and social needs of handicapped individuals, the committee bill amends Section 304 to authorize the secretary to make grants to states and public nonprofit agencies and organizations for the purpose of initiating recreational programs for handicapped individuals.
- Recreational programs for handicapped individuals are greatly needed to assist them in developing their capacity for mobility and socialization. Unfortunately, existing programming for this purpose is limited; therefore, it is the committee's intent that this authority stimulate the development of and use of more community-based recreation programs.
- It is the committee's intent that handicapped individuals participate in existing regularly scheduled recreation programs to the maximum extent feasible; the committee realizes, however, that the specialized needs of handicapped individuals may necessitate adaptive equipment and programming and specially trained personnel. The committee therefore expects that such adaptive equipment and programming as well as specialized

personnel attuned to the needs of handicapped persons will be an integral part of any recreation program initiated under this authority. It is further expected that such recreation programs should be coordinated with other recreational activities offered in the community. (Senate Report, 1978)

From a legislative funding perspective, recreation services to persons with disabilities have fared well. As a result of the amendments to the Rehabilitation Act of 1978 (PL 95-602), with reference to Sections 311 and 316, approximately $9 million have been allocated through the two sections to various agencies to make recreation facilities and programs accessible to persons with disabilities.

Education Legislation

The Individuals with Disabilities Education Act of 1990 (IDEA), PL 101-476 (Amended in 1997, PL 105-17) and Formerly Education for All Handicapped Children Act of 1975, PL 94-142

Before the date of the enactment of the Education for All Handicapped Children Act of 1975 (PL 94-142), the special education needs of children with disabilities were not being fully met. More than half of the children with disabilities in the United States did not receive appropriate educational services and more than a million children with disabilities were excluded from the public school system and did not go through the educational process with their peers. Because of the lack of adequate services, primarily within the public school system, families were often forced to find educational and social services elsewhere.

Public Law 94-142 was successful in ensuring children with disabilities access to a free appropriate public education (FAPE). However, the implementation of the act was impeded by low expectations and an insufficient focus. Over 20 years of research and experience demonstrated that the education of children with disabilities can be made more effective by having high expectations, strengthening the role of parents, and providing appropriate special education and related services such as recreation and therapeutic recreation.

In 1990, PL 101-476 amended the Education of the Handicapped Act to revise and extend the programs and purposes of PL 94-142. For example, under Related Services, the term "therapeutic recreation" was added to the existing word "recreation." Under Title IX, Section 601(a), the short title "Education of the Handicapped Act" was replaced by the title "Individuals with Disabilities Act" (IDEA). This change in wording as well as other changes, including replacing "handicaps" with "disabilities," updates the language of the law to reflect current terminology.

IDEA, the 1990 reauthorization of PL 94-142 (the Education for All Handicapped Children Act of 1975), mandates that a free appropriate public education in the least restrictive environment be provided for all children with disabilities. IDEA addresses the provision of physical education and therapeutic recreation that can be requested and delivered as part of the Individual Education Program (IEP) requirement for students with disabilities. Generally, an IEP arranges for services that need to be provided to the student during one school year. However, transition planning also needs to be done well in advance of potentially challenging transitions such as starting high school or graduation from high school. This act also assures student participation in physical education and community recreation services where appropriate. Recreation professionals and advocates should be aware that according to the provisions of IDEA, the IEP process can be used to ensure that the development of community recreation skills and participation in physical education classes are included in a student's educational program (Epstein et al., 1994).

The regulations governing implementation of the law define recreation as including

1. assessment of leisure functioning
2. therapeutic recreation
3. recreation in schools and communities
4. leisure education

The inclusion of recreation as a related service provided a rationale for the inclusion of recreation as part of the IEP and suggested a framework for the delivery of recreation services. This particular point is highlighted in a hearing in Massachusetts involving a female student, Sandra T. In this court hearing, provisions on access to, and equal opportunity to participate in, extracurricular activities in after-school hours that were offered to students without disabilities was a major issue. Dispute between the parties centered on whether Sandra's special needs indicated that an after-school therapeutic recreation/leisure education component should be included in her IEP. In short, a decision (BSEA # 3231)[2] ordered Old Rochester Regional School District to provide an after-school program of related services for Sandra T., incorporating socialization, recreation, physical development, and leisure education objectives for a minimum of six hours per week. Additionally, it was stated: "An aide shall be designated to carry out the program and a therapeutic recreation specialist shall provide a consulting and in-service program to interested teachers, etc., as well as provide direct service to Sandra individually or in a small group for a minimum of one hour per week."

Even though recreation professionals are usually not involved in IEPs, it is important that they be familiar with the process and consult materials such as Storms, O'Leary, and Williams (2000) for sample IEPs and transitional guidelines.

Developmental Disabilities

This section contains legislation that has had an impact on community recreation services for persons with disabilities.

Developmental Disabilities and Facilities Construction Act of 1970, PL 91-517

This act provided services to children and adults with developmental disabilities attributable to

---

[2]This decision was issued pursuant to the requirements of M.G.L.C. 15, 31A, C. 718, The Education of All Handicapped Children Act (20 V.S.C. 1401–1461), The Rehabilitation Act of 1973, Section 502 (20 V.S.C. 794), . . . 1980.

The National Center on Accessibility, located at Bradford Woods in Indiana, provides information and assistance regarding legal mandates to ensure access for all.
(Photo courtesy of Bradford Woods, Indiana University)

mental retardation, cerebral palsy, epilepsy, or other neurological conditions. This law was amended by PL 94-103, entitled "The Developmentally Disabled Assistance Bill of Rights Act of 1975," which added autism to the list of disabilities.

The developmental disabilities program does not provide direct services to individuals. Instead, it is oriented toward the provision of grant funds to a grantee who, in turn, provides the direct service to a population as a result of the acquired funds. Monies are awarded according to priorities established in the annual state plan.

In 1978, the DD Act was amended through passage of the Rehabilitation Comprehensive Services and Developmental Disabilities Amendments. This had an impact on the expansion of services for individuals with disabilities. It affected the Rehabilitation Act of 1973, the Developmental Disabilities Services and Facilities Construction Act, and the Developmentally-Disabled Bill of Rights Act of 1975.

The implications of these amendments to the recreation field are numerous. They allow recreation professionals opportunities to develop and implement special services, training, and research projects in the area of developmental disabilities. Some of the possibilities include (1) services necessary for community adjustment, such as counseling and educating the individual regarding leisure habits and resources for involvement in the community; (2) public awareness and educational programs to assist in the integration of individuals with disabilities into the mainstream of society; (3) coordination of all available community resources; (4) training of specialized personnel needed to service delivery or for research related to developmental disabilities; (5) development of demonstration techniques or projects to serve as a pilot for the expansion and continuation of innovative and successful programs; and (6) gathering and dissemination of information related to developmental disabilities.

The qualified recreation professional can actively involve himself or herself in the provision of quality services following acquisition of federal monies through grant writing. This law addresses the areas of facilities, research and training, demonstration projects, and special recreation programs.

Developmental Disabilities Assistance and Bill of Rights Act of 1990 (DDA), PL 101-496

The Developmental Disabilities Assistance and Bill of Rights Act (DDA), PL 101-496, was reauthorized in 1990 to provide formula grants to states for planning and training personnel to work with people with developmental disabilities. As pointed out by Epstein, McGovern, and Moon (1994), " . . . research and training programs have the capacity to obtain state, federal and private-foundation grants that can be used to fund *inclusive leisure services* within schools and communities" (p. 89) [emphasis added].

CANADIAN LEGISLATION

Canada and the United States both occupy North America and share a border. As such, the two countries have much in common. They share the same core language of English, their people share a similar culture, and both countries are deeply concerned about human rights. Because of close proximity and these similarities, there is a tendency for Canada to look to its larger, more highly developed partner for direction concerning legislation, services, and programming for people with disabilities. Many Canadians would probably agree that legislation such as the Ontario Disabilities Act (ODA) was strongly influenced by the Americans with Disabilities Act (ADA); and Canadian deinstitutionalization came out of similar social movements in the United States.

Recent research, however, shows there are notable signs of differences in values in the two coun-

tries, which in turn will influence policy and legislation. Michael Adams, president of Environics, a Canadian survey and communications consulting company, wrote in *Fire and Ice: The United States, Canada and the Myth of Converging Values* (2003) that there are many areas where our values differ. There was fear by Canadians that, under the North American Free Trade Agreement (NAFTA), the tendency to have the same values would be accelerated, which is not always a good thing according to many Canadians. Adams' research shows this is not happening and points to some value differences: there is a greater gap between the rich and poor in the United States, meaning that Canadians are more comfortable with higher taxes; there are more gun owners in the United States because Canada has stricter gun control legislation; and Americans appear to be retrenching on issues of consumption, acceptance of violence, gender and family roles, ecological concern, and global consciousness.

In terms of the role of people with disabilities in society, we also know that the United States relies more on legislation than Canada. Canadians are less prescriptive, use policy and attitude change as primary vehicles for implementing new ideas, and tend to want to negotiate solutions through the political process rather than create legislation. Americans often choose to override the political process with laws that compel, so it is no surprise that the Americans with Disabilities Act (ADA) was conceived before a Canadian disabilities act. Legislation in the United States also tends to reflect constituencies that are able to bring particular issues to the forefront. For example, the rehabilitation acts were the result of professional influence, and the ADA was more a reflection of the work of people with disabilities and advocacy organizations. This difference in reliance on legislation for creating change may be a reflection of Canada's smaller population base, which makes negotiated change more manageable. Canadian democracy is based on the British parliamentary system, which relies heavily on policy created by legislators, rather than courts. Besides, Canadian laws don't attract the same kind of attention from these different constituencies because there is no reliance on laws to enforce change (Kendrick, 2003).

As for Canada's federal government, it has less power because it is more decentralized. In theory, both Canada and the United States have national and provincial/state jurisdiction. But in Canada, the result has been more of a patchwork approach because the 10 provinces have jurisdiction over disability issues and services (Cameron & Valentine, 2001). One province, for example, might have stronger school integration legislation because education is also a provincial jurisdiction. It is problematic, in any country, if there is no coherence between the two levels of government. The Canadian Charter of Rights and Freedoms (The Constitution Act of 1982) is important because it codifies, in law, citizenship of every person with a disability in every province/territory (Section 15). However, on issues of inclusion and barriers noted earlier, the Charter has failed in areas from access to education and community living to discrimination based on disability income support, and it deserves a "C minus" because of the failure of court cases pertaining to disability that relied on the Charter (Lepofsky, 1997).

Fifteen years after the Charter, awareness of this problem led to the formation of a Federal/Provincial/Territorial (FPT) working group to address ways these discrepancies could be reduced. The outcome, *In Unison,* is a policy agreement (Federal/Provincial/Territorial Ministers Responsible for Social Services, 1998) that in theory the provinces and territories should use as a guide to address both citizenship and barriers. More particularly, it shifts control to people with disabilities and individualizes supports. It is these jurisdictional issues, however, that have hampered the development of a Canadians with Disabilities Act (CDA).

Instead, Canada is resorting to provincial legislation. Currently only one province, Ontario, has an act (ODA Bill 125, 2001) and its impact is limited because of voluntary compliance. In the United States, the federal government overrides the state on a variety of issues, so the ADA can have impact on local recreation issues. The disability movements in both countries argue for a strong presence of the federal government (Cameron & Valentine, 2001).

The Canadian Charter of Rights and Freedoms (The Constitution Act of 1982) has many sections that indirectly affect people with disabilities, such as mobility rights (Sections 6 2a and 4) and legal rights (Sections 12 and 14). However, equality rights (Section 15) have the most direct implications: (1) Every individual is equal before and under the law and has the right to the equal protection and equal benefit of the law without discrimination and, in particular, without discrimination based on race, national or ethnic origin, color, religion, sex, age, or mental or physical disability. (2) Subsection (1) does not preclude any law, program, or activity that has as its object the amelioration of conditions of disadvantaged individuals or groups including those that are disadvantaged because or race, national or ethnic origin, color, religion, sex, age, or mental or physical disability. The success of Canadian disability advocates and organizations in getting a guarantee of disability rights in the constitution has not been seen in any other country, evidence that disability had arrived as a new social movement in Canada (Boyce et al., 2001). Despite progress, Canadian legislation and policy, as in most countries, are quite fragmented in terms of ensuring access and participation for citizens with disabilities.

SUMMARY

The potential and limitations of legislation affecting persons with disabilities have been discussed in this chapter. The chapter presented legislative acts aimed at equal rights for persons with disabilities. In particular, the Americans with Disabilities Act (ADA) was highlighted. This legislation has the goal of eliminating discrimination against persons with disabilities. It is intended to enhance the employment and social opportunities for millions of Americans with disabilities to participate more fully in everyday life. Aspects of the law cover nondiscrimination in employment activities, require state and local government programs and transportation to be made accessible to and usable by persons with disabilities, and cover the accessibility by private entities such as restaurants and movie theaters. ADA has implications for the operation of recreation programs and services and should be thoroughly understood by recreation professionals so that an inclusive position is adopted.

The Rehabilitation Acts have provided monies and opportunities to hundreds of recreation students to become professionally prepared to work in a variety of leisure settings with persons who have disabilities. In addition, the Individuals with Disabilities Education Act (1990) has provided a considerable amount of federal funding for the professional preparation of recreation personnel working with children with disabilities. The Developmental Disabilities Act (PL 91-517) has provided grants to recreation agencies so leisure services can be provided in community-based programs.

Legislation has had a profound impact on the delivery of recreational services to children and adults with disabilities. Acts have made buildings and other facilities accessible to and usable by people with disabilities. Appropriated monies have helped prepare professionals and paraprofessionals and have made direct services available via demonstration programs and construction projects.

Legislation in Canada has taken quite a different turn. Because of their close proximity and similarities, Canada often looks to the United States for direction around legislation and services. While Canada does not currently have federal legislation such as the ADA, some provinces are beginning to develop legislation, such as the Ontario Disabilities Act. There are notable differences in values between the two countries, which are reflected during policy and legislative development.

SUGGESTED LEARNING ACTIVITIES

1. With regard to ADA, what are the general implications for recreation professionals and departments?

2. You are in charge of running an art program and there are several persons with disabilities who have signed up for the program. One person is in a wheelchair, another person has a hearing impairment, and a third individual is blind. Based on making reasonable accommodations as referenced in the Americans with Disabilities Act, what accommodations might you make so these individuals could participate in your art program?

3. Look up one of the pieces of legislation identified in this chapter on the Web. Figure out the most recent amendments.

4. Visit a community recreation site and assess the status of architectural barriers.

5. Discuss what Canadian and American recreationists can learn from each other.

6. Go to the library and review the IDEA. Then, write a one-page paper on how recreation could be incorporated into an IEP.

SOURCES OF ADA INFORMATION

Copies of the department's ADA regulations and publications, including the Technical Assistance Manuals for Titles II and III Common Questions: Readily Achievable Barrier Removal, Design Details! Van Accessible Parking Spaces, and information about the department's technical assistance grant program, can be obtained by calling the ADA Information Line or writing to the address listed here. All materials are available in standard print, large print, Braille, audiotape, or computer disk for persons with disabilities.

> Disability Rights Section
> Civil Rights Division
> U.S. Department of Justice
> P.O. Box 66738
> Washington, D.C. 20035-6738

Copies of the legal documents and settlement agreements mentioned in this publication can be obtained by writing to:

> Freedom of Information/
> Privacy Act Branch
> Administrative Management Section
> Civil Rights Division
> U.S. Department of Justice
> P.O. Box 65310
> Washington, D.C. 20035-5310
> Fax: 202-514-6195

The FOI/PA Branch also provides access to ADA materials on the World Wide Web at http://www.usdoj.gov/crt/foia/records.htm. A link to this website is provided from the ADA Home Page.

The *Equal Employment Opportunity Commission* offers technical assistance to the public concerning Title I of the ADA.

ADA documents
800-669-3362 (voice)
800-800-3302 (TDD)

ADA questions
800-669-4000 (voice)
800-669-6820 (TDD)

The *Federal Communications Commission* offers technical assistance to the public concerning Title IV of the ADA.

ADA documents
202-857-3800 (voice)
202-293-8810 (TDD)

ADA questions
202-418-0976 (voice)
202-418-0484 (TDD)

The *National Institute on Disability and Rehabilitation Research (NIDRR)* of the U.S. Department of Education has funded centers in 10 regions of the country to provide technical assistance to the public on the ADA.

ADA technical assistance nationwide
800-949-4232 (voice & TDD)

The *U.S. Department of Transportation* through the *Federal Transit Administration* offers technical assistance to the public concerning the transportation provisions of Title II and Title III of the ADA.

ADA Assistance Line
888-446-4511 (voice/relay)
202-366-2285 (voice)
202-366-0153 (TDD)

ADA documents and general questions
202-366-1656 (voice/relay)

ADA legal questions
202-366-4011 (voice/relay)

Project ACTION
800-659-6428 (voice/relay)
202-347-3066 (voice)
202-347-7385 (TDD)

The *U.S. Architectural and Transportation Barriers Compliance Board,* or *Access Board,* offers technical assistance to the public on the ADA Accessibility Guidelines.

ADA documents and questions
800-872-2253 (voice)
800-993-2822 (TDD)

Many of these resources are free.

CANADIAN RESOURCES

ARCH: A Legal Resource Center for Persons with Disabilities, 425 Bloor Street East, Suite 110, Toronto, Ontario, M4W 3R5. Voice (416) 482-8255, TTY (416) 482-1254, fax (416) 482-2981, e-mail library@archlegalclinic.ca, or website www.archlegalclinic.ca

Council of Canadians with Disabilities, 294 Portage Ave. Suite 926, Winnipeg, Manitoba, R3C 0B9.

Voice/TTY (204) 947-0303, fax (204) 942-4625, e-mail ccd@ccdonline.ca, website www.ccdonline.ca

Roeher Institute, Kinsmen Building, York University, 4700 Keele Street, Toronto, Ontario, M3J 1P3. Voice (416) 661-9611 or (800) 856-2207, TYY (416) 661-2023, fax (416) 661-5701, e-mail: info@roeher.ca, website www.roeher.ca

REFERENCES

Adams, M. *Fire and Ice: The United States, Canada and the Myth of Converging Values.* Toronto: Pearson, 2003.

Americans with Disabilities Act Accessibility Guidelines (ADAAG) for Buildings and Facilities; Play Areas; Final Rule. [Online]. Available: www.access-board.gov, 2000.

Americans with Disabilities Act, PL 101-336. 42 U.S.C 12101, et seq.: *Federal Registrar, 56*(44), 35544–35756, July 26, 1990.

Associated Press via Golfweb. [Online]. Available: http://www.golfweb.com/library/martin/index.html, 1998.

Bill 125, *Ontarians with Disabilities,* 2001.

Boyce, W., M. Tremblay, M. McColl, J. Bickenback, A. Crichton, S. Andrews, N. Gerein, & A. D'Aubin. *A Seat at the Table: Persons with Disabilities and Policy Making.* Montreal & Kingston: McGill-Queen's University Press, 2001.

Bullock, C., & M. Mahon. *Introduction to Recreation Services for People with Disabilities* (2nd ed.). Champaign, IL: Sagamore Publishing, 2000.

Cameron, D., & F. Valentine. *Disability and Federalism: Comparing Different Approaches to Full Participation.* Montreal, PQ & Kingston, ON: McGill-Queen's University Press, 2001.

Dattilo, J. *Inclusive Leisure Services: Responding to the Rights of People with Disabilities* (2nd ed.). State College, PA: Venture Publishing, 2002.

Department of Justice ADA Page. [Online]. Available: http://www.usdoj.gov/crt/ada/adahom1.htm, 1999.

Enforcing the ADA: A Status Report from the Department of Justice (July–September 1998).

Epstein, R. S., J. McGovern, and M. S. Moon. The impact of federal legislation on recreation programs. In M. S. Moon, Ed. *Making School and Community Recreation Fun for Everyone: Places and Ways to Integrate.* Baltimore, MD: Paul H. Brookes Publishing, 1994.

Federal/Provincial/Territorial Ministers Responsible for Social Services. *In Unison: A Canadian Approach to Disability Issues.* Ottawa, ON: 1998.

Hendy, T. The Americans with Disabilities Act insures the right of every child to play. *Parks and Recreation,* 108–117, April 2001.

Hutchison, P., & R. Mannell, Eds. Special issue: Human rights, legislation, and quality of life. *Journal of Leisurability, 7*(4), 1980.

Johnson, W., Ed. The Americans with Disabilities Act: Social contract or special privilege? Special issue of *The Annals of the American Academy of Political and Social Science, 549,* January 1997.

Kendrick, M. Comparisons between Canada and U.S. on issues related to disability, legislation, and policy from the perspective of a Canadian working in the U.S. in disability policy. Personal interview. Institute for Leadership and Community Development, August 10, 2003.

Kozlowski, J. Peripheral rule waiver is not "fundamental alternation" under ADA. *Parks and Recreation, 36*(9), 54–63, 2001.

Lepofsky, D. A report card of the Charter's guarantee of equality to persons with disabilities after ten years—What progress? What prospects? *National Journal of Constitutional Law, 7,* 263–431, 1997.

McGovern, J. N. *The ADA Self-Evaluation: A Handbook for Compliance with the Americans with Disabilities Act by Parks and Recreation Agencies.* Arlington, VA: National Recreation and Park Association, 1992.

McGovern, J. N. ADA Enforcement: Court and Administrative Decisions. NRPA Congress, 1995. Unpublished paper.

Nelson, G., J. Lord, & J. Ochocka. *Shifting the Paradigm in Community Mental Health: Toward Empowerment and Community.* Toronto: University of Toronto Press, 2001.

Nesbitt, J. The role of legislation in enabling special recreation. *Journal of Leisurability, 7*(3), 17–24, 1980.

NTRS Report, 22(3), p. 11, 1998.

Park, D. C. *Legislation Affecting Park Services and Recreation for Handicapped Individuals.* Published and distributed in part by the U.S. Department of Education, Office of Special Education, Washington, DC, and Hawkins and Associates, Washington, DC, 1980.

Pedlar, A., P. Hutchison. Restructuring human services in Canada: Commodification of disability. *Disability and Society, 15*(4), 637–651, 2000.

Reynolds, R. P., & G. S. O'Morrow. *Problems, Issues and Concepts in Therapeutic Recreation.* Englewood Cliffs, NJ: Prentice-Hall, 1985.

Schleien, S. J., M. T. Ray, & F. P. Green. *Community Recreation and Persons with Disabilities: Strategies for Integration* (2nd ed.). Baltimore: Brookes, 1997.

Senate Report on the Rehabilitation Act of 1978, PL 95-602.

Sessoms, H. D. The impact of the RSA Recreation Trainee Program, 1963–1968. *Therapeutic Recreation Journal, 14*(1), 23–29, 1970.

Storms, J., E. O'Leary, & J. Williams. *The IDEA of 1997: Transition Requirements: A Guide for States, Districts, Schools, Universities, and Families.* Minneapolis, MN: University of Minnesota, Institute on Community Integration. ERIC Number ED 441 324. 800-443-3742, May 2000.

Strenstrud, C. *A Training Manual for Americans with Disabilities Compliance in Parks and Recreation Settings.* State College, PA: Venture, 1993.

The Canadian Constitution Act of 1982, Canadian Charter of Rights and Freedoms.

Wehman, P. *The ADA Mandate for Social Change.* Baltimore, MD: Paul H. Brookes Publishing, 1993.

4

DISABLING CONDITIONS

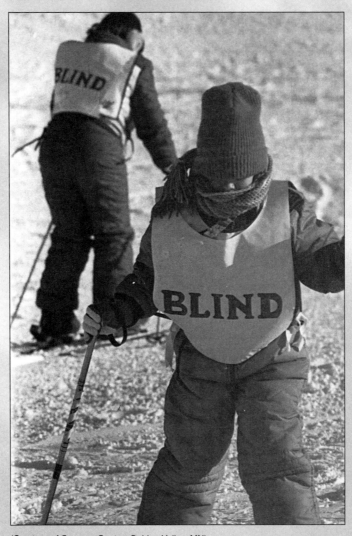

(Courtesy of Courage Center, Golden Valley, MN)

Beginning at a very young age, people are capable of observing different objects and recognizing properties that make these objects similar. Tables, for example, are recognized as large, flat surfaces usually supported by four legs. Doors have handles and open to provide access to the outside or another room. This ability to categorize objects based on common characteristics is essential to human functioning. It not only enables us to recognize things that are essentially the same, but it also allows us to distinguish between items that have different qualities and/or functions. Failing to make such judgments could be catastrophic; that is, it is essential to recognize that a chair is for sitting and a stove is for cooking, rather than vice versa.

LABELING

Categorizing, therefore, is a useful and necessary process in everyday life. However, it also presents problems. Categorizing can result in overlooking the uniqueness of each item within a category or class of objects. This is particularly troublesome when people, rather than objects, are categorized. Each human being desires to be recognized for his or her talents and assets. However, placing a categorical label on people with similar disabilities, a process known as labeling, interferes with recognizing the unique qualities of each individual with a disability. Furthermore, stereotypes may be formed, and these generalizations accentuate the differences (real or imagined) from people without disabilities.

Rosenthal and Jacobson (1968) demonstrated that labeling not only creates expectations that a member of a group will behave in a predictable way, but also can result in a self-fulfilling prophecy. In other words, a person, once labeled, may behave in a certain way *solely* because such behavior is expected of him or her. As a consequence of a self-fulfilling prophecy, a child labeled as mentally retarded may fail to achieve according to his or her cognitive capabilities because others *expect* failure. An adult with a disability may remain physically dependent on others because he or she *expects* such behavior.

Figure 4-1 summarizes the sequence just described. Placing a categorical *label* on an individual results in the formation of a *stereotype*. This stereotype results in *expectations* regarding the individual's behavior. The labeled individual behaves as predicted because of these expectations. Thus, a *self-fulfilling prophecy* has occurred that appears to confirm the stereotype. It is a vicious cycle that many authorities feel precludes the use of labels for people with disabilities. Hutchison and Lord (1979) noted,

> The problems with a label are: 1) we tend to focus upon the person's disabilities rather than abilities, and 2) we make generalizations about the whole person based upon misconceptions regarding that label; in other words, a disability tends to have a spread effect in the minds of others. (p. 18)

Hutchison and McGill (1992) observed that a label may constitute a "life sentence" if it is viewed as a "sacred truth." Too often, people believe that labels are "something that puts all the pieces of the puzzle together; indicates what to do next for someone; and reveals what the person's life is likely

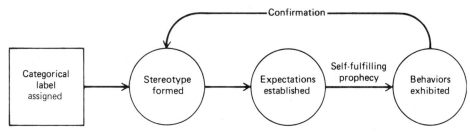

Figure 4-1   Self-fulfilling prophecy

to be like" (p. 19). Bullock and Mahon (1997) emphasized that this "rule of thumb" approach underscores the problems that can result from labeling.

Perhaps the self-fulfilling prophecy results because the *individual* focuses on the disability and makes generalizations about himself or herself. Consequently, it is sometimes difficult for a person with a disability to develop a positive self-concept. He or she may view himself or herself as different from and somehow less worthwhile than others who do not have disabilities. His or her concept of *self,* and perhaps perceptions of the entire world, are distorted by an overemphasis on the disabling condition. This overemphasis is exaggerated, if not caused, by the labeling process.

In addition to the possible consequences previously discussed, labeling someone has conceptual problems. The following questions clarify that identifying members of disability groups is not as easy as one might expect:

1. How severe does a disability or behavioral disorder have to be for a person to be classified as belonging to a disability group? For example, do people have to be legally blind before they are considered visually impaired?
2. Is it the degree of disability or the functional limitation that qualifies a person to be a member of a disability group? For example, should a person be categorized as "mentally retarded" even if he or she functions as well as most people who are not retarded?
3. Should the situation or task be taken into account in categorizing a person? For example, is a wheelchair user considered to have a disability when playing basketball, but not while eating or playing cards?
4. Does the generic term *disability* imply that people with different disabilities have common needs or problems? Should people with multiple sclerosis (who need cooler water to swim effectively) be classified under the same general term as people with cerebral palsy (who function best in warmer pool temperatures)?

The answers to these questions are not clearcut. Rosenhan (1973) provided evidence that a person may be classified as belonging to a disability group *even if he or she has no disability or functional limitation.* In Rosenhan's study, eight subjects without disabilities admitted themselves to psychiatric hospitals and, once on the wards, behaved normally. Despite exhibiting no signs of psychological disorders, these "pseudopatients" were not detected as imposters by medical personnel. To the staff members of these institutions, Rosenhan's subjects were disabled. Ironically, a few "real" patients were the only ones to recognize that Rosenhan's subjects did not truly belong in a psychiatric facility. It is often said that beauty is in the eye of the beholder. Whether someone is classified as having a disability may likewise depend on the beholder.

The Paradox of Labels

We recognize the many shortcomings and problems of labeling individuals with disabilities. It seems paradoxical, therefore, that we find it necessary to discuss people in terms of their disabilities. When used in this textbook, the term *people with disabilities* is *not* meant to imply that all people who have disabilities are alike. On the contrary, the uniqueness of each person, whether disabled or not, is a concept that recurs throughout this text. For example, people who are classified as deaf (or hearing impaired) have similar, but not identical, limitations that may result in some common problems and needs. These same individuals, however, will have widely varied personalities, attitudes, functional behaviors, and so on. As with all other human beings, people with disabilities are alike in some ways, but in other ways they are dissimilar.

If emphasis is placed on individual differences within categories, many authorities contend that labels may prove useful. Pierce (1998), for example, indicated that labels should not be completely eliminated because they are not the cause of discrimination. Moreover, they serve as a useful, though superficial, method of classifying individuals. Bullock and Mahon (1997) have pointed out that categorizing people with similar disabilities may enable recreation providers to be more "in tune" with appropriate services and assist with making programs accessible to everyone. Mandell and Fiscus (1981) also noted that labels can help professionals recognize and dispel negative stereotypes they may have regarding specific disabling conditions. It seems clear, therefore, that recreators must have some understanding of the nature of disabilities if they are to work effectively with *all* of their constituents. Although we fully recognize the potential problems of labeling, we do believe it is necessary to include selected information on a number of disabling conditions.

CONDITIONS AND CHARACTERISTICS

People with disabilities make up a surprisingly large percentage of the population. In the United States, about 54 million people (over 20% of the population) have some level of disability. Of these, 26 million (about 10% of the population) have a severe disability that places limits on their daily lives (McNeil, 1997). If recreation providers are going to provide appropriate services to all citizens, it is essential that they have some basic knowledge about disabling conditions.

The next portion of this chapter provides selected information about a variety of disabling conditions, as well as tips and techniques for offering recreation services to people who have these disabilities. The following disabling conditions are included: blindness and low vision, deafness and hearing loss, mental retardation and other learning impairments, motor impairments, psychological and behavioral disorders, brain injury, and AIDS. Although not disabling conditions per se, aging and at-risk youth have been included in this chapter because of the increasing importance of providing recreational opportunities for these persons.

It must be emphasized that the list in the prior paragraph does not include all possible categories of disability, nor are the statements that follow comprehensive in their content. The intent of each set of statements is to provide introductory applied information that may enhance the general understanding of recreators. Extensive definitions, etiologies (causes), prognoses (expected outcomes), and so on are *not* provided. The limited scope of this chapter does not allow for such depth; nor do most recreators who work in nonclinical settings require such detailed knowledge. Those desiring more depth on one or more disabling conditions are encouraged to refer to the references cited or to seek assistance from local volunteer health organizations, therapeutic recreation professionals, consumer groups, or information and referral sources.

Blindness and Low Vision

Selected Facts

- Millions of Americans are affected by visual impairments or blindness. According to Prevent Blindness American (2003), there are approximately 1,046,920 individuals in the United States age 40 and older who are blind, with an additional 3,406,280 others being visually impaired.
- Visual *acuity* is the precision or clearness with which one sees things in the environment. Visual *field* refers to the arc (degree) of vision that a person has when looking straight ahead.
- Legal blindness is defined as having measured visual acuity of 20/200 or less in the better eye with corrective lenses. In other words, a legally blind person is able to see at 20 feet or less what a person with average vision can see at 200 feet. A person with a visual field of less than an angle of 20 degrees is also legally blind. Persons who have significant, uncorrectable (e.g., surgery, eye glasses) visual impairments, yet are not legally blind, are considered to have *low vision*. Low vision is often defined as visual acuity between 20/70 and 20/200.
- If a person who is blind can perceive light in the environment but not perceive the direction of the light source, he or she is said to have *light perception*. If he or she can perceive the direction of the light source, the person has *light projection*.

- Most people with visual impairments have some vision. Only about 5% of people classified as legally blind have no vision or light perception (total blindness).
- Blindness or low vision are often present at birth, but people who have adventitious (after-birth) visual impairments will generally be able to create mental images of unseen objects based on prior sight.
- Language, motor, and cognitive skills are not significantly impaired by visual deficits, provided the person's environment has been structured to enhance development of these skills.
- Most people with blindness or low vision are not able to read Braille; those who do usually read much more slowly than a person with sight. Few Braille readers exceed 150 words per minute.
- Some people who are blind, particularly children, exhibit mannerisms known as "blindisms." These may be small or large body movements including head shaking, eye pressing, or body rocking.
- Diabetes, which may result in diabetic retinopathy, is one of the most common causes of low vision and blindness in North America. Other common vision-related diseases are glaucoma, cataracts, macular disease, and a hereditary condition known as retinitis pigmentosa. Macular disease causes a loss of central vision, whereas retinitis pigmentosa usually results in loss of peripheral vision (i.e., tunnel vision).

Tips and Techniques for Recreation Professionals

- Try to involve *all* senses in recreational activities; using sounds, tastes, smells, and textures of materials can be enjoyed by everyone.
- Glare and other lighting conditions may create difficulties for some people with visual impairments. Consult participants with blindness or low vision to determine the correct type and amount of lighting to provide because optimal conditions for vision vary from person to person.

- Placing information on audiotapes is preferable to Braille. Some commercial tapes offer compressed speech, which results from electronically cropping speech signals; thus, the speed of a recording is increased without distorting the sound.
- Bulletin boards and other visual displays (e.g., activity calendars) should use high-contrast (black-and-white), enlarged lettering.
- When walking with a person who has blindness or low vision and needs assistance, ask how he or she wishes to be guided. One preferred method, known as "sighted guide," is for the person with blindness or low vision to hold on to your elbow and walk to your side and slightly behind. Verbal cues can help to avoid obstacles.
- Be sure all directions are clear and concise, and demonstrate physical tasks. Allow individuals with blindness or low vision to be close enough to see or touch demonstrations. Use verbal information to create mental images for people with adventitious vision loss.
- Orientation to play and recreational areas is important. Prior to participation, encourage individuals to walk around the area with a guide so they become comfortable with their surroundings. Tactile maps and signs may also allow individuals who are blind to orient themselves to unfamiliar surroundings.
- When approaching a person who is blind, announce your presence using a calm, clear voice, and be sure to state your name. Do not shout or speak louder than necessary. If you need to walk away, let him or her know you are leaving. If the person uses a guide dog, do not touch or speak to the dog, unless you first ask permission from the dog's owner.

Selected Websites

- American Foundation for the Blind
  http://63.240.118.132/
- Lighthouse International
  http://www.lighthouse.org/
- National Federation for the Blind
  http://www.nfb.org/

Deafness and Hearing Loss

Selected Facts

- Hearing involves recognition of sound intensity (volume) at various frequencies (pitch). Intensity is measured by decibels (dB) and frequency is measured by Hertz (Hz).
- There is no legal definition of deafness; however, a person is considered to have profound hearing loss (i.e., deafness) if he or she is unable to hear sounds less than 90 decibels in the better ear. People are considered to be hard of hearing when hearing loss is from 25 to 90 dB.
- Hearing loss is the most common disabling condition in the United States and Canada, affecting about 10% of the population. Only a small percentage, however, have profound hearing loss. Those who have profound hearing loss are unable to understand amplified speech; they experience sound through vibrations from loud noise.
- Hearing loss occurring at birth or shortly afterward often results in delayed language development and difficulty with conceptual thinking. This is probably the greatest limitation experienced by people with hearing loss.
- Many people with hearing loss communicate by use of sign language and finger spelling. Not all people with hearing loss know and understand such communication methods, however, particularly those who lost their hearing after early childhood.
- Children with profound hearing loss often appear to be hyperactive, but their behavior frequently results from difficulty communicating with the hearing world.
- Some people with hearing loss have damage to their semicircular canals, which help control balance. Activities requiring balance, therefore, may prove difficult for these individuals.
- Many people with profound hearing loss reject the idea that deafness is a disabling condition. Rather, they consider deafness to be a cultural concept resulting from shared experiences and a unique language (i.e., sign language). People who subscribe to this interpretation of deafness

may also reject the concept of inclusion in recreational and educational programs.

Tips and Techniques for Recreation Professionals

- Whenever an individual who is deaf attends a recreational event, an interpreter should be provided to facilitate communication. Sign language and finger spelling skills (see Fig. 4-2) would also prove useful for community recreational professionals. As a last resort, write messages on a pad of paper.
- When using sign language or finger spelling, wear solid, dark-colored clothing to serve as a suitable background. Also, ensure that adequate lighting is provided.
- To gain the attention of a person with profound hearing loss, tap the person on the arm or wave your hand (not arm) near his or her visual field. You may also substitute visual cues, such as flashing lights, for auditory cues.
- When using speech to communicate with a person who has hearing loss, always face him or her and do not slow or exaggerate your speech.
- Written instructions should be expressed in short, clear sentences and difficult vocabulary words should be avoided.
- Demonstrations are the most effective method for helping persons with hearing loss to develop or improve upon activity-related skills.
- When working with children who have hearing loss, have several alternative activities prepared. To maintain their interest, it is sometimes necessary to redirect attention to a new activity.
- Participants with profound hearing loss are unable to hear audible warnings of danger (e.g., traffic noise, verbal warnings), therefore, a high degree of structure and supervision is required with some activities and environments.
- To communicate by telephone with a person who has hearing loss, consider using the nationwide "relay system" established by the ADA. This system ensures that trained telephone operators are available to relay communications

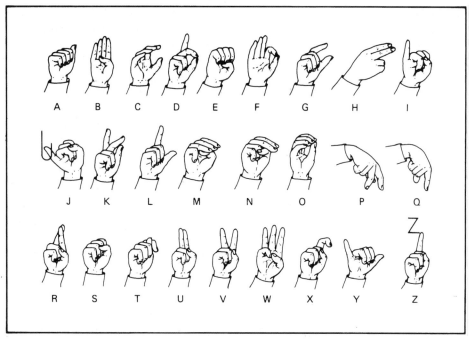

Figure 4-2   Finger spelling alphabet

between a person who is hearing and a person who is deaf or hard of hearing.

Selected Websites
- National Association for the Deaf
  http://www.nad.org/
- Alexander Graham Bell Association for the Deaf and Hard of Hearing
  http://www.agbell.org/
- National Institute for Deafness and Other Communication Disorders
  http://www.nicd.nih.gov

Mental Retardation and Other Learning Impairments

Selected Facts
- It is estimated that 2.3% to 3% of the population has mental retardation, with most (over 85%) having mild retardation. The prevalence of persons with learning disabilities

is more difficult to determine, but most estimates range from 15% to 20%.
- The most frequent known causes of mental retardation are Down syndrome, fetal alcohol syndrome, and fragile X (a genetic that is the leading inherited cause of mental retardation). About one third of mental retardation cases are due to unknown causes.
- By definition, mental retardation is a disability characterized by significant limitations both in intellectual functioning and in adaptive behavior as expressed by conceptual, social, and practical adaptive skills. This disability originates before age 18 (Information and Tips for Mental Retardation and Learning Impairments, 2003).
- People with mental retardation have subaverage intellectual functioning, but they are able to learn. Their rate of learning is slower than that of people without disabilities, however. Deficits in decision making and

problem solving may also accompany this delayed learning pattern.

- Mental retardation and other learning impairments encompass a wide range of cognitive and behavioral functioning. The level of functioning achieved by a person "is determined by the availability of training technology and the amount of resources society is willing to allocate . . . " (Dattilo & Guerin, 2001, p. 133). The greater the deficits in functioning, the greater the need for technological and societal assistance.
- According to the American Association of Mental Retardation (Information and Tips for Mental Retardation and Learning Impairments, 2003), leisure and recreation participation are fundamental in the development of a healthy lifestyle and contribute to a higher quality of life for individuals who have mental retardation. Some people with mental retardation, however, may need assistance and services to help develop independence skills to support their recreation and leisure involvement.
- The majority of people with mental retardation do not differ in physical appearance from their peers without retardation. In general, the higher the cognitive functioning of a person with a learning impairment, the less likely he or she is to have accompanying disabilities, motor deficits, or physical abnormalities.
- Socioeconomic conditions have been found to be associated with some learning impairments; for example, lower socioeconomic environments produce a higher-than-average percentage of people with mild mental retardation.
- Children with mental retardation usually experience delays in their physical, cognitive, and social development; they often exhibit behavior characteristic of children considerably younger in chronological age.
- Learning disabilities should not be confused with mental retardation. People with learning disabilities have average to above-average intelligence but do not function up to their cognitive potential. Sometimes learning disabilities affect specific types of information processing, like math or spelling skills.
- The signs of a learning disability vary widely. Problems in following directions, retaining information, performing paper-and-pencil tasks, and paying attention to appropriate cues are a few characteristics that may indicate the presence of a learning disability. Persons with learning disabilities sometimes also exhibit behavioral problems, such as hyperactivity, perceptual-motor deficits, emotional unpredictability, or aggression toward others (see the section on psychological and behavioral disorders). Learning disabilities are lifelong, but support and accommodations can compensate for specific difficulties.

Tips and Techniques for Recreation Professionals

- The wide range of behaviors and functional abilities of people with learning impairments necessitates careful consideration of each person's abilities. Assumptions about the individual based on a categorical designation must be avoided.
- Activities should be divided into manageable parts and carefully sequenced to offer a progression of skills. Repetition of important tasks may also facilitate learning. Whenever possible, it is helpful to provide a demonstration so participants with learning impairments can model the desired behavior. Also, avoid "multistep" commands when giving directions and consider using colors or shapes in place of numbers or written words.
- Assist participants with mental retardation in selecting activities that are age appropriate and require skills that are useful in community living. Some people with learning impairments have inaccurate perceptions of their capabilities; try to ensure that the challenges of an activity correspond with the skills of the participants.

- Small group and cooperative activities may facilitate social development for those with deficiencies in adaptive behavior. Activities should be structured to provide positive feedback when appropriate social skills are exhibited because effective social skills may be difficult to master.
- Use verbal instructions that are clear and easy to understand. Provide careful supervision of all activities, especially those in which accidents or injuries are possible. Be careful not to over-protect participants, however, and avoid treating an adult with mental retardation like a child.
- Start an activity at the participant's current skill level rather than at the lowest possible level. When leading an activity, provide opportunities for choice and "work toward people making constructive decisions where they devise their own alternatives, weigh the consequences of each, and choose one that meets their needs" (Bullock & Mahon, 1997, p. 182).
- Seek medical advice, including signed releases from doctors, parents, or guardians, before introducing strenuous physical activities or contact sports for persons with Down syndrome. Heart abnormalities and unstable vertebrae near the top of the spine are complications experienced by some people with Down syndrome.
- With individuals who have learning disabilities, it is important to reduce extraneous stimuli; the leader should limit the quantity of materials, directions, verbal suggestions, and so on. Care should be taken *not* to eliminate choices or limit opportunities for creativity.
- For most children with learning impairments, especially those with learning disabilities, activities should involve as many of the senses as possible. Abstractions are often difficult for such children to grasp, so visible evidence of success, such as certificates of achievement, should be used.

Selected Websites

- The ARC (Association for Retarded Citizens) http://www.thearc.org

- American Association of Mental Retardation http://www.aamr.org/
- National Center for Learning Disabilities http://www.ncld.org/

Motor Impairments

Selected Facts

- The diversity of motor impairments makes the use of generalizations exceedingly difficult, if not impossible. Some are easily identified and have reasonably predictable physical effects (e.g., amputations). Others, however, manifest in many ways and result in a wide range of functional limitations (e.g., cerebral palsy). Moreover, some neurological or neuromuscular disorders may cause dramatic fluctuations in performance from one session to the next.
- Some motor impairments are present at birth (congenital) and others occur after birth (adventitious). Most remain stable or improve, but a few are progressive. As a result, the person's functional abilities may decrease across time (e.g., muscular dystrophy).
- Motor impairments may affect almost the entire body or may affect one specific area, such as the lower extremities. Common terminology for partial or full loss of function in a part of the body includes *monoplegia* (one extremity), *hemiplegia* (extremities on one side of the body), *paraplegia* (both lower extremities), and *quadriplegia* (all four extremities, perhaps including head involvement).
- Some people with motor impairments may have accompanying disabling conditions such as learning impairments, speech difficulties, or seizure disorders. Most people with motor impairments do not have multiple disabilities, however.
- Some children and young adults who have motor impairments experience an overly protective home environment, which places additional limits on their physical or social functioning.
- Modern technology has improved the lives of many people with motor impairments.

Augmentative communication devices, for
example, have improved social interaction for
persons who have associated communication
disorders. Lightweight manual and motorized
wheelchairs have improved mobility for
wheelchairs users.

Tips and Techniques for Recreation Professionals

- Most people with motor impairments can fully
integrate into community recreational activities
if an accessible environment is provided
(see chapters 5 and 6). Minimize environmental
barriers that limit optimal independent
functioning. Adaptive equipment may help.
- Some people with motor impairments have
been overprotected at home, so encourage
challenging, but safe, activities. Emphasize
independent functioning, allowing the person to
exert control over his or her environment.
During activities, keep in mind that balance
difficulties are common among people with
mobility limitations.
- Participation in specific activities or exposure
to certain weather conditions may be
inadvisable for some people with motor
impairments. Try to discuss the demands of an
activity with participants in advance, and
consult a therapeutic recreation specialist (or
another knowledgeable professional) if there
are any doubts about the advisability of
participation.

Selected Websites

- National Spinal Cord Injury Association
http://www.spinalcord.org/
- United Cerebral Palsy http://www.ucp.org/
- Muscular Dystrophy Association
http://www.mdausa.org/

Aging
Selected Facts

- In the year 2000, there were over 36 million
Americans age 65 and older (approximately 1 in
8 Americans). By 2030, it is expected that there

will be approximately 70 million Americans age
65 and older, more than twice the number in
2000 (Administration on Aging, 2002).
- It is accepted that old age begins at 65 years of
age, but the physical, cognitive, psychological,
and social functioning of people who are older
varies considerably. People can be chronologi-
cally old yet exhibit few signs of advanced age.
Conversely, some people display physical
attributes associated with advanced age well
before their 65th birthday.
- Most individuals who are older are self-
sufficient in all aspects of their lives. Some,
however, do experience a role-reversal situation.
This happens when their offspring begin (or
attempt) to make important life decisions for the
person who is older. Such situations are
extremely frustrating and may lead to feelings
of futility and personal ineffectiveness.
- Approximately 95% of people who are older in
the United States live and function within the
community rather than in hospitals or nursing
homes.
- Advanced age is usually accompanied by
decreased visual acuity, some hearing loss
(especially of higher pitched sounds), and
decreased motor performances. However, these
declines do not place limits on most activities
until a person is well into his or her 70s or
beyond.
- In metropolitan areas, fear of crime and lack of
financial resources are two major factors that
may limit recreation and leisure participation
among individuals who are elderly. Other
factors include health considerations, lack of
companionship, and transportation difficulties.
- Contrary to stereotypes held by many, people
who are older *are* interested in sex. They can,
and frequently do, engage in satisfying sexual
relationships.

Tips and Techniques for Recreation Professionals

- It is essential that people who are older be
given opportunities to maintain personal
control over their life activities. Citizens'

councils and other organizations should be used to provide direction for community programs with participants who are elderly.

- Put to good use the skills that people who are older possess. Provide opportunities for individuals to serve as activity leaders, and try to offer a chance for them to share their life experiences with children and with people of all ages.
- Opportunities to socialize with age cohorts (those in the same stage of life) are important; flexible programs in a relaxed atmosphere should facilitate social interaction. Activities must be age-appropriate and should encourage older participants to proceed at their own pace and desired level of involvement.
- People who are older are capable of learning new information and skills. Many welcome the chance to participate in adult education classes; identify topics, subjects, and skills of interest and provide opportunities for learning.
- Visual, hearing, or motor impairments may accompany the aging process, therefore the recreation leader should be prepared to integrate tips and techniques related to these impairments, as needed.
- To the extent possible, provide "environments that support easy access to rest rooms, have flexible climate control, do not pose undue obstacles to movement around the facility, and support diminished vision and hearing with appropriate lighting and acoustical design features" (Teague, McGhee, & Hawkins, 2001, p. 245).

Selected Websites

- National Institute on Aging
  http://www.nia.nih.gov/
- National Council on Aging
  http://www.ncoa.org
- Alzheimer's Association http://www.alz.org/

✗ Psychological and Behavioral Disorders

Selected Facts

- Psychological disorders are classified in the Diagnostic and Statistical Manual of Mental Disorders, currently in its fourth edition. This manual includes over 300 categories of psychological disorders.
- Almost 16% of the U.S. population suffers from a major psychological disorder or substance abuse, and approximately 1 in 4 Americans will suffer a serious psychological disorder in their lifetime. Psychological disorders strike all races, incomes, and social strata and are more common than cancer, diabetes, or heart disease (National Institutes of Mental Health, 2003).
- Disruptive or abnormal behavior is manifested in a wide variety of ways and may result from one or more factors. Heredity, learning, physiological malfunctions, and environmental (situational) factors are often identified as contributing to problem behavior.
- For an individual to be considered to have a psychological or behavioral disorder, his or her behavior must be viewed in terms of degree, duration, or both. Extreme outbursts or withdrawal or consistently inappropriate behavior over time may indicate that professional intervention is necessary.
- Some prescription drugs may result in behaviors that appear to be signs of psychological or behavioral disorders. Many illegal drugs also have this effect on users.
- Of primary concern to most group leaders is the person whose actions distract other group members or disrupt group processes. Some behaviors, however, are not disruptive but may warrant similar attention, including extreme withdrawal, excessive shyness, submissiveness, frequent and prolonged daydreaming, fearfulness, and lack of interest in or response to environmental surroundings.
- The context in which abnormal behavior occurs, and the life situation of the individual, must be considered. Behavioral deviance is based on culturally defined norms and values. Much behavior that appears abnormal can be explained rationally by the heritage or life circumstances of the individual.

- Because of their atypical behaviors, people with psychological and behavioral disorders "experience some of the most significant barriers to recreation participation and the greatest prejudice from both the general public and recreation service providers . . ." (Bullock & Mahon, 1997, p. 236).

Tips and Techniques for Recreation Professionals

- Group leaders should become familiar with behavior management techniques and use them when necessary. Some specific techniques for dealing with problem behavior are included at the end of this chapter.
- No single technique of behavior management has been found effective with all people. Regardless of the technique used, consistency and empathy are essential. Be specific and firm about expected behavior, and express expectations in a clear and calm manner. Refrain from expressing negative emotions (e.g., blaming, threatening). If it becomes necessary to express displeasure, do so calmly and clarify that the *behavior,* not the person, is the concern.
- The presence of appropriate behavioral models in a warm and understanding environment may do a great deal to reduce or eliminate inappropriate behavior. Patience and acceptance of individual differences are also important.
- Learn to identify the physiological and psychological effects of popular (i.e., recreational) drugs. In addition, side effects of drugs used to treat psychological disorders should also be considered. These may include "hypersensitivity to sun exposure, fine motor tremors, weight gain, inability to eat certain foods, blurred vision, dry mouth, sedation, and stiffness of movement" (Bullock & Mahon, 1997, p. 247).
- If an individual's behavior appears to warrant outside intervention, seek the assistance of a qualified mental health professional.

Selected Websites

- American Psychological Association
  http://www.apa.org/
- National Association on Mental Illness
  http://www.nami.org
- National Institutes of Mental Health
  http://www.nimh.nih.gov/

Brain Injury

Selected Facts

- Brain injury (also referred to as head injury or closed head injury) is caused by trauma to the brain, usually resulting from an external blow to the head (e.g., auto accident, fall) or internal injury (e.g., embolism). The effects may be temporary or long term, and recovery is often slow. "Intellectual ability may cease to improve after a period of time, but memory, social, and behavioral functions may improve over long periods of time" (Dattilo, 2002, p. 333).
- The majority of brain injuries are caused by motor vehicle accidents. Violence and falls are also frequent causes of brain injury. Less frequent, but of particular concern to recreation providers, are brain injuries caused by participation in recreational activities.
- The extent of impairment resulting from brain injury varies according to the severity of the injury and the specific portion of the brain most affected by the injury. For example, a person whose injury is greatest to the frontal portion of the brain may have significant difficulty with planning and initiating actions. Injury that is primarily to the back portion of the brain, however, is more likely to cause difficulty with visual perception and memory.
- The effects of brain injury vary greatly from person to person and often involve more than cognitive functioning. Ineffective social skills and limitations in motor functioning may also be associated with brain injury.
- Persons with brain injury often display one or more of the following characteristics: excessive talkativeness, impulsiveness, lack of inhibition, deficits in memory, inability to interpret

situations accurately, and difficulty with time management.

- Depending on the nature and variety of the injury, a person with brain injury may be unaware of his or her limitations. In addition, the person may be unaware of the effects his or her behaviors have on others.

Tips and Techniques for Recreation Professionals

- Recreation leaders should become familiar with effective behavior management techniques. Many people who have brain injury need guidance with appropriate behavior in social situations. Such guidance should reinforce appropriate behaviors and, without being punitive, emphasize the consequences of inappropriate behaviors.
- When memory deficits are associated with brain injury, repetition of information, skills, and so on is helpful. Keep in mind that the individual with a brain injury often does not realize that he or she has recently made a statement, asked a question, or performed a task. Try to respond to each repetition as if it were the first time.
- Initially, recreational activities should be *highly* structured for participants who have brain injury. Start with relatively simple (but age-appropriate) tasks that are sequenced in small, manageable steps. Doing so will facilitate success and encourage advancement to more complex tasks.
- Give directions in clear, concise, and concrete ways, and try to supplement verbal instructions with demonstrations and visual cues. Try to avoid abstract concepts and generalizations.
- Leadership of most activities that include participants with brain injury requires highly attentive supervision. The leader must be ready to intervene in any situation that has the potential for accidents or injuries because the participant with brain injury may not recognize appropriate actions or his or her own limitations.

Selected Websites

- Brain Injury Association of America http://www.biausa.org
- Brain Injury Resource Center http://www.headinjury.com/
- National Resource Center for Traumatic Brain Injury http://www.neuro.pmr.vcu.edu/

Acquired Immunodeficiency Syndrome (AIDS)

Selected Facts

- There are approximately 800,000 to 900,000 people currently living with Human Immunodeficiency Virus (HIV) in the United States, with an estimated 40,000 new HIV infections occurring each year. As of December 2000, 774,467 AIDS cases were reported in the United States with many more cases reported among men than women and children. Since the first reported case in 1981, AIDS has claimed 448,060 lives through December 2000 (Centers for Disease Control, 2003). Projections indicate that before the disease is eliminated, everyone in North America will know at least one person with AIDS.
- HIV is *not* transmitted by casual contact, nor can one get HIV from sweat, saliva, or tears. HIV is transmitted through bodily fluids such as semen and blood. Unprotected sexual contact and sharing needles or syringes with an infected person are the most common methods of transmission. Also, a baby may be born with HIV if the mother is infected.
- At present, AIDS is a chronic disease that cannot be cured. Medical treatment, however, can prevent or postpone associated illnesses and delay the onset of AIDS after infection with HIV. Improved treatment has resulted in a greater number of individuals living with AIDS in the United States (322,865 in 2000). This growing population suggests an increased need for HIV prevention programs for HIV-infected individuals and for increased treatment and care services (Centers for Disease Control, 2003). The average length of time between

being infected with HIV and the onset of AIDS is more than 10 years. A person infected with HIV is capable of transmitting the virus even though he or she does not show any symptoms of being ill.

- Prescription drugs have enabled persons with HIV to live longer, more productive lives. However, these drugs often have side effects that have an impact upon recreation participation. These side effects may include "nausea, vomiting, abdominal discomfort and diarrhea" (Grossman & Caroleo, 2001, p. 301).

- Despite being protected by the Americans with Disabilities Act, people with HIV and AIDS often experience prejudice, discrimination, and social stigma. As a result, feelings of alienation, social isolation, and despair are frequently experienced by persons with HIV and AIDS.

- There is evidence that many recreation professionals have misconceptions about HIV and AIDS; moreover, they also have limited knowledge about high-risk behaviors and steps to reduce the risks of infection (Glenn & Dattilo, 1993; Grossman & Caroleo, 1992).

- Physical problems associated with AIDS may include loss of energy, loss of weight, bladder/bowel incontinence, and problems with coordination. Persons with AIDS also experience a wide variety of nutritional problems associated with their illness or medication (Caroleo, 1988). In addition to physical problems, most persons with AIDS will experience dementia during the latter stages of their illness. Symptoms may include impaired memory and concentration, confusion, and slowing of mental processes.

Tips and Techniques for Recreation Professionals

- Become knowledgeable about HIV and AIDS. Use that knowledge to provide appropriate environments and activities for participants with HIV or AIDS.
- Provide an atmosphere that enables participants with AIDS to feel relaxed, welcome, and

supported by staff members. Friends and family members of participants with HIV or AIDS should be encouraged to attend. Enjoyable recreation-related activities that include family members have been found to boost the immune system of persons with HIV and AIDS (Goleman, 1994).

- Serve refreshments at events because reduced caloric intake may compound the severity of the disease (Grossman & Caroleo, 2001). If refreshments are provided, be sure to provide choices that are consistent with dietary requirements of persons with AIDS. For example, foods high in yeast, fat, or lactose may be prohibited for some participants with AIDS.

- Include individuals with HIV or AIDS in activities and programs *and* in the program planning process. Coping with AIDS requires discipline and necessitates adherence to physician directives; therefore, it is important to provide ample opportunities for choice and personal control during leisure. Activities that provide outlets for socialization and stress reduction are also important for persons with HIV and AIDS.

- All recreation providers should include prevention education in conjunction with programs and activities. To date, prevention (e.g., safer sex practices) is the only method of controlling the spread of HIV infection and AIDS.

Selected Websites

- AIDS.ORG http://www.aids.org/
- American Foundation for AIDS Research http://www.amfar.org/cgi-bin/iowa/index.html
- Center for Disease Control Divisions of HIV/AIDS Prevention http://www.cdc.gov/hiv/dhap.htm

✗ Youth-at-Risk

Selected Facts

- The term *youth-at-risk* means different things to different people. As used in this textbook, it refers to children and adolescents who, for a variety of reasons, are at risk of becoming juvenile offenders.

- Youth-at-risk often come from socially disadvantaged backgrounds, lack basic academic skills, experience feelings of alienation and futility, and have limited support from family members. Most of these young persons do not succeed in school and many fail to complete their secondary education. The number of school dropouts is particularly high among minorities and those with low socioeconomic status.

- Most youth-at-risk have low self-esteem; they experience, or have experienced, extremely stressful home environments. Family-related stressors include parental separation or divorce, physical and/or sexual abuse, alcoholism, and frequent residential moves. For many, peers (e.g., gangs) replace the family as the primary source of support, affiliation, and behavioral guidance.

- Delinquent and other behaviors that deviate from society's norms (e.g., physical aggression, disorderly conduct, destruction of property) usually occur during free time. Moreover, they may provide youth-at-risk with fun and other feelings associated with leisure experiences (Aguilar, 1991; Reimer, 1981). Substance abuse is also an issue for youth-at-risk. "The age when young people first start using alcohol and other drugs is a powerful predictor for later substance abuse, especially if use begins before age 15" (Kuntsler, 2001, p. 95).

- Many factors help create *resiliency* among youth-at-risk (i.e., they resist criminal behavior and make positive contributions to communities). Some *protective factors* that promote resiliency include knowledge of neighborhood resources, presence of caring adults, positive attitudes toward the future, and perceived competence (Allen & McGovern, 1997). Initiation of recreation programs that focus on resiliency has been found to decrease local crime rates (Witt & Crompton, 1997).

Tips and Techniques for Recreation Professionals

- Recreation leaders need to provide stimulating activities that can provide youth-at-risk with high degrees of personal challenge. Outdoor adventure programs and ropes courses are two commonly used activities that offer a progression of challenges to participants. Such activities also foster important interpersonal skills, such as acceptance of others and cooperation with group members. In addition, outdoor adventure programs assist participants to develop a more realistic view of self (Gillis, 1992).

- Programs and activities should emphasize autonomy and choice making. Youth-at-risk should be active contributors to the program planning process, and activities should be structured to optimize decision making and personal control among participants.

- Education regarding socially acceptable leisure participation should be incorporated into recreation programs. Educational activities that promote small group interaction and interdependence among group members may be particularly helpful because acceptance of peers is important to many youth who are at-risk.

- Create a positive, caring, and accepting environment for youthful participants by displaying genuine interest in them and their experiences. Providing unconditional support and universal acceptance may be the most important programming principle for youth-at-risk (Allen, Paisley, Stevens, & Harwell, 1998). Also, encourage their family members to become actively involved in recreation programs and activities. Fees for services should be kept to a minimum because financial constraints are significant for many youth-at-risk.

- Peers who are appropriate role models for youth-at-risk should be encouraged to attend programs and share how they successfully adjusted to the demands of society. Recreation leaders and adults in the

community may also serve as mentors to youth-at-risk, offering guidance, support, and understanding.
- Early intervention is vitally important; therefore, recreation programs should be available to preschool and preteen youth considered to be at-risk. The most effective way of dealing with socially deviant behavior is to prevent it before it begins.

Selected Websites
- Children, Youth and Families at-Risk Program (CYFAR)
  http://www.reeusda.gov/4h/cyfar/cyfar.htm
- National Network for Child Care
  http://www.nncc.org/
- Children, Youth and Families Education and Research Network (CYFERnet)
  http://www.cyfernet.org/

✗ Attention Deficit Hyperactive Disorder (ADHD)

Selected Facts
- According to numerous data sources, approximately 4% to 6% of the U.S. population has ADHD.
- Adults and children diagnosed with ADHD typically display certain characteristic behaviors over a period of time (the behaviors typically are evident prior to the age of 7 and are displayed consistently for a period of time greater than 6 months).
- The most common behaviors associated with ADHD are:
  1. distractibility (inability to sustain attention to tasks),
  2. impulsivity (impaired impulse control and difficulty with delayed gratification), and
  3. hyperactivity (physically restless and excessively activity).
- According to the *DSM IV* (*Diagnostic and Statistical Manual of Mental Disorders*), specific behaviors associated with ADHD include difficulty attending to tasks; making careless mistakes or failing to attend to details;

may not seem to be listening when spoken to, failing to follow directions; losing or forgetting important things; feeling restless and/or fidgeting with hands or feet; running, squirming, or climbing excessively; talking excessively; and having difficulty waiting a turn.
- ADHD is believed to be caused by improperly working chemicals in the brain and is believed to be a neurological disorder. It is also suggested that genetics may play a part. For example, when one family member is diagnosed with ADHD, there is a 25% to 35% probability that another family member also has ADHD. This is an increase over a 4% to 6% probability in the general population.
- ADHD is *not* believed to be caused by poor parenting, poor schools, poor teachers, or too much sugar.
- It is estimated that one half to two thirds of children with ADHD will continue to have significant problems with ADHD behaviors and symptoms as adults, which often can have an impact on their occupations, families, and social relationships.

Tips and Techniques for Recreation Professionals
Note: Although ADHD is found in both children and adults, ADHD begins at childhood. Therefore, the following tips and techniques are directed toward children in an effort that some of the approaches will have positive long-term outcomes as the children grow into adulthood.

- If a child is continuously exhibiting some of the symptoms associated with ADHD, talk to the child's parents about the behaviors that you are observing. The child may or may not have ADHD; do not assume or attempt to diagnose the child. First, learn from the parents about techniques they have successfully used to minimize the observed problem behaviors. If a child has been diagnosed with ADHD, most parents will disclose this information and provide helpful approaches to managing the behaviors associated with ADHD.

- Determine from the parents whether the child is taking any medications that may be having an impact on his or her behavior (either positive or negative). If the child is taking a medication, learn the effects and side effects associated with the medication.
- Make sure to always speak to the child in a respectful manner. "Putting down" a child can only serve to further damage a child's self-esteem and may contribute to increases in inappropriate behavior.
- Try to structure the environment to allow for social or peer support. Perhaps identify another child to serve as a "social buddy." Social buddies can be either an individual or a group of individuals who can provide assistance to the child with ADHD in difficult situations. The buddies can prompt and reinforce appropriate behavior by demonstrating such behaviors for the child with ADHD when appropriate. Critical selection and training of "buddies" is paramount to the success of this approach (Asher & Gordon, 1998, p. 45).
- Try to help the child plan ahead. Before engaging the child in an activity or program, review with the child what he or she might expect and "troubleshoot" any obstacles that the child might encounter (Asher & Gordon, 1998, p. 44). Give the child an opportunity to think ahead of time how he or she might handle a situation that may cause problems *before* they arise (e.g., what to do if the child is teased or is rejected). This approach empowers children to act for themselves without authoritative intervention, and thus serves to boost confidence and self-esteem.
- Finally, praise the child for any positive behavior and any small successes. Praise and recognition of positive behaviors usually result in repeated positive behaviors over time.

Autism Spectrum Disorder (ASD)

Selected Facts

- ASD typically appears during a child's first three years. It is a neurological disorder that affects brain functioning impacting the normal development of the brain in the areas of communication and social interaction.
- Children and adults who have ASD most often have problems in both verbal and nonverbal communication resulting in secondary problems in social interaction and leisure or play activity.
- ASD affects approximately 1.5 million Americans, both children and adults. According to the Centers for Disease Control and Prevention, it is estimated that 2 to 6 per 1,000 individuals are affected by some form of ASD.
- The number of cases of ASD is increasing each year at a rate of 10% to 17%. At this rate, the ASD Society of America estimates that the prevalence of ASD could reach 4 million Americans within the next decade.
- Boys are four times more likely to be diagnosed with ASD than girls. There is no difference in ASD rates across race, ethnicity, social boundaries, income, lifestyle, and educational levels.
- The cause for ASD is largely unknown, although it is generally believed to be caused by abnormalities in brain structure or function.
- ASD is *not* caused by poor parenting and is not considered a mental illness. No psychological factors have been found to contribute to the development of ASD.
- ASD is generally diagnosed by ruling out all other potentially contributing causes for the exhibited behaviors. Diagnosis is based on observation of the individual's behavior, communication, and developmental progress. Early diagnosis typically results in better long-term outcomes.
- In addition to communication and social interaction difficulties, many children with ASD have sensory difficulties. The child may be hypersensitive or hyposensitive to stimuli or materials and/or may have difficulty integrating senses.
- Some individuals with ASD exhibit repetitive and/or dangerous inappropriate behaviors. These behaviors might include hand flapping,

rocking, finger snapping, headbanging, and self-mutilation. Many of these behaviors are thought to be the result of problems with sensory integration.

Tips and Techniques for Recreation Professionals

- As with ADHD, take some time to talk to the individual's parents or guardian about your observations. Learn about the individual's interests, his or her abilities, and what have been traditionally successful approaches to working with the individual.
- Consult the parents/guardians when inappropriate behaviors arise. Learn what approaches have been most successful when attempting to minimize or eliminate the behavior. Consult an appropriate ASD professional, if needed. The goal is for the person and any other participants to have a safe environment in which to participate.

- If the person has an augmented communication system that he or she uses, learn how to use the system. Example systems include using pictures to identify needs/desires and computers for audible communication.
- Provide activities that are appropriate to the age and abilities of the person. Modify and adapt activities as needed.
- If appropriate, provide art and music activities to aid in sensory integration. These activities provide tactile, visual, and auditory stimulation.
- Utilize songs to aid in speech development and language comprehension.
- Offer opportunities for participation in art activities to provide a nonverbal method for individuals to express themselves safely.
- If possible, provide animal therapy (i.e., therapeutic horseback riding) to improve coordination and motor development and to aid in sensory integration.

SUMMARY

The traditional approach to recreation with persons who have disabilities is to focus extensively on characteristics that distinguish people with special needs from the general population. Medical terminology, facts and figures, and therapeutic interventions are often stressed. We feel, however, that this traditional approach overlooks the uniqueness of each person with a disability. Rather than give detailed characteristics and data for all disabling conditions, we have presented selected information that should be useful to any recreational professional. Readers interested in additional information regarding data, characteristics, techniques, and terminology associated with specific disabling conditions are encouraged to visit the selected Websites at the end of sections in this chapter. Additional print resources include:

Adams, R., A. Daniel, & L. Rullman. *Games, Sports and Exercises for the Physically Handicapped* (4th ed.). Philadelphia: Lea and Febiger, 1991.

Austin, D. R., & M. E. Crawford, Eds. *Therapeutic Recreation: An Introduction* (3rd ed.). Englewood Cliffs, NJ: Prentice-Hall, 2001.

Batshaw, M. L., & Y. M. Perret. *Children with Handicaps: A Medical Primer* (3rd ed.). Baltimore: Paul H. Brookes, 1992.

Bullock, C. C., & M. J. Mahon. *Introduction to Recreation Services for People with Disabilities: A Person-Centered Approach* (2nd ed.). Champaign, IL: Sagamore, 2000.

Caplan, B., Ed. *Rehabilitation Psychology Desk Reference.* Rockville, MD: Aspen, 1987.

Chilman, C. S., Ed. *Chronic Illness and Disability.* London: Sage, 1988.

Coyne, P., & A. Fullerton, Eds. Supporting individuals with Autism Spectrum Disorder in recreation. Champaign, IL: Sagamore, 2004.

Dell Orto, A. E., & R. P. Marinelli. *Encyclopedia of Disability and Rehabilitation.* New York: Simon & Schuster, 1995.

Eisenberg, M. G., R. L. Glueckauf, & H. H. Zaretsky Eds. *Medical Aspects of Disability: A Handbook for the Rehabilitation Professional* (2nd ed.). New York: Springer, 1999.

Erickson, M. T. *Behavior Disorders of Children and Adolescents: Assessment, Etiology and Intervention.* (3rd ed.). Englewood Cliffs, NJ: Prentice-Hall, 1998.

Garrison, S. J., Ed. *Handbook of Physical Medicine and Rehabilitation Basics.* Philadelphia: Lippincott, 1995.

Garrison, W. T., & S. McQuiston. *Chronic Illness during Childhood and Adolescence.* London: Sage, 1989.

Gethings, L. *Person to Person: A Guide for Professionals Working with People with Disabilities* (3rd ed.). Baltimore: Paul H. Brookes, 1997.

Henderson, G., & W. V. Bryan. *Psychosocial Aspects of Disability* (2nd ed.). Springfield, IL: Charles C. Thomas, 1997.

Marinelli, R. P., & A. E. Dell Orto. *Psychological and Social Impact of Disability* (4th ed.). New York: Springer, 1999.

McWirter, J., B. T. McWirter, E. H. McWirter, & R. J. McWirter. *At-Risk Youth: A Comprehensive Response for Counselors, Teachers, Psychologists, and Human Service Professionals* (3rd ed.). Belmont, CA: Brooks/Cole, 2004.

Mobily, K. E., & R. D. MacNeil. *Therapeutic Recreation and the Nature of Disabilities.* State College, PA: Venture, 2002.

Quinn, P. *Understanding Disability: A Lifespan Approach.* Thousand Oaks, CA: Sage, 1998.

Swanson, H. L., K. R. Harris, & S. Graham, Eds. *Handbook of Learning Disabilities.* New York: Guilford, 2003.

SUGGESTED LEARNING ACTIVITIES

1. Explain the concept of a self-fulfilling prophecy. How do you think expectations could cause behavior?

2. Write a two-page paper that gives your opinion on the topic "Should Labels Be Used to Identify People with Disabilities?"

3. Learn the finger spelling alphabet pictured in Figure 4-2. Practice this alphabet by finger spelling a message to friends (they can use Figure 4-2 to interpret your message).

4. Use the Web to research one disabling condition and

   a. Add two facts to the "Selected Facts" listed in the chapter;

   b. Add two suggestions to the "Tips and Techniques" provided in the chapter.

REFERENCES

Administration on Aging, Department of Health and Human Services. A Profile of Older Americans: 2002—Future Growth. [Online]. Available: http://www.aoa.gov/prof/Statistics/profile/2.asp, 2003.

Aguilar, T. E. Social deviancy. In D. Austin & M. E. Crawford, Eds. *Therapeutic Recreation: An Introduction.* Englewood Cliffs, NJ: Prentice-Hall, 1991, pp. 100–118.

Allen, L. R., & T. D. McGovern. BBM: It's working! *Parks and Recreation, 32*(8), 48–55, 1997.

Allen, L. R., K. Paisley, B. Stevens, & R. Harwell. Top 10 ways to impact at-risk youth in recreation programming. *Parks and Recreation, 33*(3), 80–85, 1998.

Asher, M. J., & S. B. Gordon. *The AD/HD Forms Book: Identification, Measurement, and Intervention.* Champaign, IL: Research Press, 1998.

Bullock, C. C., & M. J. Mahon. *Introduction to Recreation Services for People with Disabilities: A Person-Centered Approach.* Champaign, IL: Sagamore, 1997.

Centers for Disease Control and Prevention. Trends. In *Combating Complacancy—HIV Prevention, Geneva '98.* [Online]. Available: http://www.cdcnpin.org/geneva98/trends/trends_1.htm, 1999.

Centers for Disease Control, Publication: HIV/AIDS Update. [Online]. Available: www.cdc.gov/nchstp/od/news/At-a-Glance.pdf, 2003.

Dattilo, J. *Inclusive Leisure Services: Responding to the Rights of People with Disabilities* (2nd ed.). State College, PA: Venture, 2002.

Dattilo, J., & N. Guerin. Mental retardation. In D. R. Austin & M. E. Crawford, Eds. *Therapeutic*

Recreation: An Introduction (3rd ed.). Boston: Allyn and Bacon, 2001, pp. 130–156.

Fact Sheet on Attention Deficit Hyperactivity Disorder (ADHD/ADD). [Online]. Available: http://add.org/content/abc1.htm, 2003.

Gillis, H. L. Therapeutic uses of adventure-challenge-outdoor-wilderness theory and research. Paper presented at the Coalition for Education in the Outdoors, 1992.

Glenn, C., & J. Dattilo. TR professionals' attitudes toward and knowledge of AIDS. *Therapeutic Recreation Journal, 27,* 253–261, 1993.

Goleman, D. Seeking out small pleasures keeps immune system strong. *The New York Times,* May 11, 1994, p. c11.

Grossman, A. H., & O. Caroleo. A study of AIDS risk-behavior knowledge among therapeutic recreation specialists in New York State. *Therapeutic Recreation Journal, 26*(4), 55–60, 1992.

Grossman, A. H., & O. Caroleo. HIV disease. In D. R. Austin & M. E. Crawford, Eds. *Therapeutic Recreation: An Introduction* (3rd ed.). Boston: Allyn and Bacon, 2001, pp. 297–317.

Hutchison, P., & J. Lord. *Recreation Integration.* Ontario, Canada: Leisurability Publications, 1979.

Hutchison, P., & J. McGill. *Leisure, Integration and Community.* Concord, Ontario, Canada: Leisurability Publications, 1992.

Information and Tips for Mental Retardation and Learning Impairments. [Online]. Available: www.aamr.org, 2003.

Information and Tips for Autism. [Online]. Available: www.autism-society.org, 2003.

Information and Tips for ADHD. [Online]. Available: www.adhd.com, 2003.

Kuntsler, R. Substance abuse. In D. R. Austin & M. E. Crawford, Eds. *Therapeutic Recreation: An*

Introduction (3rd ed.). Boston: Allyn and Bacon, 2001, pp. 94–112.

Mandell, C. J., & E. Fiscus. *Understanding Exceptional People.* St. Paul, MN: West Publishing, 1981.

McNeil, J. M. Americans with Disabilities: 1994–95. *Current Population Reports,* U.S. Department of Commerce, Bureau of the Census, Economics and Statistics Administration (P70-61). Washington, DC: Government Printing Office, August 1997.

National Institutes of Mental Health, Mental Illness Facts. [Online]. Available: http://www.mhsource.com/resource/mh.html, 2003.

Pierce, J. T. Linguistic factors as they relate to attitudes towards persons with disabilities. *Journal of Applied Rehabilitation Counseling, 29,* 31–36, 1998.

Prevent Blindness America. Vision Problems in the U.S. [Online]. Available: http://www.preventblindness.org/resources/vision_data.html, 2003.

Reimer, J. W. Deviance as fun. *Adolescence, 16*(61), 39–43, 1981.

Rosenhan, D. L. On being sane in insane places. *Science, 179*(4070), 250–253, 1973.

Rosenthal, R., & L. Jacobson. *Pygmalion in the Classroom: Teacher Expectations and Pupil's Intellectual Development.* New York: Holt, Rinehart & Winston, 1968.

Teague, M. L., V. L. McGhee, & B. A. Hawkins. Geriatric practice. In D. R. Austin & M. E. Crawford, Eds. *Therapeutic Recreation: An Introduction* (3rd ed.). Boston: Allyn and Bacon, 2001, pp. 233–254.

Witt, P. A., & J. L. Crompton. The at-risk youth recreation project. *Parks and Recreation, 32*(1), 54–61, 1997.

PART

II Service and Facility Planning

(Photo by Ralph W. Smith)

Equal access to recreation programs and facilities is the thrust of chapter 5, Barriers to Recreation Participation. This chapter discusses intrinsic, environmental, and communication barriers that prevent leisure participation by individuals with disabilities, along with means to overcome these barriers.

Chapter 6, Design of Accessible and Usable Recreation Environments, concerns designing appropriate recreation environments for all people, including persons with disabilities. A major portion of the chapter is devoted to guidelines and recommendations for creating accessible and usable public park and recreation facilities. A special section on playground design concludes chapter 6.

Featured in chapter 7, The Planning Process, is a discussion of how to create recreation programs that facilitate inclusion of persons with disabilities. Needs assessment, selection and modification of activities, and implementation of inclusive recreational activities are highlighted. In addition, an overview of program evaluation is presented, including a detailed discussion of Importance-Performance Analysis.

The final chapter in this section is chapter 8, Selective Examples of Community Services. This chapter presents information on several outstanding community-based inclusive and special recreation programs. Each program is highlighted and the philosophy and goals of each are outlined.

5 BARRIERS TO RECREATION PARTICIPATION

(Courtesy of *New Mobility Magazine*)

Many factors shape an individual's recreation and leisure behavior. People who live in Florida, for example, are much less likely to go snow skiing than people living in Colorado. Individuals with limited financial resources may find it impossible to afford recreational luxuries such as vacation homes or resort trips. People from specific regions or cultural backgrounds may refuse to participate in activities that others from different backgrounds find acceptable and enjoyable. As with this last example, some of these factors provide a framework for *choice*. The individual freely chooses either to participate or not to participate in an activity that is available and attainable. Many factors exist, however, that may deny freedom of choice. In the first two examples cited, location and lack of money serve as barriers to participation.

As indicated in literature on constraints to recreation participation (e.g., Crawford, Jackson, & Godbey, 1991; Jackson, 1991; Jackson, Crawford, & Godbey, 1993; Jackson & Scott, 1999), everyone experiences such barriers. There is no doubt, however, that people with disabilities experience more and greater barriers than people without disabilities. The following expression, based on a quote from George Orwell's *Animal Farm,* summarizes the situation: "We are all created equal but some of us are more equal than others." When it comes to the opportunity to participate in recreation and leisure activities, people without disabilities are clearly "more equal" than their peers who have disabilities.

One single step can deny wheelchair users the right to enter a building independently. The absence of an interpreter may prevent a person who is deaf from understanding a play. Individuals who have mental retardation may be excluded from participation in many events unless an effort is made to include tasks appropriate to their cognitive abilities. Collectively, these and other barriers have a negative impact on the life satisfaction of persons with disabilities (Hendershot, 2003). Hendershot noted that reducing barriers would enable persons with disabilities to increase their community participation and the result would be

increased satisfaction with their lives. Citing data from a National Organization on Disability study, Hendershot wrote, "At every level of mobility limitation, from none through moderate to most severe, persons who participated more in the community were more likely to be very satisfied with their lives." Yet, if recreation professionals are going to assist in the effort to improve lives by removing barriers to recreation and leisure activities, they must be able to recognize more than the obvious barriers previously cited. They must constantly be alert to the *many forms* that barriers take, and attempt to eliminate or minimize the impact these barriers have on individuals with disabilities.

TYPES OF BARRIERS

The multitude of barriers preventing individuals with disabilities from full leisure participation can be divided into three major categories: (1) *intrinsic* barriers, which result from the individual's own limitations and may be associated with a physical, psychological, or cognitive disability; (2) *environmental* barriers, composed of the many external forces that impose limitations on the individual with a disability; and (3) *communication* barriers, which block interaction between the individual and his or her social environment.

Intrinsic Barriers

Like everyone else, individuals with disabilities face constraints that result from their own physical, emotional, or cognitive limits. These intrinsic barriers may be directly associated with their disabilities, but they also may arise from other factors such as parental overprotection or inadequate educational opportunities. Regardless of their causes, intrinsic barriers are permanent or temporary limitations that reside within the individual. As illustrated in Figure 5-1, such barriers may block fulfillment of the individual's needs, desires, and interests. The following sections describe intrinsic barriers that may reduce a person's ability to participate in recreation and leisure activities.

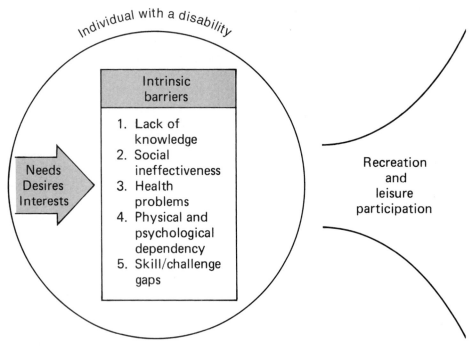

Figure 5-1   Intrinsic Barriers

Lack of Knowledge

Many people are not able to realize their maximum leisure functioning because they lack essential information. Knowledge of programs, facilities, and other recreation and leisure resources, for example, is needed to make informed choices. Knowledge of support services, such as modes of transportation, also may be necessary for them to participate in a particular recreational activity.

Some people with learning disorders or mental retardation may be incapable of learning about recreational opportunities. Usually, however, knowledge deficits arise from inadequate information or a lack of opportunities to learn about recreation resources. The 2000 N.O.D./Harris Survey on Community Participation, for example, found that lack of awareness over what activities exist within the community was cited by 40% of their sample as a barrier to community involvement (National Organization on Disability, 2001b). Likewise, Hutchison (1980) found that the people with physical disabilities in her study con-

sidered a lack of information on available services to be an important barrier to recreation participation. As noted by the National Organization on Disability (1993), "The gap in the level of participation in American life means [people with disabilities] are going to be less informed on most issues" (p. 1).

Even people with disabilities who *do* know what recreational activities are available may not know their legislative rights to access these services. One study, for example, found that 12 years after the passage of the Americans with Disabilities Act, 1 in 5 persons with disabilities was still unaware of the law's existence (National Organization on Disability, 2002). An individual cannot participate in a recreational activity if he or she is unaware either of its availability or of his or her right to attend the activity. This lack of knowledge can impose a severe restriction on the recreation behavior of anyone, but especially on people with disabilities who face so many other barriers to participation.

Social Ineffectiveness

For many reasons, some individuals with disabilities have ineffective social skills. Parental overprotection and segregation from peers without disabilities are two of the most frequently mentioned reasons. In addition, youngsters with disabilities often receive inadequate feedback on appropriate behavior in various social situations. Regardless of their origin, however, ineffective social skills have a profound effect on an individual's participation in leisure activities (Bedini, 1993; Sherrill, 2003; Sneegas, 1989).

People often form their own self-images from their interactions with others. How others react to them provides cues that combine to produce a view of their self-worth. A person who lacks the social skills needed to get positive and consistent feedback from others may encounter interference with his or her vital process of self-concept formation. This is especially true if skill deficits in other areas of a person's life limit his or her feelings of personal control and effectiveness. Bowe (1978) noted the impact of poor self-concepts among individuals with recent disabilities. He wrote that a "vicious cycle" results, in which "damaged self-concepts... lead to lowered aspirations and increased isolation, further handicapping the disabled individuals" (p. 35).

Health Problems

Most people with disabilities lead relatively pain-free and illness-free lives. Still, some types of disabilities do present recurring health problems. In a study of Canadians with disabilities, Ferris (1987) found that respondents often cited ill health as a barrier to physical activity. Furthermore, some conditions, such as rheumatoid arthritis and glaucoma, are accompanied by frequent and often severe episodes of pain. It is easy for others not to recognize the limitations imposed by pain because pain is invisible. Condor (1995) noted that it is a constant mental challenge for someone in pain to relate his or her experience to others.

Some types of disabilities also have contraindications, a term meaning that a particular behavior may result in medical complications or injury.

Rough or contact activities may be contraindicated for a child with hemophilia, and lengthy exposure to the sun may be contraindicated for people taking certain types of medication.

A word of caution: Recreators must remain aware that giving *too* much attention to health-related matters may result in overprotection. Care must be given to ensure the *optimum* level of attention to health-related barriers so that maximum participation is encouraged.

Physical and Psychological Dependency

Any child who grows into adulthood experiences a gradual progression toward physical and psychological independence. Total independence from others is neither achievable nor desirable, but most people strive for a level of independence that allows them to feel at least partially in control of their environment. Unfortunately, many people who have disabilities do not achieve their potential for independent functioning. Dattilo (2002), for example, observed that people who have limited knowledge and skills, plus few opportunities for choice, may experience a condition known as *learned helplessness*. The person who learns to be helpless stops trying to explore his or her environment and loses opportunities for enjoyment in leisure. From the moment a disability occurs or is discovered, the person with a disability may be overprotected and overassisted by others. As Wright (1983) noted, "A certain amount of protection is good; more than that is detrimental" (p. 403). Over time, this situation renders the individual physically or psychologically incapable of achieving a desired level of independence.

When a disability makes an individual physically dependent on others, the limits imposed are obvious. In some cases, an attendant or aide may be necessary to enable a person to participate in activities. It is not always easy for the person with a disability to ask for physical assistance, however. Szychowski (1993) wrote that asking for assistance "in some ways requires greater strength of spirit than it takes to face a monster [whitewater] rapid, for in those moments we risk intimacy and vulnerability" (pp. 20–21).

Psychological dependency is not always as obvious as physical dependency, but it can be even more limiting. Moore and Dattilo (1993), for example, theorized that differences in nature-related trail preferences between persons with and without disabilities may have resulted from "a willingness on the part of people with disabilities to accept limited accommodations as a result of 'internalized oppression'" (p. 28). Family members, friends, and rehabilitation professionals are capable of fostering an atmosphere of psychological dependency (i.e., internalized oppression) for people with disabilities. Sometimes this situation is reciprocal, meaning that the person with a disability receives feelings of satisfaction from being protected and patronized, while the person without a disability enjoys being needed by someone viewed as "less fortunate." Thus, both have their needs met by the other.

When psychological dependency occurs, the person's capacity for personal growth and self-development is severely limited (Wright, 1983). Many of the barriers faced by people with disabilities require personal initiative, creative thought, risk taking, and perseverance in action. These qualities do not develop fully in an atmosphere of psychological dependency. That some rehabilitation professionals encourage their clients to be dependent also compounds this problem. As noted by Illich, Zola, McKnight, Caplan, and Shaiken (1977), "Life is paralyzed in permanent intensive care" (p. 27).

Skill/Challenge Gap

Csikszentmihalyi (1975, 1997) has studied enjoyment of activities for many years. He has proposed that enjoyment of an activity is most often possible if the participant perceives that the challenges of an activity are in balance with or slightly above his or her skills. If the challenges are thought to be excessive, worry or anxiety may limit the chance for enjoyment. If the challenge is considered too easily achieved, boredom often results. Many individuals with disabilities do not possess skill levels appropriate for enjoying a number of leisure pursuits. Moreover, the presence of a skill/challenge gap may interfere with efforts to integrate individuals with

disabilities into mainstream society (Miller, 1989). Sometimes the nature of their disabilities limits skill development, but often they do not get the opportunity to develop skills that could enhance participation. As a result, they correctly perceive that many activities are too challenging for their present skills. The result is usually nonparticipation.

This skill/challenge gap has many implications for recreation professionals. Proper progression in teaching specific skills may enable a person with a disability to gain the expertise necessary for participation. Also, an activity may be modified to accommodate the current skills of a participant with a disability (see chapter 7). Keep in mind that the participant's *perception* of his or her skill level is a critical factor. Underestimating one's own skill may result in withdrawal from participation, whereas overestimating one's own skill may prove embarrassing or even dangerous. Many overconfident skiers, for example, have ended up in the hospital because they thought they were ready for the advanced slopes. As Bregha (1980) observed, the ability to select appropriate leisure pursuits requires more than knowledge of what is available or permissible. "Something deeper is required: the knowledge of oneself as well as one's milieu" (p. 31).

Environmental Barriers

No matter how successfully a person with a disability copes with intrinsic barriers to recreation participation, he or she will also be faced with external forces that limit participation. Figure 5-2 illustrates the idea that these external forces, known as environmental barriers, may block the actions that a person takes toward participation in recreation and leisure activities. Unlike intrinsic barriers, environmental barriers are imposed on the individual by societal or ecological conditions. Thus, the person is less likely to feel that he or she can overcome such barriers through individual action. Many intrinsic barriers can be partially or completely overcome through personal efforts such as physical rehabilitation, educational programs, and counseling. The solution to environmental barriers is much more complex and, therefore, more

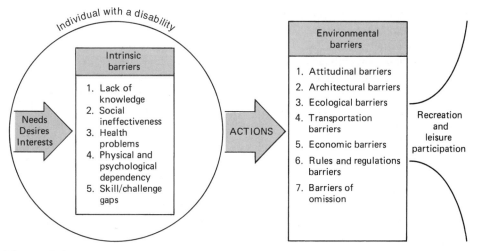

Figure 5-2   Environmental Barriers

frustrating for individuals with disabilities. The following environmental barriers limit recreation and leisure participation for many persons with disabilities.

Attitudinal Barriers

Of all the barriers to participation faced by individuals with disabilities, attitudinal barriers are probably the most limiting. They form what Schleien, Ray, and Green (1997) have called "an invisible wall of exclusion" (p. 62). The attitude concept is discussed in depth in chapter 2, but it is important here to examine the types of behaviors that reflect barrier-producing attitudes. These behaviors, which may be exhibited by family and friends or by strangers, can be divided into three categories: (1) *negative* behaviors; (2) *paternalistic* behaviors; and (3) *apathetic* behaviors. To give readers a better understanding of these behaviors, we have provided the following information:

1. *Negative Behaviors.* From time to time, every person with a disability is subjected to behaviors that arise from negative attitudes toward people who are "different." Some of these behaviors are obvious, while others are subtle. One obvious example of negative behavior is ridiculing or mocking the person

with a visible disability. Less obvious, though, is avoidance of people with disabilities. Whether from fear, dislike, or discomfort, many people without disabilities avoid eye contact and maintain exaggerated social distance when in the presence of people with visible disabilities (Langer, Fiske, Taylor, & Chanowitz, 1976). Obsolete and derogatory labels, such as "cripple," "deaf and dumb," and "crazy," are also examples of negative behaviors. Such terms are not only demeaning, but their use encourages others to behave negatively toward people with disabilities. These acts of prejudice and discrimination (i.e., negative behaviors) create an atmosphere of *oppression* for persons with disabilities that is deep-seated and pervasive (Barnes & Mercer, 2003; Longmore, 2003). Ervin (1997) noted that if you have a disability, "the odds are pretty enormous that you are oppressed." He added, "After all these years, I suddenly understood what it was about that 'physically challenged' stuff that always made me cringe in pain. No wonder it always rang so false. We're not challenged! We're oppressed!" (p. 67).

2. *Paternalistic Behaviors.* Many people without disabilities treat adolescents or adults

who have disabilities like children. (Often they treat children with disabilities like infants!) Unlike negative behaviors, paternalistic actions frequently arise from a desire to show a "favorable" view of people who have disabilities. Unfortunately, the message conveyed by paternalistic behavior is that people with disabilities lack competence, maturity, and the capacity for independence. Longmore (2003) observed that paternalism denies self-determination; therefore, people with disabilities are "schooled in social incompetency, and then their confinement to a socially invalidated role is justified by that incompetency" (p. 220). Head patting, giving undue praise, and providing help when it is not needed are examples of paternalistic behavior. The underlying concept is that the person without a disability is superior to the person who has a disability. This supposed superiority creates an atmosphere of condescension that then justifies the person without a disability making unilateral decisions about what is best for people who have disabling conditions. Hahn (2003) emphasized the impact of paternalism by calling it "perhaps the most serious and intractable hindrance to the advancement of the rights of people with disabilities" (p. 39).

3. *Apathetic Behaviors.* People who are apathetic toward individuals with disabilities express no feelings of sympathy, understanding, or caring toward people who have disabilities. Rather than being negative or paternalistic, such people ignore the needs and concerns of people with disabilities. They behave as if such people did not exist. Doug Wakefield, who is blind, talked about one personal experience with public apathy. Doug and his guide dog were using Washington's subway system. They got off the train at an unfamiliar station, and Doug did not know the direction of his exit. His guide dog, trained to keep him from dangerous situations, preceded Doug as he

paced back and forth on the landing trying to determine the appropriate direction. Despite that it was obvious Doug and his dog were pacing aimlessly, none of the passengers and bystanders offered assistance. Some people may have failed to help because of negative feelings, but Doug felt that most were apathetic toward his dilemma. Ironically, public apathy prevented him from climbing out of a Washington subway station, but in 1981, Doug Wakefield was part of a team of individuals with and without disabilities who scaled Mt. Rainier (Wakefield, 1981).

The effects of attitudinal barriers on persons with disabilities are overwhelming. Heyne, Schleien, and McAvoy (1993), for example, found that "fearful and negative attitudes about people with disabilities" was one of the most frequently reported obstacles to friendship development between persons with and without disabilities. Moreover, the negative attitudes of some recreation professionals has been cited as a major barrier to successful inclusion (Maryland-National Capital Park and Planning Commission, 1993; National Organization on Disability, 2003; Schleien et al., 1997). In his poignant and eloquent book *The Body Silent,* Robert Murphy (1987) described the effects of a progressive disability on his daily activities and social relationships. He wrote, "The greatest impediment to a person's taking full part in his society are not his physical flaws, but rather the issue of myths, fears, and misunderstandings that society attaches to them" (p. 113).

Architectural Barriers

Structures such as buildings, walkways, and so on, that are usable by nondisabled people but present obstacles for people with disabilities, are known as architectural barriers. These barriers limit mobility and often deprive individuals with disabilities access to worthwhile leisure activities. David Park (1977), the National Park Service's Chief of Special Programs and Populations, noted, "A major reason many persons with disabilities do not participate in existing recreation programs is simply that facilities are not physically accessible and barrier-free" (p. 129).

Despite legislation (e.g., ADA) and the U.S. Access Board's efforts to increase accessibility in the United States, architectural barriers continue to be a significant problem for persons with disabilities. Percy (2003), for example, documented that over one half of settlements in ADA legal cases were due to architectural barriers. Not all persons with disabilities are affected by architectural barriers; however, about one in four report having problems with access to public buildings (Kaye, 1998). Architectural barriers give an unspoken message to these individuals: Society is not concerned with the needs of people who have disabilities. In effect, they are second-class citizens. The result is often frustration, anger, and alienation. As one person expressed, "I am not a shut in, I am a shut out" (Bruck, 1978, p. 21).

Progress toward eliminating architectural barriers has been made during the past decade (Barnes & Mercer, 2003), but there is still much work to be done. Freedom of mobility and access to programs are rights that should be extended to *every* citizen. (See chapter 6 for an in-depth examination of architectural barriers.)

Ecological Barriers

Physical obstacles that occur in the natural environment may be termed ecological barriers. Hills, trees, sand, rain, snow, and wind are some examples. The physical impact of such barriers is roughly the same as that of architectural barriers, but there are two important differences. First, ecological barriers are much less frustrating for individuals who have disabilities, because they are not intentionally constructed by human beings. Therefore, they are not reminders of societal insensitivity toward people with disabilities. "I have to accept the fact that I will never backpack unassisted through the wilderness," commented one wheelchair user, "but I deserve the right to go to the store independently!"

The second difference between ecological and architectural barriers is that legislation cannot be used to counteract ecological barriers. Rather than eliminating ecological barriers, the main emphasis must be on minimizing their impact on people with disabilities. Careful advance planning may help minimize or avoid ecological barriers. For example, prior to participating in a nature walk, the individual with a disability can ensure that the program leader selects an access route that avoids ecological barriers such as gullies or large tree roots. Sometimes, however, overcoming rather than avoiding an ecological barrier may offer a greater reward. Satisfaction and pride are feelings that we *all* receive when we face and overcome nature's obstacles.

Transportation Barriers

The lack of usable and affordable methods of transportation often prevents individuals who have disabilities from benefiting from available community resources, including recreation services (Martin et al., 2002; National Organization on Disability, 2001a). A U.S. Department of Transportation study, for example, found that about 560,000 people with disabilities in the United States never leave their homes because of transportation difficulties (U.S. Department of Transportation, 2003). Automobile or van modifications are expensive; mass transportation is often inaccessible, unsafe, or inconvenient (Cleigh, 2003); and specially arranged (dial-a-ride) programs are few and often have many restrictions. Even when accessible public transportation is available, it usually requires considerable advance planning and constricts the lives of persons with disabilities. Murphy (1987) wrote:

> The inability to drive was more than a retreat from mobility, for it was one more step away from spontaneity and the free exercise of will. Whereas I could once act on whim and fancy, I now had to exercise planning and foresight. . . . This loss of spontaneity invaded my entire assessment of time. It rigidified my short-range perspectives and introduced a calculating quality into an existence that formerly had been pleasantly disordered. (p. 76)

Although some recreational programs do offer transportation services, these are usually segregated programs that do not meet the needs of all people who have disabilities. Too often, the person with a disability faces the choice of either staying home or imposing on family and friends by requesting transportation to recreational activities (Barnes & Mercer, 2003).

Currently, the U.S. government has no national policy on transportation for individuals who have disabilities. Until such a policy is formulated and accompanied by a commitment to fund it, many people with disabilities in the United States will continue to face difficulties in finding and affording transportation to recreational programs.

Transportation barriers are particularly apparent when it comes to air transportation. The ADA covers most travel-related services in the United States, but air travel is addressed by the Air Carrier Access Act of 1986 (ACAA). Enforcement of this law is entrusted to the Department of Transportation (DOT), but many are critical of the DOT's enforcement efforts. Quigley (1995) spoke for many people with disabilities when he wrote:

> Our only "protection" is a toothless tiger of a law that allows the airlines to get away with systematic outrages against passengers with disabilities. This is true because the ACAA provides no penalties for violations, nor does it provide any provision for attorney fees for the person with a disability. Instead, DOT logs the complaint into the record and occasionally meets with airlines to request that they improve services. This "enforcement" is like using a peashooter to get the attention of a thick-skinned elephant. . . . It simply does little good to create disabled-adapted rooms on cruise ships, hotels and resorts, and to make buildings more accessible, when people with disabilities can't get from point A to point B on our nation's airlines! (p. 11)

Canada, unlike the United States, has had a national policy on transportation of persons with disabilities since 1983. The Coalition of Provincial Organizations of the Handicapped (COPOH, 1987) stated that the Canadian national policy guarantees for persons with disabilities "reasonable, reliable, and equitable transportation services and facilities; dignified travel; no unreasonable terms and condi-

tions of travel; and self-determination" (p. 6). In addition, a Canadian Transportation Commission ruling known as the Kelly Decision has profound implications for the traveler who has a disability. This decision, an outcome of Clarris Kelly being denied transport because she was traveling without an attendant, established four significant principles: (1) self-determination (the traveler with a disability decides whether he or she requires an attendant); (2) one person/one fare (an attendant travels without charge); (3) equality of access (architectural barriers must not prevent travel); and (4) dignity of risk (travelers with disabilities are entitled to take the same risks as everyone else) (COPOH, 1987). As part of Canada's National Strategy for the Integration of Persons with Disabilities, "Transport Canada is working closely with all levels of government and the private sector to achieve equal access" ("Flying High," 1993, p. 17).

Such steps to improve transportation for persons with disabilities are of vital importance because, as Bowe (1979) noted, the availability of transportation "expands the alternatives from which a [person with a disability] can design his or her life" (p. 484).

Economic Barriers

Even in times of low unemployment, job opportunities are more limited for people who have disabilities. Furthermore, when they are able to find employment, individuals with disabilities frequently find themselves in low-paying positions with limited opportunity for advancement. These difficulties are compounded by higher-than-average expenses, such as for special transportation arrangements or personal care assistance. Studies in the United States and Canada (Kaye, 1998; Leitman, Cooner, & Risher, 1994; McNeil, 1997; National Organization on Disability, 2001b; Roeher Institute, 1988) have emphasized the economic plight of many people who have disabilities. Generally, people with disabilities have considerably less disposable income than people without disabilities; thus, their leisure activity choices and life experiences are constrained by their economic circumstances (Bridge & Gold, 1989). Rimmer,

People with disabilities usually have less income than people without disabilities. Unfortunately, many have greater expenses as well.
(Reprinted with permission from "There's Lint in Your Bellybutton! A Disabled Fable" by Audry King, © 1987 Canadian Rehabilitation Council for the Disabled [CRCD])

Rubin, and Braddock (2000), for example, surveyed African American women with disabilities and found that the cost of an exercise program was *by far* the biggest barrier to participation faced by these women. Moreover, even when enough money is available to participate in activities outside the home, there may not be sufficient funds to fully enjoy the experience. Ferrel (1989) provided a poignant illustration of this point:

> Finally, I saved enough to pay for a week-end retreat and to go home each night by taxi. I enjoyed meeting new people and discovering

new feelings of relaxation. The opportunity to go out for dinner afterwards with the group was important to me, but I felt peculiar when I could only afford to order an appetizer. My lack of income, rather than my disability, made me feel different from the others. (p. 15)

Interestingly, some studies have found that people with disabilities do not perceive lack of money to be a significant barrier to leisure participation (Caldwell & Adolph, 1989; Ferris, 1987). Nevertheless, these and other investigations have noted that people with disabilities often report recreational pursuits that are home based and require minimal expenditure of money. Economic barriers may also place greater limits on those who have severe disabilities. McNeil (1997) found that employment was over three times higher for persons without severe disabilities (76.9%) than for those with severe disabling conditions (26.1%).

It is entirely possible that financial limitations, rather than personal preferences, determine the nature of leisure participation for many people who have disabilities. As Crawford (1989) stated, "For most, the economics of disability determine what life at the sidelines is like" (p. 8).

Rules and Regulations Barriers

Historically, people with disabilities have faced many rules and regulations that limited their ability to participate in all aspects of our society. Examples of rules and regulations barriers include educational opportunities systematically denied to people with severe disabilities; literacy tests prevented many capable people with disabilities from voting; and employers overtly discriminated against people with disabilities by establishing requirements that were unrelated to job performance.

In 1997, for example, the PGA attempted to prevent Casey Martin from riding in a golf cart in PGA Tour golf events. The PGA cited the rule that all competitors must walk during competition. Martin, who has a lower-extremity disability, could not compete without the aid of a golf cart. Jay Hass, a member of the PGA Tour's policy board, summed up the board's position by stating, "The issue is should we be allowed to make our rules that people abide by. We need to be able to do that" (*Washington Post,* 1998). A court of law disagreed, however. Martin, citing the ADA, sued the PGA and won the right to compete using a golf cart.

Rules and regulations are necessary if society is to function effectively. At the same time, they must not be used as an excuse to exclude people with disabilities from participation in leisure activities. Susan Sygall (1985), a highly independent wheelchair user, described the excellent accessibility at the National Theatre in England, but then stated, "Would you believe they refused to sell us two 'wheelchair seats'

because we didn't have an able-bodied chaperone?" (p. 50). Such incidents provide evidence that fair rules and regulations, plus sensible enforcement, are needed if individuals with disabilities are to have equal access to recreation-related activities.

Barriers of Omission

Most environmental barriers to participation are actions or obstacles that limit people who have disabilities. Sometimes, however, what is *not* done creates barriers as well. The failure of society to provide for the needs of individuals who have disabilities results in barriers of omission. The following are examples of such barriers:

- Lack of appropriate education opportunities, including education for leisure.
- Lack of available recreation services that provide for people who have disabilities. Specifically, individualized services are needed to allow a person with a disability to function at his or her maximum level.
- Failure to publicize adequately those programs that could offer appropriate services to people who have disabilities.
- Lack of affordable and high-quality personal care assistance for persons with severe disabilities.
- Failure to include participants with disabilities in the planning and implementation of leisure services.
- Lack of appropriate technology to maximize the leisure functioning of individuals with disabilities.
- Failure to enforce existing legislation that would reduce other barriers to participation.
- Lack of adequate leisure role models for youngsters with disabilities and adults with recent disabilities.

Communication Barriers

The locus of intrinsic barriers is primarily within the individual. Environmental barriers are external forces. Communication barriers, however, cannot be thought of as either primarily intrinsic or extrinsic to the individual with a disability. Communication barriers result from a reciprocal

Effective communication requires *active* participation by both the sender and receiver of a message. For people with physical disabilities who have speech difficulties, pointing to letters on a "letter board" may facilitate this two-way interaction.
(Courtesy of The League: Serving People with Disabilities, Inc., Baltimore, MD)

interaction between individuals with disabilities and their social environment. There is an old expression "It takes two to tango." It also takes two to establish effective communication; a message needs to be sent, but it must be received as well.

Orelove and Sobsey (1996) have referred to the reciprocal nature of communication as "mutuality." If mutuality is to occur, the sender *and* the receiver must be active participants in the process. This is true whether the message is spoken or written. If the message sender is not able to make the message clear enough to be understood by others, an *expressive* block limits communication. On the other hand, if a clearly expressed message is not received correctly, a *receptive* block interferes with the communication process.

Communication barriers are rarely caused exclusively by expressive blocks or receptive blocks, however. An individual with speech difficulties may find it impossible to pronounce words clearly. This difficulty could be an expressive block to communication. The listener, however, may not concentrate on what is said or take the time to ask for unclear words to be repeated. Thus, the listener could be responsible for a receptive block. Most communication barriers between people with and without disabilities result from a combination of expressive blocks and receptive blocks. If effective communication is to occur, *both* individuals with disabilities and society at large must make an effort to overcome expressive and receptive blocks to communication.

People who are deaf are probably the most familiar individuals affected by communication barriers. To varying degrees, however, most people with disabilities experience communication barriers. Many youth with behavioral disorders feel that their parents do not listen to them. Their parents, in turn, may complain that they do not even speak the same language. Some people with physical disabilities claim that politicians do not listen to their complaints. At the same time, these politicians express frustration because they feel that activists with physical disabilities do not want to discuss the problems of funding social programs.

Communication difficulties experienced by people with disabilities can be compounded if cultural or language differences exist. Iera (1994) observed that "there is a low participation of people with disabilities of non-English speaking background within recreation services" (p. 2). Perhaps communication barriers are primarily responsible for low participation.

The importance of communication barriers such as those just discussed cannot be overemphasized. Communication links the individual who has a disability with his or her environment. A two-way dialogue needs to exist between persons with disabilities and the rest of society, including individuals and societal institutions. If blocks are allowed to interfere with this communication, there is little hope of overcoming the many barriers to participation.

OVERCOMING BARRIERS

It is important to recognize that individuals with and without disabilities regularly overcome their personal barriers to recreation participation. Research on constraints to recreation participation for persons both with and without disabilities confirms that the presence of barriers (i.e., constraints) does not necessarily limit participation in activities (Henderson, Bedini, Hecht, & Schuler, 1993; Hubbard & Mannell, 2001; Jackson & Rucks, 1995). Rather, people who are faced with barriers often "negotiate" their way through or around these barriers. People with disabilities are *not* powerless against the many barriers listed

previously; however, they may require assistance to negotiate some barriers they face. As a result, recreation professionals have the *obligation* to work for the reduction or elimination of these barriers. Despite this obligation, many people with disabilities point out that the community, including leisure service providers, fails to reach out to them. This is particularly true for persons who have severe disabilities (Hendershot, 2003).

Perhaps personnel from community organizations do not reach out to their neighbors with disabilities because removing barriers to participation seems like an overwhelming task. Most recreators rightfully feel that their jobs are so time-consuming that they have little time for additional efforts. Much of what needs to be done to remove barriers, however, can be accomplished within the scope of a recreator's job. The following concepts may help recreation professionals to provide the proper atmosphere for reducing or eliminating barriers to participation.

Provide Accessible Programs

It is essential that recreation professionals respond to the intent of the ADA (see chapter 3) by planning and implementing programs that are accessible to persons with disabilities. This means more than simply providing ramps into buildings; it involves planning programs that avoid as many barriers to participation as possible. The following suggestions may assist with this process:

- Offer activities that (a) include a range of cognitive and physical skill requirements, (b) allow for proper skill progression, (c) give opportunities for both formal and informal involvement, and (d) encourage cooperative interaction between participants with and without disabilities.
- Coordinate activities offered with public transportation schedules, and consider establishing car or van pools to activities.
- Ensure that buildings and facilities, including parking lots, comply with Americans with Disabilities Act Architectural Guidelines for accessibility.

Accessible and inclusive programs encourage cooperative interaction between persons with and without disabilities. (Courtesy of *VSA arts*, www.vsarts.org)

- Develop ways for economically disadvantaged individuals to "pay" for services that require fees; for example, in-kind services such as volunteer work could be used. Some authorities (Hutchison & McGill, 1992; Schleien et al., 1997) have proposed that community recreation services be offered on a "sliding scale." Thus, persons with lower incomes would pay less for services.
- Coordinate programs with agencies and organizations that specialize in services to people with special needs, thus ensuring that a continuum of services is available within the community.
- Publicize programs thoroughly and advertise that they are accessible to people with disabilities (including interpreters for participants who are deaf).

- Offer programs that provide *social accessibility* for everyone. For persons who are deaf, this means "encouraging, validating, and promoting recreation participation with others who share the same communication method" (Oliva & Simonson, 2000, p. 85).

Establish Priorities for Action

The traditional approach to overcoming barriers to participation has been for the recreation professional to concentrate on intrinsic barriers. This approach involves using recreation participation to improve the person's social, physical, or cognitive functioning. Emphasis may be on improving a person's disability or "problem," or it may be on strengthening the person's abilities. Regardless, this traditional approach means that the recreation professional focuses on changing the participant.

A number of authorities (Howe-Murphy & Charboneau, 1987; Longmore, 2003; Schleien et al., 1997; Wright, 1980) have challenged this traditional approach, however. They contend that professionals should not focus solely on changing individuals with disabilities, but should work toward reducing or eliminating environmental barriers. In 1980, Hutchison developed and used a Barriers to Community Involvement scale to determine the impact of 13 intrinsic and environmental barriers. Her results "suggest that disabled persons largely see barriers to community involvement as lying beyond themselves" (p. 10). She stated that this was a "noteworthy finding and should be analyzed further, since much of the focus in rehabilitation, education, and vocational services is upon changing disabled persons rather than the community" (pp. 10–11). The individual with a disability does not live in a vacuum. If people with disabilities are to become fully integrated into society, most authorities agree that *both* intrinsic and environmental barriers must receive everyone's attention.

Although recreational professionals can and should help to reduce or eliminate intrinsic and environmental barriers, the *unique* contribution that recreators can make is with the third type of barrier—communication barriers. By eliminating communication barriers as their first priority, recreators can help provide a vital link between individuals with disabilities and their social environments. Once this is accomplished, the job of overcoming other barriers will become much easier.

Facilitate Communication

Providing accessible programs is one way to facilitate communication between individuals with and without disabilities. Such programs bring people together and offer an opportunity for interpersonal communication. Recreation professionals must do more than just bring people together, however. Recreators should set an example for their constituents without disabilities by interacting appropriately with people who have disabilities. Additionally, recreators should aid the communication process between people who have disabilities and society's policymakers.

People who lack experience interacting with individuals with visible disabilities sometimes feel uncomfortable initiating conversation. Hesitancy and some discomfort are normal reactions to any unfamiliar situation, so recreators should expect to feel uneasy at first. It is essential to overcome these initial feelings, however. Before long, the person's disability will become less noticeable, and his or her "uniqueness" will become apparent. The following tips for interacting with an individual who has a disability are modified from "When You Meet a Handicapped Person," by an unknown author. They provide an excellent guideline for community recreators.

- Remember, a person with a disability is a person *first*. He or she is like anyone else, except for specific physical or mental limitations.
- Just be yourself, and show friendly personal interest in him or her.
- Learn basic signs and finger spelling for talking with individuals who are deaf.
- Talk about the same things you would with anyone else.
- Give physical assistance only if requested by the individual.
- Independence is important to everyone. If the situation dictates, perhaps ask, "Do you need assistance?"
- Be patient and let the person with a disability set the pace in walking or talking.
- Don't be afraid to laugh with him or her.
- Don't be overprotective or shower the individual with kindness. Don't offer pity or charity.
- Avoid making up your mind in advance about the capabilities of the person. You may be surprised how wrong you can be in making judgments about the individual's interests and abilities.

Facilitating interpersonal communication is extremely important. It is equally important, however, for recreators to facilitate communication between individuals with disabilities and leaders in the community. Hendershot (2003), Hutchison and McGill (1992), Sable and Gravink (1995), and many others have stressed the necessity for people with disabilities to express their own needs to policymakers. Hutchison (1980) noted, "As with many other change movements, greatest progress will be made when those oppressed by negative attitudes and poor services take an active role in changing attitudes and practices which block community involvement" (p. 7). Recreation professionals should search for ways to assist with this process. The following are some possibilities:

- Assist in the development of consumer groups, which bring together people with disabilities who have similar needs, interests, and goals.
- Analyze the community's power structure (Jewell, 1983), identify decision makers, and assist efforts to increase their awareness of barriers to participation.
- Keep abreast of meetings, hearings, and so on, that offer opportunities for people with disabilities to express their views.
- Provide consumers with information and resources that may be useful in discussions with policymakers.
- Offer seminars on interpersonal communication for people with disabilities to include ways to improve expressive and receptive communication.
- If necessary, serve as an advocate to speak for people with disabilities who are unable to articulate their own needs.
- Form partnerships with local organizations or chapters that have constituents with disabilities. Examples include rehabilitation centers, assisted living facilities, and volunteer organizations (e.g., ARC, Easter Seals).

Foster Empowerment

Empowerment is an important concept for recreation service providers to know and understand. According to Chamberlin (1997), the key elements

of empowerment are self-esteem, assertiveness, access to information, and the ability to make choices. In addition, an empowered person needs the resources to implement the choices that are made. Similarly, Dickerson (1998) divided empowerment into three general attributes, including self-determination, social engagement, and a sense of personal competence. Empowerment means that a person with a disability has positive feelings toward self and can effect positive outcomes in his or her life. Recreation professionals should work to foster empowerment in the lives of participants who have disabilities.

One essential way for recreation professionals to promote empowerment is to encourage individuals with disabilities to identify, develop, and use social support networks. Taylor, Sylvestre, and Botschner (1998) have referred to social support as a *dynamic social activity.* Rather than viewing social support as something one person provides to another, this conceptualization emphasizes "supportive relationships, made up of many incidental day-to-day interactions that, taken together, give the people involved a sense of mutual support" (p. 6).

The family is probably the most important source of social support for the majority of people who have disabilities. Christopher Reeve (1998), the actor who sustained a spinal cord injury during an equestrian event, underscored this point. Immediately after his accident, his wife Dana said to him, "You're still you, and I love you." Reeve wrote that Dana's statement "meant more to me than just a personal declaration of faith and commitment. In a sense it was an affirmation that marriage and family stood at the center of everything, and if both were intact, so was your universe" (p. 54).

The family is not a person's only source of social support, however. Friends, coworkers, and acquaintances can also foster a supportive environment, and community leisure activities provide an ideal avenue for building a strong support network. When people with disabilities experience open and accepting communities, they develop "texture" in their everyday lives (Pedlar, Haworth, Hutchison, Taylor, & Dunn, 1999). Living a textured life means developing and maintaining multiple relationships on multiple levels, and social multiplicity provides the foundation for empowerment.

Additional suggestions for recreation professionals to foster empowerment among participants with disabilities include:

- Offering inclusive programs that provide successful experiences and meaningful interactions among participants (see chapter 7).
- Forming self-help groups that focus on overcoming barriers to recreation participation.
- Hiring persons with disabilities to work in recreation leadership positions (paid and volunteer).

- Including persons with disabilities on recreation policy-making boards and committees.
- Offering community awareness programs that delineate issues, provide information, and identify relevant resources.

Hutchison and McGill (1992) have observed that achieving empowerment is a lifelong struggle, but social support and empowerment enable a person to "dream" of what can be. "When people's dreams are compared to the current situation, the barriers to meeting these dreams and the challenges that result can be easily identified" (p. 216). Social support and empowerment not only help a person with a disability to identify barriers, they enable him or her to overcome them.

Summary

Barriers to participation in recreation and leisure activities are experienced by everyone, but people who have disabilities face more and greater barriers than their nondisabled peers. Some of these barriers are *intrinsic;* they result from the individual's own limitations. Other barriers are *environmental;* they are caused by external forces that impose limits on the individual. Finally, some are *communication* barriers, which block interaction between the individual and his or her social environment. Although recreation professionals can assist with overcoming all types of barriers, they should establish the elimination of communication barriers as their first priority. By reducing or eliminating communication barriers, recreators can help create a vital link between people with disabilities and their social environments. Properly nourished, this link will lead to empowerment of persons with disabilities and elimination of most barriers to participation.

Suggested Learning Activities

1. Make a list of 10 items regarding elimination of barriers to recreation participation that you would address if asked to testify before your city council.
2. Explain how an individual's perception of his or her skill can act as a barrier to recreation participation.
3. Access the website for the National Organization on Disability (www.nod.org). On this site, find recent research on the status of persons with disabilities in the United States. Using the data from this research, write a three-page paper entitled "The Impact of Barriers to Community Participation for Persons with Disabilities."
4. Interview the director of a community recreation program and determine what actions are being taken to eliminate barriers to participation in that program. Discuss the strengths and weaknesses of these actions.
5. Of the three types of barriers outlined in the chapter, which is the key to reducing or eliminating most other barriers to participation? Explain why.
6. Interview an individual with a disability and determine (a) his or her recreational needs, interests, and desires; and (b) intrinsic, environmental, and communication barriers that limit his or her participation.
7. Read three journal articles on the concept of empowerment. Write a short paper explaining why empowerment is important for persons with disabilities.

REFERENCES

Barnes, C., & G. Mercer. *Disability.* Cambridge, U.K.: Polity, 2003.

Bedini, L. A. Transition and integration in leisure for people with disabilities. *Parks & Recreation, 28*(11), 20–24, 1993.

Bowe, F. *Handicapping America: Barriers to Disabled People.* New York: Harper and Row, 1978.

Bowe, F. Transportation: Key to independent living. *Archives of Physical Medicine and Rehabilitation, 60*(10), 484, 1979.

Bregha, F. J. Leisure and freedom re-examined. In T. L. Goodale & P. A. Witt, Eds. *Recreation and Leisure and Issues in an Era of Change.* State College, PA: Venture Publishing, 1980, pp. 30–37.

Bridge, N. J., & D. Gold. An analysis of the relationship between leisure and economics. *Journal of Leisurability, 16*(2), 10–14, 1989.

Bruck L. *Access: The Guide to a Better Life for Disabled Americans.* New York: Random House, 1978.

Caldwell, L., & S. Adolph. Economic issues associated with disability: And then there is leisure. *Journal of Leisurability, 16*(2), 19–24, 1989.

Chamberlin, J. A working definition of empowerment. *Psychiatric Rehabilitation Journal, 20*(4), 43–46. 1997.

Cleigh, W. C. Is there any safety—or equality—for gimps? *Ragged Edge On-line.* [Online]. Available: http://www.ragged-edge-mag.com/0703/0703ft6.html, July/August 2003.

Condor, B. For the chronically ill, managing pain is no easy task. *The Island Packet,* March 14, 1995, p. C1.

COPOH. Transportation and disabled citizens: Policies on eligibility and reciprocity. *Journal of Leisurability, 14*(1), 4–12, 1987.

Crawford, C. A view from the sidelines: Disability, poverty, and recreation in Canada. *Journal of Leisurability, 16*(2), 3–9, 1989.

Crawford, D. W., E. L. Jackson, & G. Godbey. A hierarchical model of leisure constraints. *Leisure Sciences, 13,* 309–320, 1991.

Csikszentmihalyi, M. *Beyond Boredom and Anxiety.* San Francisco: Jossey-Bass, 1975.

Csikszentmihalyi, M. *Finding Flow: The Psychology of Engagement with Everyday Life.* New York: BasicBooks, 1997.

Dattilo, J. *Inclusive Leisure Services: Responding to the Rights of People with Disabilities* (2nd ed.). State College, PA: Venture, 2002.

Dickerson, F. B. Strategies that foster empowerment. *Cognitive & Behavioral Practice, 5,* 255–275, 1998.

Ervin, M. The joy of oppression. *New Mobility, 8*(40), 67, 1997.

Ferrel, M. No income: No leisure. *Journal of Leisurability, 16*(2), 15–16, 1989.

Ferris, B. F. Reflection on the physical activity patterns of disabled Canadians: Challenges for practitioners. *Journal of Leisurability, 14*(2), 18–23, 1987.

Flying high. *Abilities, 17,* Spring 1993.

Hahn, H. Accommodations and the ADA: Unreasonable bias or biased reasoning? In L. H. Krieger, Ed. *Backlash against the ADA: Reinterpreting Disability Rights.* Ann Arbor, MI: University of Michigan Press, 2003, pp. 26–61.

Hendershot, G. Community participation and life satisfaction. [Online]. Available: http://www.nod.org/content.cfm?id=1371, May 29, 2003.

Henderson, K. A., L. A. Bedini, L. Hecht, & R. Schuler. Women with physical disabilities and the negotiation of leisure constraints. Paper presented at the Canadian Congress on Leisure Research, Winnipeg, Manitoba, Canada, May 1993.

Heyne, L. A., S. J. Schleien, & L. H. McAvoy. Friendship Development between Children with and without Developmental Disabilities in Recreational Activities. Paper presented at the 1993 Symposium on Leisure Research, San Jose, CA, October 1993.

Howe-Murphy, R., & B. G. Charboneau. *Therapeutic Recreation Intervention: An Ecological Perspective.* Englewood Cliffs, NJ: Prentice-Hall, 1987.

Hubbard, J., & R. C. Mannell. Testing competing models of the leisure constraint negotiation process in a corporate employee recreation setting. *Leisure Sciences, 23,* 145–163, 2001.

Hutchison, P. Perceptions of disabled persons regarding barriers to community involvement. *Journal of Leisurability, 7*(3), 4–16, 1980.

Hutchison, P., & J. McGill. *Leisure, Integration and Community.* Concord, Ontario: Leisurability Publications, 1992.

Iera, R. *Re-thinking Recreation for People with Disabilities of Non-English Speaking Background.* Brunswick, Victoria: Action on Disability within Ethnic Communities, Inc., 1994.

Illich, I., I. K. Zola, J. McKnight, J. Caplan, & H. Shaiken. *Disabling Professions.* London: Marion Boyers, 1977.

Jackson, E. L. Special issue introduction: Leisure constraints/constrained leisure. *Leisure Sciences, 13,* 203–215. 1991.

Jackson, E. L., D. W. Crawford, & G. Godbey. Negotiation of leisure constraints. *Leisure Sciences, 15,* 1–11, 1993.

Jackson, E. L., & V. C. Rucks. Reasons for ceasing participation and barriers to participation: Further examination of constrained leisure as an internally homogeneous concept. *Leisure Sciences, 15,* 217–230, 1993.

Jackson. E. L., & V. C. Rucks. Negotiation of leisure constraints by junior-high and high-school students: An exploratory study. *Journal of Leisure Research,* 27, 85–105, 1995.

Jackson, E. L., & D. Scott. Constraints to leisure. In T. L. Burton & E. L. Jackson, Eds. *Leisure Studies: Prospects for the Twenty-First Century.* State College, PA: Venture, 1999, pp. 299–321.

Jewell, D. C. Comprehending concepts of community power structure: Prerequisite for recreation-integration. *Journal of Leisurability, 10*(1), 24–30, 1983.

Johnson, M. *People with Disabilities Explain It All for You.* Louisville, KY: The Advocado Press, 1992.

Kaye, H. S. Is the status of people with disabilities improving? *Disability Statistics Abstract #21,* May 1998.

Langer, E. J., S. Fiske, S. E. Taylor, & B. Chanowitz. Stigma, staring, and discomfort: A novel-stimulus hypothesis. *Journal of Experimental Social Psychology, 12*(5), 451–463, 1976.

Leitman, R., E. Cooner, & P. Risher. *N.O.D./Harris Survey of Americans with Disabilities.* New York: Louis Harris and Associates, 1994.

Longmore, P. K. *Why I Burned My Book and Other Essays on Disability.* Philadelphia: Temple University Press, 2003.

Martin, K. A., A. E. Latimer, C. Francoueur, H. Hanley, K. Watson, A. L. Hicks, & N. McCartney. Sustaining exercise motivation and participation among people with spinal cord injuries. *Palaestra, 18*(1), 38–40, 51, 2002.

Maryland-National Capital Park and Planning Commission. *Survey on Community-Based Therapeutic Recreation Programs and Services.* Riverdale, MD: Author, 1993.

McNeil, J. M. Americans with Disabilities: 1994–95. *Current Population Reports,* U.S. Department of Commerce, Bureau of the Census, Economics and Statistics Administration (70–61). Washington, DC: Government Printing Office, August 1997. Available: http://www.census.gov/prod/3/97pubs/p70-61.pdf

Miller, H. L. Integration of disabled people in mainstream sports: Case study of a partially sighted child. *Adapted Physical Activity Quarterly, 6,* 17–31, 1989.

Moore, R. L., & J. Dattilo. Greenway preferences: A comparison between people with and without disabilities. In *Abstracts from the 1993 Symposium on Leisure Research* (p. 28). Arlington, VA: National Recreation and Park Association, 1993.

Murphy, R. *The Body Silent.* New York: Holt, 1987.

National Organization on Disability. *What Is the Community Participation Gap?* [Online]. Available: http://www.nod.org/content.cfm?id=971, January 3, 2003.

National Organization on Disability. *Awareness of ADA at All-Time High.* [Online]. Available: http://www.nod.org/content.cfm?id=1095, July 24, 2002.

National Organization on Disability. *Overall Community Participation of People with Disabilities.* [Online]. Available: http://www.nod.org/content.cfm?id=132, July 24, 2001a.

National Organization on Disability. *Barriers to Community Participation.* [Online]. Available: http://www.nod.org/content.cfm?id=146, July 24, 2001b.

Oliva, G., & A. Simonson. Re-thinking leisure services for deaf and hard of hearing persons: A new paradigm. *Parks and Recreation, 35*(5), 78–85, 2000.

Orelove, F. P., & D. Sobsey, *Educating Children with Multiple Disabilities: A Transdisciplinary Approach* (3rd ed.). Baltimore: Paul H. Brookes, 1996.

Park, D. Recreation. In the White House Conference on Handicapped Individuals, *Volume One: Awareness Papers* pp. 119–131. Washington, DC: The White

House Conference on Handicapped Individuals, 1977.

Pedlar, A., L. Haworth, P. Hutchison, A. Taylor, & P. Dunn. *A Textured Life: Empowerment and Adults with Developmental Disabilities.* Waterloo, Ontario, Canada: Wilfried Laurier University Press, 1999.

Percy, S. L. Administrative remedies and legal disputes. In L. H. Krieger, Ed. *Backlash against the ADA.* Ann Arbor, MI: University of Michigan Press, 2003, pp. 297–322.

Quigley, M. Airlines: Still crimping travel. *New Mobility, 6*(26), 11, 1995.

Reeve, C. *Still Me.* New York: Random House, 1998.

Rimmer, J. H., S. S. Rubin, & D. Braddock. Barriers to exercise in African American women with physical disabilities. *Archives of Physical Medicine and Rehabilitation, 81,* 182–187, 2000.

Roeher Institute. *Income Insecurity: The Disability Income System in Canada.* Downsview, Ontario: The G. Allan Roeher Institute, 1988.

Sable, J., & J. Gravink. Partners: Promoting accessible recreation. *Parks and Recreation, 30*(5), 34–40, 1995.

Schleien, S. J., M. T. Ray., & F. P. Green. *Community Recreation and People with Disabilities: Strategies for Inclusion* (2nd ed.). Baltimore: Brookes, 1997.

Sherrill, C. Should social inclusion be a major goal of physical education? *Palaestra, 19*(2), 56–57, 2003.

Sneegas, J. J. Social skills: An integral component of leisure participation and the therapeutic recreation services. *Therapeutic Recreation Journal, 23*(2), 30–40, 1989.

Speaking out: Walk or ride? *The Washington Post,* January 18, 1998, p. D4.

Sygall, S. Travelling tips. *The Exceptional Parent, 15*(8), 50–51, 1985.

Szychowski, E. River of dreams. *Sports'n Spokes, 18*(1), 19–22, 1993.

Taylor, A. R., J. C. Sylvestre, & J. V. Botschner. Social support is something you do, not something you provide: Implications for linking formal and informal support. *Journal of Leisurability, 25*(4), 3–13, 1998.

U.S. Department of Transportation. Transportation difficulties keep over half a million disabled at home. *Issues Brief,* Number 3, April 2003.

Wakefield, D. Personal communication, 1981.

Wright, B. A. Developing constructive views of life with a disability. *Rehabilitation Literature, 41*(11–12), 274–279, 1980.

Wright, B. A. *Physical Disability—A Psychosocial Approach.* New York: Harper and Row, 1983.

6

DESIGN OF ACCESSIBLE AND USABLE RECREATION ENVIRONMENTS

(Photo by David R. Austin)

In the past, a vast number of recreation facilities in the United States have been usable only by persons who do not have disabilities. Today, however, there is a growing public consciousness regarding environmental design for persons with disabilities. This consciousness is manifested by the Americans with Disabilities Act of 1990.

This chapter deals with the design of appropriate recreation environments for all people, including persons with disabilities. Initial coverage is given to common terms and pertinent legislation. The major portion of the chapter is devoted to a discussion of guidelines and recommendations for creating usable public recreation facilities, with special attention directed to playgrounds.

TERMINOLOGY

For the purpose of this chapter, it is necessary to define two important terms often found in the literature concerning recreation environments designed to meet the needs of persons with disabilities. These terms are *physical accessibility, usability,* and *universal accessibility,* and each is defined as follows:

- *Physical accessibility* refers to the elements in the constructed environment (site or building) that allow approach, entrance, and use of facilities by persons with disabling conditions. The term is often used to indicate that a facility complies with specified standards to permit use by those whose sensory or physical impairments might otherwise limit their use of the facility.
- *Usability* refers to a constructed environment providing the opportunity for maximum use by those with sensory or mobility impairments. Occasionally, the word is used with the term *accessibility* to indicate that a facility not only meets minimum accessibility standards but is usable by individuals with disabling conditions.
- *Universal accessibility* refers to an encompassing design approach that strives to ensure environments are usable by the broadest possible spectrum of people, rather than being designed only with the thought of accommodating the needs of people with or without disabilities. For example, universal design allows for the provision of ramps that accommodate not only wheelchair users but mothers with baby strollers and bicyclists. While a brief background and principles are to be provided at the end of this chapter, a central notion behind universal accessibility is to design environments for people who are diverse in size and abilities and to avoid segregating or stigmatizing any users.

THE EXPANDING ROLE OF ASSISTIVE TECHNOLOGY

We regularly employ a variety of "high" and "low" technologies in our recreational pursuits. For instance, we use "high tech" golf clubs with graphite shafts. Our survival in sports such as scuba diving and rock climbing depends on technology. Sometimes our use of technology in recreation is relatively "low tech," such as using softball gloves when playing a game of catch, but technology still can play a vital part in the recreation experience. Few recreation activities require "special" equipment for persons with disabilities to take part because they usually employ the same technologies others use (Austin & Hamilton, 1997; Longmuir & Axelson, 1996). On those occasions where people with disabilities encounter obstacles, another application of technology can be used to overcome them through the use of *assistive devices,* sometimes known as *assistive technology devices* (ATDs) (Cook, 2002; Lewis, 1998).

PLAE, Inc. (1993) has proposed three categories for assistive technology for recreation: personal, activity-specific, and environmental. Personal technology includes assistive devices that individuals use or wear to enhance their abilities. Examples include eyeglasses, hearing aids, and handgrip cuffs. Activity-specific assistive devices include chairlift-compatible monoskies for downhill skiing, hand cycles, tactile game boards, and beep balls. Environmental technologies include ramps that allow access to recreation areas, swimming pool lifts, and signs to provide information about trails. Ideally, environmental technologies will employ the concept of universal design to assure facilities are accessible to all individuals, with and without disabilities. The focus of this chapter is this third category, the recreation environment.

LEGISLATION

Growing public awareness of the problems of persons with disabilities has led to several pieces of federal legislation that have an effect on the design of recreation facilities. Chief among these are the Architectural Barriers Act of 1968 (PL 90-480), Section 504 of the Rehabilitation Act of 1973 (PL 93-112), and the Americans with Disabilities Act of 1990 (PL 101-336).

The language of PL 90-480 and PL 93-112 dictates that the needs of persons with disabilities be considered by those recreation agencies that use federal funds. The Architectural Barriers Act specifies that "Any building, or facility, constructed in whole or in part by federal funds must be made accessible to and usable by the physically handicapped." Section 504 of the Rehabilitation Act states, "no otherwise qualified handicapped individual in the U.S. . . . shall solely, by reason of his handicap, be excluded from participation in, be denied the benefits of, or be subjected to discrimination under any program or activity receiving federal assistance." The Americans with Disabilities Act (ADA) prohibits discrimination against people with disabilities. The ADA extends the Architectural Barriers Act to all public facilities regardless of funding. It is the mandate of the government of the United States that recreational facilities open to the public be accessible to all people. In addition, many state and local laws stipulate barrier-free architectural design for public facilities. For more detailed information on legislation, see chapter 3.

To enforce areas covered under the Architectural Barriers Act and Americans with Disabilities Act, the U.S. Architectural and Transportation Barriers Compliance Board (Access Board) was created. The Access Board serves as the nation's only independent federal agency whose primary mission is accessibility for people with disabilities. A mandate to the Board is the development of accessibility guidelines under the ADA. In 1991, ADA accessibility guidelines were published to set forth standards for public buildings and facilities. These are referred to as ADAAG (ADA Accessibility Guidelines) (PLAE, Inc., 1993). In 1994, the Access Board appointed a Recreation Access Advisory Committee to develop specific ADA accessibility guidelines for all recreation areas. In 2002, the Access Board issued final guidelines for recreation facilities (Architectural and Transportation Barriers Compliance Board, 2002). For information on the guidelines, the reader may reach the Access Board's website (www.access-board.gov) or contact the Access Board (800-USA-ABLE).

GENERAL GUIDELINES FOR PLANNING RECREATION FACILITIES

Dimensions—Space Requirements

A basic point of departure in thinking about design components for persons with disabilities is to deal with dimensional requirements. To do this, space requirements for an average adult wheelchair user are considered because designs to accommodate this individual should ensure spaces large enough for other persons.

Wheelchair Dimensions

Dimensions for an average, manual, adult-sized wheelchair (Fig. 6-1) are as follows:

- The length of the chair will be 42 in. to 48 in. With another 6 in. required for toe space, the total length required for wheelchair users is 48 in. to 54 in.
- The width of the average wheelchair is 22 in. to 26 in. When collapsed, the most commonly used wheelchairs are 11 in. wide.
- The height of the seat from the floor is approximately 19 in.

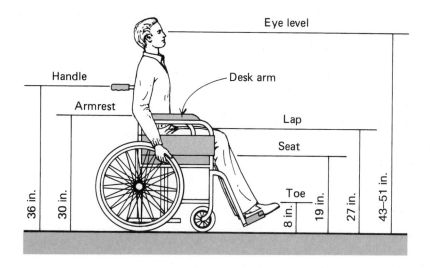

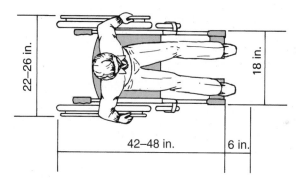

Figure 6-1   Dimensions of Adult-Sized Wheelchairs

- It is 27 in. from the floor to the user's lap and 30 in. from the floor to the armrests.
- The height of the pusher handles is 36 in. from the floor.

Some specially equipped adult-sized wheelchairs may exceed these dimensions. Children's wheelchairs will be smaller than those designed for adults. The junior-sized chair has a seat 16 in. wide and 18 in. from the floor. Thus, space requirements such as the turning radius will necessarily be reduced for children.

Space Requirements for Maneuvering Wheelchairs

The following are space requirements for those using standard, adult-sized wheelchairs:

- A turning radius of 60 in. × 60 in. is required to make a full 360° turn.
- A minimum width for a corridor or path that allows a pedestrian and a wheelchair user to pass is 48 in., although a wider width to accommodate two wheelchairs to pass is recommended.

- The minimum width for a corridor or path that allows two wheelchairs to pass is 60 in. minimum, although a space of 72 in. would be recommended.
- A minimum door opening width of 32 in. is needed by a person who uses a wheelchair.
- The width of a corridor or path with a door or gate should exceed the width of the door or gate by 18 in. to 24 in. to allow the space needed to maneuver the chair while opening the door or gate.

Reaching from a Wheelchair

Each wheelchair user is unique in his or her range of reach because of differences in size, strength, range of motion, and degree of involvement. The reach dimensions presented here are averages. Devices should therefore be placed well within the figures presented so they may be accessible to all.

- The reach for a wheelchair user facing a wall and reaching diagonally is approximately 48 in. from the floor. Thus, switches, telephones, and other such devices should be placed less than 48 in. from the floor. Minimum height is 15 in. from the floor.
- An upward side reach can be made to the height of 54 in. from the floor. A downward side reach can be made down to 9 in. from the floor. Thus, shelves and cabinets should be placed within the range of 9 in. to 54 in. from the floor.
- An average person in a wheelchair can reach a maximum of 25 in. across a table when seated at the table. A comfortable reach would be less. Thus, relatively narrow shelves and work spaces are dictated.

Special Considerations for Other Persons

General concepts to consider when planning areas and facilities for other populations are as follows:

- Some persons experience difficulty in operating devices that call for grasping or twisting because of chronic impairments that affect the skills required to manipulate objects (such as doorknobs). Therefore, devices should be chosen that make it possible to manipulate the objects without the need to grasp or twist.
- Persons may lack the strength and stamina needed to be successful in completing tasks such as opening heavy doors or using revolving doors. Decreased strength and stamina may particularly be a problem for older people. Doors should not be heavy to open, and rest areas should be considered in all recreation facilities, especially along paths.
- For those with visual impairments, raised letters should be used on signs.
- The use of different textures on walks or paths may be used to provide location cues to persons who have visual impairments. Textured borders on the edge of paths are an example of such a cueing aid.
- Audible cues may be provided, such as bells signaling once for an up elevator, twice for a down elevator, or verbal announcements of each floor on the elevator.
- For those with severe auditory impairments, signage is particularly important. Signs with precise and clear messages should be placed at a height within the range of vision of both children and adults.
- Simplicity should be a keynote in design for persons possessing mental disabilities. For example, signs should be as simple as possible (i.e., use short words or easily understood symbols). In the design of buildings and other facilities, ambiguity should be avoided to minimize uncertainty and confusion.

PARKS AND OUTDOOR RECREATION AREAS

Numerous design elements are found within park and outdoor recreation areas. Although in the section that follows, a number of these elements will be treated as separate entities, it is critical to remember the importance of the physical relationship among these design elements. Unless it is possible to get from one area to another, the value of making a specific area accessible is minimized.

Gilbert (1987) has noted an interrelationship among design and other elements critical to accessibility of parks and outdoor recreation areas. Citing the results of a Canadian survey, Gilbert identified four key issues related to park access:

1. Transportation—To get to the [parks and historic] areas and to get around inside the park.
2. Accessibility—The need to remove all barriers to enable participation by all.
3. The need to consider disabilities other than physical disabilities.
4. The need for more education programs to impact on society's attitudes toward persons with disabilities. (p. 27)

The emphasis in this chapter is on design elements. However, the design characteristics discussed are interrelated and have important psychosocial implications for park and recreation facility users, particularly those who have disabilities.

Signage

Identification, directional, and information signs are helpful to all users of park and recreation facilities. Proper signage is particularly beneficial for persons with hearing and speech disabilities, because they may not be able to communicate with others to obtain information.

The international symbol of accessibility (see Fig. 6-2) should be displayed at the entrance and at various points within the park or recreation area to inform people that it provides access for persons with disabilities. Facilities within the park or recreation area that should be appropriately marked with the symbol include rest rooms, entrances to buildings, trails, and picnic areas. In addition, all parking spaces designated for use by individuals with disabilities should be clearly marked with the symbol of accessibility, and where diagrams or maps are provided, the symbol should be used to indicate accessible buildings or areas.

Signs should be placed at a height within the range of vision and reach for both children and adults. Preferably, signs should be located at eye level (between 43 in. and 51 in.) for wheelchair users. Consistency should be employed in height and location when mounting signs so that they may be found easily.

For ease in reading, signs should be made with light-colored characters or symbols on a dark background and have a nonglare surface. Identification signs for rooms (including rest rooms) should have raised characters, using the standard alphabet and Arabic numbers, because the vast majority of persons with severe visual impairments do not read Braille. The characters should be at least 5/8 in. in height but no higher than 2 in. They should be raised a minimum of 1/32 in. and have clearly defined edges. Signs with raised letters can also be used to identify and interpret points of interest. Most authorities would probably agree, however, that sighted guides or audiotape devices are more effective means of presenting information.

Figure 6-2   International Symbol of Accessibility

Parking

Special parking accommodations are required for persons with disabilities. These spaces allow drivers with disabilities who need extra space to transfer safely. Those with stamina limitations and individuals with visual impairments who must have safe access to and from parking areas may also use accessible spaces. Because of this, parking spaces need to be located as close as possible to the shortest accessible route to the building or area being used. Accessible paths (with a minimum 48 in. width) adjacent to parking areas must be wide enough to allow for the possibility of parked cars overhanging the walkway. Accessible parking stalls must be at least 9 ft. wide. Passenger access aisles (at least 60 in. wide) next to the stalls for cars permit persons who have disabilities to gain access to automobiles. The overall dimensions of the area should be approximately 14 ft. wide (including the 60 in. zone for the access aisle) and 18 ft. long.

One accessible space must be provided in lots that hold 25 cars or less. In lots holding up to 100 cars, an additional accessible space must be added for each 25 spaces (i.e., 2 accessible spaces in a 50-space lot, 3 in a 75-space lot, 4 in a 100-space lot). Lots having 101 to 150 spaces must have 5 accessible spaces and lots with 151 to 200 must have 6. Lots of 201 to 300 spaces need 7 accessible spaces. Those with 301 to 400 need 8 accessible spaces and those with 401 to 500 spaces require 9 accessible spaces. For lots of 501 to 1,000 spaces, 2% of the spaces must be accessible. Finally, in lots of 1,001 spaces or more, the required number of accessible spaces is 20 plus 1 per 100 above 1,000. One out of every 8 accessible stalls (but at least one) must be designed as van accessible. Van stalls, like those for cars are 9 ft. wide, but the access aisle must be at least 96 in. (as compared to 60 in. for cars). These stalls shall be designated as "van accessible."

Both car and van accessible stalls must be painted solid blue with a white international symbol of accessibility, or must be outlined in blue with a 3-ft.-square accessibility symbol. Finally, a sign at least 70 square in. in size, displaying the international symbol of accessibility, should be posted so the bottom edge is at least 80 in. above the surface.

Additional Design Information for Access Aisles

Access aisles need to be provided for accessibility. As previously noted, the space for cars must be at least 18 ft. in length. An aisle, with a minimum width of 60 in., must run along the entire length of the parking space. The aisle should be on the passenger side of each space. The exception is when the aisle is shared by two accessible spaces (a design feature that is not preferable). Van spaces must have a wider aisle than normal accessible spaces. Van accessible aisles need to be 96 in. wide. Exit from the access aisle must be the same level as the parking space or a curb ramp needs to be provided. The slope of the curb ramp cannot exceed 1:12 (8.33%).

Passenger Loading Zones

Sometimes pull-off areas are designed as designated passenger loading zones. In such cases, a 60 in. wide access aisle must be provided directly adjacent to the vehicle pull-up area. The access aisle must be the same length as the pull-up area, that is 20 ft. The access aisle must also be at the same level as the vehicle pull-up area or a curb ramp must be provided, that cannot exceed 1:12 (8.33%).

Two common types of curb ramps are the ramp with a returned curb (Fig. 6-3) and the flared ramp (Fig. 6-4). If there is a flare on the sides of the ramp, it should be no steeper than 1:8 (12.3%). No matter the type, curb ramps should be a minimum of 36 in. wide. Ramps should be constructed to blend at a common level with the street or parking lot and the walk. It is recommended that the entire curb ramp be made to contrast in color and texture with the walk surface so that it is not a hazard for those who have visual impairments.

Walks and Trails

Parks and outdoor recreation areas commonly provide walks to connect major buildings with other areas. Trails are also common features in parks and outdoor recreation areas.

When walks join parking lots and streets, they must be made to meet the level of the other surfaces. In many instances, curbs are not constructed in park and recreation areas so that there is a natural blending of walks with parking lots and streets. Illustrations presented in the previous section cover

Figure 6-3   Returned Curb

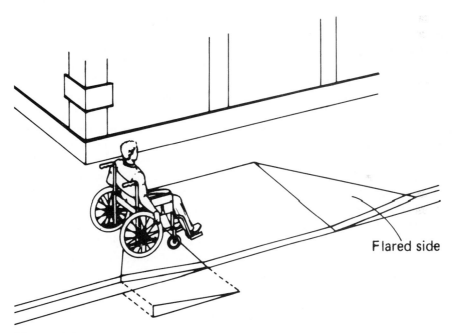

Figure 6-4   Flared Ramp

the design features when curb ramps are necessary in parking facilities. These same principles may be employed when a walk meets a street or driveway. Design features become far more complex, however, when walks meet the intersection of two curbed streets. It is recommended that information be sought from experts or illustrated literature on

accessibility be reviewed to obtain alternatives for designing acceptable curb ramps at intersections.

Walks should be a minimum of 48 in. wide. However, a width of 60 in. to 72 in. is preferable so that wheelchairs can easily pass. Walk gradients should not exceed 1:20 (5%) and preferably should be less. If a walk does approach the maximum grade or is unusually long, rest areas with benches and room for wheelchairs should be provided. Surfaces in front of rest stops should be textured differently than the walk to provide location cues for persons with visual impairments. Nonslip surfaces such as brushed concrete or asphalt are recommended for the overall walk surface. Minimum use of expansion joints is also recommended, and where joints are used they should not exceed 1/2 in.

For persons with visual impairments, it is important to consider objects that may protrude over or beside walks. A vertical clearance of at least 80 in. must be provided above walks. For instance, tree branches must be kept trimmed so someone with a visual impairment does not get struck by a branch. The lowest part of objects protruding into a walk must be no more than 27 in. above level of the walk so that persons with visual impairments can detect them.

Most authorities object to the designation of "handicapped trails." An alternative to designating trails for the use of persons with disabilities is to provide several different types of recreational trails within a park or outdoor recreation area. The trail system can then reflect a wide range of user preferences and abilities. *A Guide to Designing Accessible Outdoor Recreation Facilities* (1980), published by the U.S. Department of Interior, suggests five classifications for trails. A brief description of each follows.

- Class I trails are short (0 ft. to 1/4 mi.), hard surface (concrete or asphalt) trails with very little grade (a maximum of 1:50 or 2% slope). The recommended width is 48 in. (one way) to 72 in. (two ways). Rest areas with benches, shelters, and interpretation stations are placed every 100 ft. to 150 ft.
- Class II trails are 1/4 to 1 mi., surfaced with asphalt, wooden planking, or solidly packed crushed stone, and may have a slope of 1:20 (5%). The width for Class II trails is 36 in. to 48 in. (one way) to 48 in. to 60 in. (two ways). Rest areas with benches, shelters, and interpretation stations are placed every 200 ft. to 300 ft.

- Class III trails are 1 to 3 mi. long, are surfaced with a firm, well-compacted material (such as pea gravel), and may have a slope of 1:12 (8.33%). The width of the trail is 36 in. to 48 in. Rest areas consist of occasional natural benches and interpretation stations where needed (using 500 ft. to 600 ft. as a guideline.)
- Class IV trails are 3 to 10 mi. in length, are surfaced with bound wood chips or class 5 gravel mixed coarse, and may have a slope of 1:8 (12.5%). The trail width is 24 in. to 36 in. A rest area or interpretation station is located every mile.
- Class V trails are more than 10 miles, have surfaces that are sandy or made of rocks or rough, unbound wood chips, and that follow the slope of the land or use steps. The width of the trail is not defined and rest areas are not developed unless there is a particularly unique feature that requires interpretation.

By employing this five-level classification system or a similar system, parks and recreation professionals can provide appropriate levels of experiences to suit persons with a variety of interests and abilities. Proper signage is important to the successful use of such a trail system, because users must be informed of the length and difficulty of each trail.

An alternative means to the classification system is the mapping of trails using computerized mapping techniques to provide users objective data on the difficulty of each trail. Such maps offer much more specific and objective information than can a general classification system (Axelson & Chelini, 1993).

Beneficial Designs, Inc. has developed still another approach termed the Universal Trail Assessment and Mapping Process (UTAP). UTAP provides objective information on five key elements of trail access information. These are (1) grade, (2) cross slope, (3) width, (4) surface, and (5) obstacles. This information is helpful to persons determining whether the trail is appropriate for their use. For instance, information about the grade and cross slope may be particularly important to individuals

Ecological barriers, such as hills and rough terrain, may limit independent participation by wheelchair users. Accessible walks and trails enable most people with disabilities to enjoy nature without depending on others for assistance.
(Courtesy of *Sports 'n Spokes*/Paralyzed Veterans of America)

who use assistive mobility devices. Information about the width of the trail may be vital to persons using mobility devices such as wheelchairs, walkers, or strollers because narrow points in the trail can block them. Information on the firmness and stability of trail surfaces is critical to persons who may use crutches, canes, walkers, or wheelchairs. Beneficial Designs, Inc. has developed trail access symbols to indicate trail characteristics to potential users. These symbols can be displayed on pocket maps, visitor kiosks, or signs near trails (National Center on Accessibility, 1997).

A particularly interesting approach to trail design is displayed by the "All People's Trail," located in the Shaker Lakes Regional Nature Center in Cleveland, Ohio. The "All People's Trail" is a completely accessible trail constructed of wood and concrete. The use of wood allowed the designers to elevate parts of the trail so that all can enjoy being in the middle of a marsh area; overlooking a small waterfall; looking down into a creek; and, in general, having a new perspective from which to view nature. The trail truly provides a unique outdoor experience in which all may participate.

Picnic Areas

Picnic tables need to be designed to accommodate wheelchair users. Usually this is accomplished by designing picnic tables so that a wheelchair user can sit comfortably at one end of the table. Paths should lead to at least some of the tables in any picnic area, and grills should be usable by those in wheelchairs. Specific dimensions for tables and grills are provided in the following section on furnishings.

Furnishings

Site furniture includes tables, grills, benches, drinking fountains, and telephones. *Picnic tables* should be a minimum of 27 in. from the underside of the table to the ground and should allow 19 in. clearance in depth and 30 in. in width for knee space. *Grills* 30 in. in height and located adjacent to hard surfacing can be most easily used by wheelchair users. While not all grills in any picnic area need to accommodate persons who use a wheelchair, a number should be provided adequate to the needs of the population using the facility. *Benches* with setting heights of 17 in. to 19 in. and widths of no more than 18 in. are ideal. Backrests and arm supports should be included. Benches should be set back so that they do not obstruct walkways, and adequate space should be provided around them so that a wheelchair user can sit in his or her wheelchair beside someone seated on the bench. *Drinking fountains* should be surrounded with paved areas to provide easy access and avoid mud puddles. Hand-operated levers allow the greatest ease in turning on the water. For adults, the spout should preferably be 34 in. to 36 in. from the paved area. For children, the height should be approximately 30 in. A push-button public *telephone* should be located on a hard surface for use by persons with disabilities. The entrance to the phone should be at least 30 in. wide to allow wheelchair users access to the coin slot, receiver, and push buttons. It is best to plan for the highest operable part of the telephone to be no more than 54 in. from the surface.

WATER-RELATED AREAS AND PLAYFIELDS

Some of the most popular recreational activities take place in water-related areas. The section that follows discusses swimming, fishing, and boating facilities.

Beaches

Sand—a highly desirable element at the beach—can create difficulties for wheelchair users and others who may have mobility impairments. Designers must, therefore, make certain there is access through the sand to the water. It has been recommended (National Center on Accessibility, 1994) that all beaches provide at least one accessible surface to and across the sand, continuing to the water. Concrete walks can be constructed. An alternative is to build a stabilized sand path. A soil stabilizer may be sprayed onto the sand or mixed with the sand to form a hardened surface. Another alternative is to purchase commercially available accessible surfaces, such as Lattice or Diamond Rubber Mat, that can be placed on the sand to form a walkway (Hamilton, 2002). No matter what method is used, the walk or path should not be steep (a maximum slope of 8.33% is recommended), and it should lead to the water's edge or to swimming platforms or docks. Where platforms or docks do not extend into the lake, a concrete pad can be constructed so that there is a hard surface under the water to aid the entry of persons with disabilities. Sometimes handrails (placed at about 32 in. in height) are constructed to follow the walk and entry into the water.

Pools

The best pool design is one that allows people who have disabilities to choose from several options to enter the water. One means to aid entry is to construct a ramp a minimum of 36 in. wide. Such a ramp should have a slip-resistant surface, handrails that are 33 in. to 38 in. high, and a slope of no more than 8.33%. A second means is to provide steps with treads at least 18 in. wide. Steps should be deep enough to allow adults to sit on them. Handrails can be provided along the steps, and the clear width between handrails must be between 33 and 38 in. It would also be helpful to have a second rail 6 in. above the nosings (the projecting edge of a step). A third means for people to enter the pool is for them to sit on the pool deck and swing their legs over the side into the water. A portable device with steps can be placed on the deck so that wheelchair users may transfer to it and then move down its steps to deck level. A final means of helping people with disabilities into a pool is a hydraulic lift. Such a lift will normally not be required. However, in instances when large persons must be assisted into the pool, the hydraulic lift can be helpful.

The popularity of wave pools and leisure pools has brought about the development of zero-depth entry designs. This design is similar to a beach where the end of the pool begins at the deck level and slopes, at a gradual rate, to a depth of about 60 in. This zero-depth entry offers people with disabilities a level of independence because it provides natural access that is always available. Wheelchair users use an aquatic chair or a personal chair to enter, as they would using a ramp. Zero-depth pools also allow children and older adults easy entry (Hamilton, Mispagel, & Bloomer, 1996).

An extensive swimming pool study was conducted by the National Center on Accessibility for the U.S. Access Board (Hamilton et al., 1996). One finding from the study was that persons with disabilities most often preferred lifts, ramps, stairs, and zero-depth entries for entry. Stairs, however, were preferred only by those persons who were ambulatory. Among the 76 recommendations that came out of the study were two dealing with pool entry. One was that at least one accessible means of entry should be provided and should be located on an accessible route, and that when there is only one accessible means to entry, it should be a lift, ramp, or zero-depth entry. A second pool entry recommendation was that pools with more than 300 linear ft. of pool wall should provide at least two accessible entries.

Fishing Piers

Fishing piers can be constructed to meet the needs of persons with disabilities. Fishing piers should be accessible by a walk or hard surface pathway. It is important that the walk or path blend with the pier so there is no difference in level between the two. The surface of the pier should have spaces of less than 1/2 in. between the planks. Around the bottom edge of the pier, there should be a kick plate to keep foot pedals of wheelchairs from slipping off the pier, which should be at least 2 in. high. Handrails or armrests and bait shelves should be provided. Probably the best design is to build an armrest no more than 34 in. high with a slope of approximately 30°, so that the railings do not obstruct fishing for people using wheelchairs. This board can be used by those fishing to rest their arms and fishing poles. An 8 in. to 12 in. bait shelf about 30 in. from the surface of the pier offers a place for fishing gear. If children are the principal users of the pier, then slightly reduced heights would be appropriate for the armrest and bait shelf. Benches and some type of shaded seating area are other features that may enhance fishing piers.

Boat Docks

As with fishing piers, access to boat docks should be over hard surface walks or paths, and there should be no difference in level between the dock and the walk or path. Again, as in the case of the fishing pier, spaces between planks should be no wider than 1/2 in. Handrails may be constructed around the edge of the dock where they do not restrict access to boats.

PLAYFIELDS WITH SEATING AREAS

Ticket Booths

At least one ticket booth must be accessible although it is desirable to have more. The front of the booth needs to have a level surface area of 30 in. by 48 in. The ticket window or counter must not be higher than 36 in. above the surface

Fishing piers, if properly constructed, can provide access to persons who use wheelchairs or other mobility aids. (Courtesy of Bradford Woods, Indiana University)

to accommodate persons who use wheelchairs. The counter should be 36 in. wide.

Seating Areas

The number of wheelchair spaces that need to be provided depends on the seating capacity of the facility. One space is required for a capacity of 4 to 25. Two spaces are required for 26 to 50, four for 51 to 300, six for 301 to 500, and six plus one per 100 additional seats for more than 500. Spaces provided for wheelchair users cannot be segregated and wheelchair seating must be provided at each seat pricing level. The size of the space depends on approachability. If the user can pull forward into the space, the space needs to be 33 in. by 48 in. If maneuvering from the side is necessary, then a space of 33 in. by 60 in. is required. A companion seat must be made available next to the wheelchair space.

RECREATION BUILDINGS

This section covers accessibility information about recreation buildings. Both exterior and interior design elements are discussed.

Exterior Circulation and Entrances

Designated parking spaces need to be located as near as is practical to the accessible entrance of each recreation facility. The guidelines on parking noted earlier in the chapter provide more exact information on design features for parking areas.

Ideally, the approach to the entrance of the building will not be on a slope, or any slope will be minimum. The suggested guidelines for walks presented earlier in this chapter may be applied when designing walks leading to buildings. Chief among design considerations for walks are their grade, width, and surface.

All major entrances to recreation buildings should be made accessible to avoid having persons with disabilities use the back door, service entrance, or other similar entrance. Involved in this principle is not only respect for individuals with disabilities but the need for all persons to have access to major exits in cases of emergency.

The surface directly in front of entrances should be level or have only a slight slope (no more than 2%). When an automatic door is not provided, adequate space should be allowed on either side of the door to permit wheelchair users to easily open the door. Manual doors should be equipped with handles that do not require grasping or a twisting motion of the wrist. The door should have a width of at least 32 in. and should have a threshold of no more than 1/2 in. to allow wheelchair access. The pressure required to open the door should never exceed 15 lb. for exterior doors and is preferably much less than this maximum. Revolving doors are not practical, because they cannot be used by people who use wheelchairs.

Ramps

Both exterior and interior ramps may be used in recreation buildings. Any walk or path may be designated a ramp if it has a slope of 5% or more. While curb ramps may be slightly steeper, other ramps should not exceed a slope of 8.33% (1:12 ratio) with a slope of 5% preferred (1:20 ratio). Handrails on both sides are a necessity on practically all ramps (except curb ramps) to protect people or to provide support. Handrails on ramps are placed around 34 in. to 38 in. in height. However, if the building is often used by children, a second set of handrails 24 in. in height should be added. Handrails should extend 12 in. beyond both ends of the ramp if handrails are not continuous.

The minimum width for ramps is 36 in., with 60 in. needed for ramps over which wheelchairs often pass. A level space at least 5 ft. in length and as wide as the ramp should be provided at the approach and at the top of the ramp. Long ramps or ramps with turns should have level platforms to allow users to rest or to negotiate the turn. On long, straight-run ramps, a rest platform of 3 ft. in length is recommended. Turning platforms are larger. The platform for a ramp with one 90° turn should be 60 in. deep by 60 in. long. For a switchback type of ramp, the turning platform needs to be at least 8 ft. deep and 5 ft. wide.

Stairs

Stairs and elevators should be provided in addition to ramps because some persons have difficulty using ramps. Persons wearing leg braces and others may trip if the nosing of stair steps is squared; therefore, a smooth nosing on steps is recommended. As with ramps, handrails should be installed on both sides of the stairs. The handrails (between 1 1/4 in. and 1 1/2 in. in diameter) should be placed about 34 in. to 38 in. above the stair nosings and should extend 12 in. beyond both the top step and the bottom step. A second set of handrails should be provided in recreation facilities that serve children. These should be placed 24 in. above the surface of the steps.

Tactile warning devices can be used as cueing aids for persons with visual impairments to alert them of stairs. For example, in buildings with carpeting or vinyl tiles, rubber tiles can be laid at the top of stairs to offer a surface tactile warning signal. It is important that tactile warning signals remain consistent throughout the building. Finally, adequate lighting on stairs is necessary to allow users to detect the step nosing.

Elevators

Elevators should be placed in an area close to the main entrance of the building and in the normal path of travel of building users. The elevator call buttons should be located so wheelchair users can reach them. It is recommended that the center of the button panel be 42 in. from the floor. Raised numbers can be placed on the button panel to identify the floor. These numbers should be raised a minimum of 1/32 in. from the surface and be at least 5/8 in. high. They should have clearly defined edges. To be easily seen, the numbers should contrast in color with the background on which they are placed. Brailled characters should also identify buttons.

Visual and audible cueing devices should be used to indicate the direction of an approaching elevator car. Visual signals can be given by installing arrow-shaped direction indicators. The up indicator arrow should be white and the down arrow red. Audible cues can be given by signals that sound once for up cars and twice for down cars.

The inside of the elevator car must be large enough to accommodate at least one person in a wheelchair and allow this individual to move to a position from which he or she can operate the elevator controls. The controls need to be located so that the highest button is no more than 54 in. from the floor of the elevator. All control buttons need to be at least 3/4 in. in their smallest dimensions. Emergency controls should be located below the standard controls so that they are accessible to

wheelchair users. Also inside the car should be handrails mounted on the side walls (and preferably rear wall) at a height of 30 in. to 32 in. from the floor of the elevator.

It is necessary that all elevators be adjusted so that, when stopped, the floor of the car is level with the building floor. Elevator doors should have safety edges and door-opening sensing devices to prevent the door from closing and injuring someone entering or leaving the car. Door reopening should remain effective for at least 20 seconds.

Transient Lodging

Newly constructed or remodeled transient lodging units must provide for the needs of people with disabilities. Ideally, all resort, lodge, or cabin bedrooms will be made accessible to persons who have physical disabilities. If this is not possible, then a certain percentage of rooms should accommodate individuals who have disabilities. ADA

Signage is important but should only be used when necessary. The signs in front of this transient lodging facility are not needed, and they may bring unwanted attention to occupants with disabilities.
(Photo by David R. Austin)

standards call for one accessible room per 25 total rooms, up to 100 (e.g., three accessible rooms per 75 total rooms). Five accessible rooms are required for 101 to 150 rooms, six for 151 to 200, seven for 201 to 300, eight for 301 to 400, and nine for 401 to 500. For establishments with 501 to 1,000 rooms, 2% of the total number of rooms are required to be accessible, and in those with more than 1,001 rooms, there must be 20 accessible rooms, plus one for each 100 over 1,000.

Hallways and corridors should be a least 44 in. wide if occupancy exceeds 50 people and 36 in. wide if occupancy is 50 or fewer. All doors should have a minimum width of 32 in. Accessible sleeping rooms need to have a 36 in. clear width maneuvering space located along both sides of a bed. However, if there are two beds, this requirement can be met by providing a 36 in. wide maneuvering space located between two beds. The floor should be unwaxed. If carpeting is used, it should be low-pile, wall-to-wall carpet so that wheelchairs can move easily on it.

It is important that essential elements are of the proper height. The top of the mattress on the beds should be approximately the same height as the seat of the wheelchair to allow for ease in transferring. Controls such as light switches and thermostats should be placed within reach of wheelchair users, at a maximum of 4 ft. from the floor. Windows should be easy to open and close by persons who use wheelchairs. Ideally, windows will be placed low enough so people who use wheelchairs may be able to see the out-of-doors from them.

Closets and other clothing-storage facilities should be designed with wheelchair users in mind. Closets should allow ease in entry and should have hanging rods within comfortable reach. Spring-close or self-closing drawers should be avoided.

Many of the suggestions in the next section on rest rooms can be applied to bathrooms for bedroom units. The floor space of individual bathrooms for bedroom units will be much smaller than for public rest rooms. Therefore it is important to design individual bathrooms so that those who use wheelchairs can close the door for privacy and have sufficient room to move about.

Rest Rooms

Within any given park and recreation area, it is important to have at least one public rest room for each sex that accommodates persons with disabilities. Accessible rest rooms should be identified by a 12 in. gender symbol centered 60 in. above the floor and raised 1/4 in. from the door surface. The international symbol of accessibility should also be displayed if not all rest rooms in a facility are accessible.

Rest room entry corridors must be 44 in. wide, or 48 in. wide if wheelchair users are required to turn around an obstruction to enter. Inside the rest room, a minimum of 5 ft. by 5 ft. of clear floor space must be provided so that wheelchair users can have sufficient turning space. There must be at least 44 in. between all fixed elements in the rest room to allow wheelchairs to move through the room.

At least one accessible toilet stall should exist in each rest room. There must be 48 in. of clear space outside the stall door. Doors must open outward and have an opening of 32 in. if the stall is entered from the front and 34 in. if the stall is entered from the side. In the stall, there must be 18 in. from one wall to the centerline of the toilet. The overall width of the stall must be at least 36 in. There must be 48 in. between the front of the toilet and the door (or opposite wall for side-entry stalls). The toilet seat should be 17 in. to 19 in. from the floor to allow ease in transferring.

Grab bars must be placed 33 in. above the floor. On a tank-type toilet, they may be 36 in. above the floor. The rear grab bar needs to be at least 36 in. long, while the side grab bar must be at least 42 in. long. An outside diameter of 1 1/4 in. to 1 1/2 in. is required for grab bars, which should be exactly 1 1/2 in. from the wall. Grab bars should support at least 250 lb.

Men's rest rooms should have at least one wall-mounted urinal. Accessible urinals should be placed with the basin lip not more than 17 in. from the floor and the rim projecting at least 14 in. from the wall.

The lavatory should be mounted to provide a 29 in. clearance from the floor, with a maximum height to the top of the rim of 34 in. All pipes under the lavatory should be covered or insulated to protect wheelchair users from burning themselves. This is particularly important for protecting those without sensation in their legs.

Towel racks, towel dispensers, hand dryers, and other such devices should be placed so that they are easily accessible to wheelchair users. These should be placed no higher than 40 in. from the floor.

Showers are sometimes found in rest rooms or locker rooms in recreation facilities. If showers are provided, they should accommodate persons who have disabilities. Shower stalls equipped for individuals with disabilities should not have thresholds (or only slight thresholds) and should have nonslip surfaces. On each shower stall, a hinged seat should be mounted 33 in. to 36 in. from the floor so that it can be unfolded during shower use. Grab rails are a necessity and should be placed at a height of approximately 18 in. Water control levers should allow for ease in gripping and, along with the soap tray, should be placed between 38 in. and 48 in. from the floor. The provision of a handheld diversionary showerhead with a flexible hose allows those seated to shower more easily.

Concluding Statement on the Design of Parks and Outdoor Recreation Areas

Many sources of information on design considerations for people with disabilities are available to parks and recreation professionals. No matter what the source of information, it is important to consider *all* parts of the facility, because these must flow together to ensure that the area is truly accessible. Table 6.1 provides a checklist that may be used to determine the accessibility of park and recreation facilities.

Within this chapter and Table 6.1, an attempt has been made to stipulate ADA accessibility guidelines from the *Federal Register* (1991). Readers may wish to refer to publications such as McGovern (1992) or Goltsman, Gilbert, and

Wohlford (1993b) for further details on ADA standards. The U.S. Architectural and Transportation Barriers Compliance Board (Access Board) is to publish ADA guidelines specifically for amusement parks, boating and marine facilities, golf facilities, playgrounds, sports facilities, and outdoor developed facilities (such as ski areas and campgrounds). The Access Board may be contacted at 1331 F Street NW, Suite 1000, Washington, DC 20004-1111 (http://www.access-board.gov). The National Center on Accessibility (NCA) offers the latest information regarding accessibility. NCA is located at 105 N. Morton Street, Suite #109, Showers Building, Bloomington, IN 47404.

Although the design of facilities to meet the needs of children has been mentioned several times, the central focus of this chapter has been on adults. If children are the primary users of a facility, their needs should be given a great amount of consideration. Those planning facilities for children should remain ever conscious of the need to accommodate children with disabling conditions. One of the primary play areas of children is the playground. The final portion of this chapter deals with the design of playgrounds to accommodate the child who has a disability.

PLAYGROUNDS

Through play, children develop intellectually, emotionally, and motorically. As stated in *The Universal Playground: A Planning Guide* (1990), "Play is an essential activity for all children. It is one way children explore their world" (p. 9). Stout (1988) has written: "A safe, accessible, and challenging playground encourages social interaction and physical and mental exercise. All children have the right of access to appropriate play opportunities" (p. 653).

In the past, children with disabilities have not had the play opportunities they have needed to develop social and physical skills. Playgrounds have not been designed to allow them to develop the competencies to interact with confidence with

TABLE 6.1	Checklist for Accessibility of Park and Recreation Facilities

Signage

1. Is the international symbol of accessibility displayed at the entrance?
2. Is the international symbol of accessibility displayed at various points within the facility to inform persons of accessibility?
3. Are parking spaces designated for use by persons with disabilities marked with the symbol of accessibility?
4. Do diagrams or maps provide the symbol of accessibility to indicate accessible buildings or areas?
5. Are signs located at eye level (43 in. to 51 in.) for wheelchair users?
6. Are signs made with light-colored characters of symbols on dark backgrounds?
7. Do identification signs for rooms (including rest rooms) have raised characters at least 5/8 in. in height but no greater than 2 in.?
8. Are signs placed near the closest approach?
9. Are signs well lighted, if used at night?
10. If used, are exhibit labels large enough to read?

Parking

1. Is a loading zone 20 ft. long available, with a 60 in. area parallel to the auto allowing the car door to open fully?
2. Is the loading zone separated from the walk by a curb, bollards, or similar objects?
3. Is there a curb ramp if a curb is next to the loading area?
4. Are accessible van spaces 9 ft. wide and 18 ft. long with 96 in. access aisles?
5. Are car spaces 9 ft. wide and 18 ft. long with 60 in. access aisles?
6. Do spaces have provisions to keep cars from overhanging walks?
7. If a curb exists, is there a curb ramp?
8. Are curb ramps no more than 8.33% grade?
9. Are curb ramps made to contrast in color and texture with the walk surface?
10. Are adequate numbers of spaces provided for persons with disabilities?

Walks and Trails

1. Are walks that join parking lots and streets made to meet the level of the other surfaces?
2. Are walks at least 48 in. wide?
3. Are walk gradients 5% or less?
4. Do walks approaching the maximum grade, or those unusually long, have rest areas? Are surfaces in front of the rest areas textured differently than the walks?
5. Do walks have nonslip surfaces?
6. Do trails reflect a wide range of user preferences and abilities?
7. Are trails clearly marked for length and degree of difficulty?
8. Are overhanging tree branches on trails cut?
9. Are textural changes used on hard surface trails to indicate interpretations or rest areas?

Picnic Areas

1. Are picnic tables designed to accommodate wheelchair users (with a minimum of 27 in. to the ground and 19 in. from the end of the table to the undersupport)?
2. Do paths lead to some of the picnic tables? Grills?
3. Are grills approximately 30 in. in height?
4. Do benches have sitting heights of 18 in. to 20 in. and widths of no more than 18 in.? Are brackets and arm supports included?

(Continued)

TABLE 6.1	*(Continued)*

5. Is there adequate space around benches so that wheelchair users may sit beside someone seated on the bench?
6. Are drinking fountains set in paved areas? Do they stand 34 in. to 36 in. from the ground for adults? 30 in. for children?

Telephones

1. Is a push-button public telephone available? Is it located on a hard surface?
2. Is the entrance to the phone at least 30 in. wide?
3. Is the highest operable part of the telephone no more than 54 in. from the surface?
4. Are telephones equipped for persons with hearing impairments?

Water-Related Areas

1. Are pathways provided on beaches through the sand to the water?
2. Are paths sloped no more than 8.33%?
3. Is the pool designed to allow persons to enter the water by means of a ramp? Steps? Portable device with steps placed on the deck? Hydraulic lift? Zero-depth entry?
4. Do beaches provide at least one accessible surface to the water?
5. Are fishing piers made accessible by providing a path to them?
6. Do the surfaces of docks and piers have spaces of less than 1/2 in. between planks?
7. Is there a kick plate at the bottom edge of fishing piers? Are handrails provided?

Buildings and Ramps

1. Are designated parking spaces for persons with disabilities located near the entrance?
2. Are all major entrances accessible?
3. Are surfaces in front of entrances level or have only a small slope?
4. Are entry doors at least 32 in. wide with a threshold of no more than 1/2 in.?
5. Are manual doors equipped with proper handles?
6. Are doors relatively easy to pull open?
7. Are ramps on a slope of 8.33% or less?
8. Are there proper handrails on ramps?
9. Are ramps at least 36 in. wide? Do they have nonslip surfaces?
10. Are level spaces (5 ft. in length or more) provided at the approach and at the top of the ramps?

Stairs and Elevators

1. Are stairs and elevators provided in addition to ramps?
2. Do stair steps have smooth nosing?
3. Are handrails on both sides of the stairs?
4. Are handrails 34 in. to 38 in. from the surface of each step? Do they extend 12 in. beyond both the top step and the bottom step?
5. Are tactile warning cues provided to alert persons with visual impairments to stairs?
6. If the building serves children, are handrails provided 24 in. from the surface of each step?
7. Are stairs adequately lighted?
8. Are elevators placed near the main entrance?
9. Are elevator cars large enough to accommodate at least one person who uses a wheelchair and to allow that person to move to a position to operate the controls?
10. Are elevator buttons easily accessible to wheelchair users?

(Continued)

TABLE 6.1	*(Continued)*

11. Are raised numbers placed on the button panel?
12. Are visual and auditory cueing devices used to indicate the direction of approaching elevator cars?

Transient Lodging

1. Do doors have a clear opening of at least 32 in.?
2. Are hallways and corridors at least 36 in. wide?
3. Does floor space in rooms permit wheelchair users to move freely around furniture?
4. Do floors have nonslip surfaces? If carpeting is used, is it low-pile, wall-to-wall carpet?
5. Are light switches and other controls within reach of wheelchair users (a maximum of 4 ft. from the floor)?
6. Are bed mattresses approximately the same height as the seats of the wheelchair users who usually occupy the room (i.e., children or adults)?
7. Do closets allow use by wheelchair users?

Rest Rooms

1. Is there at least one rest room for each sex that accommodates persons with physical disabilities?
2. Can wheelchair users easily enter the rest rooms?
3. Is there a minimum of 5 ft. × 5 ft. of clear floor space to provide turning space for wheelchair users?
4. Are toilet stalls at least 36 in. wide? Equipped with doors at least 32 in. wide that open outward? Equipped with grab bars approximately 33 in. high and 42 in. long with an outside diameter of 1 1/4 in. to 1 1/2 in.?
5. Is the seat in toilet stalls 17 in. to 19 in. from the floor and designed for persons with disabilities?
6. Does the men's rest room have at least one wall-mounted urinal with a basin lip of not more than 17 in. projecting at least 14 in. form the wall?
7. Is the lavatory mounted to provide 29 in. clearance from the floor with a maximum height to the top of the rim of 34 in.?
8. Are drain pipes and hot water pipes covered or insulated?
9. Are mirrors, towel racks, dispensers, hand dryers, and other such equipment placed so they are easily accessible to wheelchair users, no more than 40 in. from the floor?
10. Do showers, if provided, accommodate persons with physical disabilities by having no thresholds (or only slight thresholds)? Nonslip surfaces? A hinged seat, mounted 18 in. from the floor? Grab rails at 33 in. to 36 in.? Control levers between 38 in. and 48 in. from the floor?

other persons or with their physical environment. Before the passage of ADA, Smith (1989) noted:

> It appears that our nation's community playgrounds offer few architecturally barrier-free play opportunities to children with disabilities. Only 14 percent of the play equipment surveyed was designed for use by a child in a wheelchair, and only 16 percent of the play equipment provided for wheelchair accessibility up to the equipment. The latter is particularly disturbing because a child who uses a wheelchair might be able to transfer onto and use a conventional play structure, *providing* he or she could position the chair adjacent to the equipment. (p. 88)

The situation described by Smith will never occur again. ADA requires that playgrounds be readily accessible to, and usable by, individuals with disabilities. All playgrounds must provide play opportunities for children with varying abilities. This does not imply that every piece of equipment must be usable by every individual. For example, if a playground has apparatus for swinging or sliding, it must offer comparable experiences for all children. If it has several swings and slides, the playground is considered to be accessible if children with disabilities can use one of the swings and one of the slides (Landscape Structures, Inc., 1997). By constructing playgrounds to serve all children, children both with and without disabilities can gain experiences playing with children possessing different characteristics. Such exposures have the potential to broaden the understandings of all children regarding individual differences (Schleien, 1993). In addition, among the many positive outcomes of such integrated play experiences are appropriate responses to peer aggression, increased social and cognitive skills, and improved communication skills for children with disabilities (Odom, Strain, Karger, & Smith, 1986). Therefore, from all perspectives, it makes sense for playgrounds to be designed so they are usable by *all* children.

The Inadequacy of Traditional North American Playgrounds

Traditional playgrounds were seemingly designed to serve two primary purposes. Apparently, the major reason for the establishment of playgrounds was to provide gross motor activities. The slides, swings, merry-go-rounds, seesaws, and monkey bars of the traditional playground certainly do not encourage types of play other than motor behaviors. The second major purpose of the design was evidently to allow ease of maintenance. This was commonly done by having all apparatus made of steel and usually placing this equipment in a sea of asphalt. Traditional North American playgrounds, to say the least, were unimaginative in design and built with the needs of the maintenance crews in mind.

What Should Playgrounds Be Like?

Unquestionably those responsible for traditional American playgrounds failed to provide well-designed play areas for our children. But what should playgrounds be like? A number of authors have attempted to answer this question (e.g., Caesar, 1999; Cook, 2002; Harrison, 1993; Hudson & Thompson, 2001; Malkusak, Schappet, & Bruya, 2002; Schappet, Malkusak, & Bruya, 2003;

Spencer, 2003; Wadell, 2001). Most of these authors have given consideration to the needs of children with disabilities in their writings. Still other authors (e.g., Christensen & Morgan, 2003; Goltsman et al., 1993b; Hudson & Thompson, 2001; PLAE, Inc., 1993) have published works that have focused specifically on designing playgrounds that meet the needs of children with disabilities.

In reviewing this body of literature, four broad areas of concern emerge. These are (1) accessibility, (2) health and safety considerations, (3) the provision of an interesting and challenging environment, and (4) the need for variety. The sections that follow review these four areas.

Accessibility

Children who use wheelchairs, children using crutches or other mobility aids, and children with leg braces have been regularly denied play experiences because play areas have not been accessible. To be sure, physical accessibility is a primary issue in the design of playgrounds.

A number of design features can be employed to make an outside play area accessible. The following recommendations for increasing accessibility have been drawn from *The Accessibility Checklist* (Goltsman et al., 1993b) and final rules for play areas by Access Board (Architectural and Transportation Barriers Compliance Board, 2000).

An Accessible Route

The first item to consider in designing a playground is to provide an accessible route of travel to the play area. The access route, or path, is essential to allow entry to the play area and then to wind its way throughout the playground so that each piece of apparatus intended to be used by children with disabilities can be reached. Further, the path needs to be designed in such a way that it allows children with disabilities complete integration into the entire play area. The surface of the path must be safe, firm, stable, and slip-resistant. Paths must be 60 in. wide, although 88 in. is preferable so that two children using wheelchairs can easily pass. Gentle curves,

This playground design offers safety, novelty, challenge, and accessibility to users.
(Preschool developmental play center designed by Dr. Louis Bowers, University of South Florida;
Photo by David R. Austin)

not sharp angles, should be used in laying out the path system. Steep slopes should be avoided. Paths should not exceed a grade of 5% (1:20), with slopes of 3% or 4% preferred. Cross slopes should not exceed 1:50. Finally, space close to each piece of apparatus to be used by children with disabilities should be provided so that children can park their wheelchairs or leave crutches or walkers to give them the freedom to crawl or use the apparatus for support while exploring the play environment. The turnaround/parking space next to the apparatus needs to be a minimum of 5 ft. in diameter to allow wheelchair users to turn around.

Ramps

Ramps allow a means for children to access elevated equipment. They should be at least 36 in. in width, although some authorities (Goltsman, Gilbert, & Wohlford, 1993a) recommend a minimum width of 44 in. A maximum slope of 1:12 must be provided for all ramps (Architectural and

Transportation Barriers Compliance Board, 2000), although at least one source (i.e., PLAE Inc., 1993) has recommended a maximum slope of 1:20. The cross slope should not exceed 1:50. The length of a ramp is not to exceed 12 ft. with landings at the bottom and top of ramp runs of a minimum of 60 in. in diameter. Ramps are well suited to replace stairs or ladders. For example, a ramp can provide access to a slide. Freestanding ramps need to be designed to prevent the child from accidentally slipping off the edge. This may be done by two means—curbs and handrails. The top of handrail gripping surfaces shall be 20 in. minimum to 28 in. maximum above the ramp surface. However, handrails should not be required at ramps located within ground level use zones (Architectural and Transportation Barriers Compliance Board, 2000).

Transfer Platforms and Handholds

Children in wheelchairs may access equipment by means of transfer platforms. The act of transferring onto a transfer platform is similar to transferring onto a bed. It has been estimated that 40% to 60% of wheelchair users will transfer out of their chairs onto the play apparatus (Landscape Structures, Inc., 1997). A transfer platform must be located along an accessible route. The deck of the platform needs to be 11 in. to 14 in. above the ground for 2- to 5-year-olds and 14 in. to 17 in. for 5- to 12-year-olds. The platform should be at least 24 in. wide with a minimum depth of 14 in. Handholds, or grab bars, should be mounted on the apparatus to help children transfer from the chair to the platform (Goltsman et al., 1993b). Some more examples of transfer supporters include rope loop, a loop type handle, poles, or bars.

Railings

Railings can be used to enable children to move about the playground more easily. Children with balance problems can use the equipment by supporting themselves with the railings. Children who have visual impairments can employ the railings to guide their movements. The use of bright paint on the rails can serve as visual cues for children who are partially sighted. It is important to make the railings the proper height to accommodate the children using them. The diameter of the railing is also important. For children with mobility limitations, a railing of 3/4 in. to 1-1/2 in. has been recommended by *The Accessibility Checklist* (Goltsman et al., 1993a). Another source (*A Playground for all Children,* 1978) has suggested that handrails should have a diameter of no more than 3/4 in. to allow ease in use by amputees with hooks.

Elevated Areas

Elevated areas can be constructed to allow children in wheelchairs to engage in sand and water play or to complete gardening projects. Freestanding sand and water tables, which accommodate children who use wheelchairs, can be purchased or constructed. Their trays should not be more than 30 in. to 34 in. above the ground, with at least 27 in. between the underside of the table and the ground and 19 in. of knee space. For sand play, a

mound can be covered with sand. A small wall can be constructed to surround the cutout area (an indentation cut into the mound). It is important that the cutout area be the correct height (approximately 30 in.) for allowing the child to easily reach the sand. Garden boxes can be built of railroad ties, which can be stacked to form boxes and filled with soil. Again, proper height is important (20 in. to 30 in.). The child who uses a wheelchair should be able to reach the soil from his or her wheelchair or by transferring from the wheelchair to sit on the top rail. Most designers believe that children should be afforded the option to leave their wheelchairs whenever they desire. Therefore, it is probably best not to overdesign playgrounds by building too many elevated areas, because this may discourage children from leaving their wheelchairs.

Health and Safety Considerations

A nationwide survey of playground equipment in U.S. community parks (Thompson & Bowers, 1989) documented a myriad of health and safety problems. Analyzing the results of this survey, Smith (1989) has listed many *significant* problems that reveal that "our nation's playgrounds may simply be too unsafe for use by the people for whom they were built—children" (p. 85). A few commonsense measures, however, can help ensure a safe and healthy play environment that challenges children without posing undue risks. Several recommendations follow under the headings of general considerations, surfacing, and apparatus. Primary sources for this section are *A Guide to Designing Accessible Outdoor Recreation Facilities* (1980), Henderson (1997), Landscape Structures, Inc. (1996), PLAE, Inc. (1993), and Thompson & Bowers (1989).

General Considerations

One often-neglected element on playgrounds is seating for adults who accompany children to the play area and who wish to have a comfortable vantage point from which to view the child at play (Thompson & Bowers, 1989). Benches should, if possible, be in a shaded area. Protection from the sun should also be provided for the children. Trees or shelters may be used for this purpose. For some, a shaded area is a desirable convenience. For others it is essential. Children taking certain medications may need to avoid exposure to the sun to prevent nausea, severe sunburns, or other harmful reactions. Those who do not perspire normally must have shade to avoid becoming overheated. Other children who lack skin sensitivity may be burned by contact with metal parts on apparatus that have become hot from exposure to the sun (Pittsburgh Architects Workshop, 1979). Another general consideration is to provide accessible rest rooms and drinking fountains a short distance from the playground. Easy access to water is imperative for some persons with physical disabilities who require regular fluid intake (Smith, 1981). Finally, a fence with gates (32 in. to 48 in. wide) that can be locked should be provided around playgrounds adjacent to a street or those used primarily by young children.

Surfacing

Falls to the surface account for 60% (Henderson, 1997) to 75% (Landscape Structures, Inc., 1996) of all playground injuries. Compounding the seriousness of playground falls is that they tend to be among the most serious playground injuries because head-impact injuries often result. Therefore, when considering playground surfacing, shock absorbency is perhaps the most important factor to be considered in playground safety. Henderson (1997) has proclaimed that: "Shock absorbency is the most critical consideration in choosing a playground surface" (p. 86).

Another important consideration in playground surfacing is accessibility. Children who use wheelchairs or have mobility impairments need to be able to maneuver across the surface. While surfacing in potential fall zones can be chosen primarily for shock absorbency, at least the portion of the surface that provides a path to playground equipment must be accessible.

In the past, common types of playground surfaces have been of loose-fill materials, such as sand, pea gravel, and wood chips. These common surfaces provide some measure of shock absorbency so they offer an alternative for use in fall zones under and around apparatus. But these natural loose-fill materials create surfaces that are usually inaccessible. New alternatives to the natural loose-fill materials are beginning to emerge. One, a synthetic loose material manufactured by Landscape Structures, is known as "PlayTurf." The manufacturer claims its synthetic loose material provides better fall protection than traditional loose-fill surfaces while offering accessibility for wheelchair users and others using walking aids. Even the manufacturer, however, admits that any type of loose-fill materials can be problematic in that they tend to become unevenly distributed and their volume is reduced over time through attrition (Landscape Structures, Inc., 1996).

There are alternatives to loose-fill materials that offer shock absorbency and accessibility. These are made of synthetic compact materials. They include poured-in-place rubber surfaces that are seamless and look like carpeting, premanufactured rubber tiles, and synthetic turf on foam mats. The disadvantage of these synthetic materials is that they are more expensive than traditional surfacing materials. Their advantage lies in the lowering of maintenance costs. Because of the higher cost of the synthetic materials, sometimes more traditional materials are used within the fall zones of play equipment to provide shock absorbency while synthetic materials are used to form accessible paths. (Landscape Structures, Inc., 1996; PLAE, Inc., 1993; Wallach, 1997). When assessing commercially available playground surfacing, the buyer should ask for the results of shock absorbency testing by the American Society for Testing and Materials (ASTM), the type of installation required to assure accessibility, and what maintenance is required (Henderson, 1997).

Apparatus

It is a good idea to be sure that any piece of playground equipment purchased meets the ASTM standard for public use playground equipment safety and the Consumer Product Safety Commission (CPSC) federal guidelines for public playground safety (Wallach, 1997). For those who may wish training on issues related to safe playground equipment, the NRPA regularly offers comprehensive playground safety training through its National Playground Safety Institute (NPSI) (Hendy, 1997).

There are specific safety concepts that need to be kept in mind when planning apparatus for children with disabilities. For instance, for children with strength limitations, those who have amputations or paralysis, and others who can benefit from the stabilization provided, safety belts can be useful additions to molded full-support swing seats. Stabilization is a critical factor to be considered in selecting or designing equipment for children with disabilities. There is a noticeable absence of support devices on many traditional pieces of playground equipment. Swings, spring animals, and similar pieces require a great deal of balance and control; the lack of some type of device to provide back and leg support makes their use difficult for many children. Therefore, to allow these children safe access to this equipment, alternations need to be made (Pittsburgh Architects Workshop, 1979). Specific guidelines for making adaptations for slides and swings are provided later in this chapter.

It is important that *everyone* be able to move safely about play areas. Swings and other rapidly moving equipment should have barriers strategically placed to protect all passersby, but especially those with visual limitations (Thompson & Bowers, 1989). To enable children with strength or mobility limitations to move safely, handholds and handrails should be installed on equipment where appropriate.

A final area of concern is that of height. A great deal of analysis should go into the selection of equipment and its installation to be sure it is safe for the user. Smaller children naturally need smaller apparatus. Other design concepts, such as building slides into hillsides or using climbing ropes or platforms set on one another to allow children access to a slide, not only eliminate the need for a ladder but reduce the danger of having a child fall from a high place.

The Provision of an Interesting and Challenging Environment

Besides being unsafe to varying degrees, most community parks in the United States feature play structures "dominated by traditional pieces of equipment that offer children limited opportunities for social interaction, creative expression, and fine motor development" (Smith, 1989, p. 85). There are, however, several concepts that could be used to provide interesting, challenging, and developmentally sound playgrounds for *all* children. The concepts that follow are based largely on the work of Caesar (1999), Frost and Klein (1979) and Moore and the University of Wisconsin-Milwaukee group (Moore, Cohen, Oerbel, & van Ryzin, 1979).

Multiple Skill Level

The play environment should provide for multiple levels of skill so that the child is challenged without unreasonable demands being made on his or her abilities. Ideally, there is just enough challenge to stimulate the child to try the next skill level. Therefore, it is important to provide graded levels of complexity on the playground. For example, there may be several ways to reach the top of a slide, each of which may be slightly more challenging to the child. These might range from a ramp to platforms to climbing a cargo net. Such alternatives also provide clear points of accomplishment so the child will realize he or she has succeeded at the task. All children, and particularly children with disabilities, need successes to build positive self-concepts.

Opportunities for Sensory Stimulation

Children need opportunities for all sorts of sensory stimulation. Playgrounds should offer a wide variety of sensory experiences including things to feel, smell, see, and hear (Hart, 1989). For example, surfaces can be made to have different textures so that children with visual impairments can learn to discriminate between types of surfaces. Flowers and other plants can be grown to offer visual beauty as well as pleasing aromas. A variety of

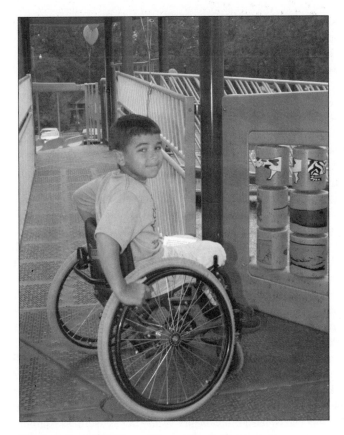

Playgrounds should offer safety, novelty, challenge, *and* accessibility to users.
(Courtesy of Game Time)

colors can be used on the playground, and some equipment may be designed so that children can manipulate it to produce sounds.

Soft Playthings

Not all equipment must be made of steel or wood. Pits made of covered foam rubber have been designed to allow children with severely limited mobility to express themselves through motion by moving their bodies on the soft, giving surface. An air-filled apparatus is another soft alternative. While originally designed for fast-food restaurants and family entertainment centers, Soft Contained Play Equipment (SCPE) has found its way into public playgrounds as more park and recreation

departments are investing in SCPE playgrounds. SCPE playgrounds have been described as "oversized gerbil cages" in that, "The equipment is totally encapsulated" (Iverson, 1998, p. 79) in modular units with "mazes of tunnels; climbers; slides; and moving, jiggling, and twisting components . . ." (Iverson, 1999, p. 55). SCPE playgrounds are constructed out of soft, forgiving materials made of plastic, vinyl, and netting. Iverson (1999) has defined SCPE as: "a play structure made up of one or more components where the user enters a fully enclosed play environment that utilizes pliable materials" (p. 56). Iverson (1999) has gone on to explain that "SCPE playgrounds offer wonderful play opportunities for children with all types of disabilities. Some children get tremendous enjoyment from merely sitting in the ball pool, while others can crawl through the playground, making choices regarding which way to go" (pp. 57–58).

Equipment Placement to Facilitate Continuous Play

Play should be allowed to flow naturally from one activity to another. In the placement of equipment, consideration should be given to possible alternative play behaviors once a particular activity ends. The child should be given several alternatives from which to choose his or her next play activity. For example, are opportunities other than returning for more sliding available at the bottom of the slide? Play patterns can grow and expand if adequate environmental cues are provided to the child. On the other hand, overstimulation at decision points must be avoided for those children not yet ready to tolerate dealing with too many stimuli.

Props for Play

A storage shed on a playground can hold any number of props that can be used by children in play. Included can be things that can be used in sand and water play and gardening. Some of these might be buckets; cups; pots; pans; watering cans; and child-size shovels, rakes, trowels, and scoops. Other types of props for play include: toys for creative play (e.g., miniature cars and animals); toys for dramatic play (e.g., dolls and movable furniture); materials for sensory play (e.g., clay and chalk); materials for construction (e.g., hollow wooden blocks and plastic crates); wheeled toys (e.g., trikes and wagons); outdoor toys (e.g., balls and hula hoops); and materials for quiet play (e.g., books and games) (Caesar, 1999).

The Need for Variety

Closely related to the need for an interesting and challenging environment is the necessity for variety in play environments. The content for this section, like the one that preceded it, has been drawn primarily from the works of Caesar (1999), Frost

and Klein (1979), and Moore and his colleagues (1979).

Broad Range of Areas and Equipment

The playground should provide for almost any imaginable type of play in which children normally engage. Children certainly need equipment that allows for gross motor activity. But children also require places for play involving organized games, drama, building things, growing edible plants, and other activities. Defined boundaries should set apart the more active areas from other areas of the playground. One means of zoning the playground is by building waist-high railings throughout the play area. Such a railing system also serves as a guide for children with visual impairments and enables children with leg braces, crutches, canes, and walkers to stabilize themselves as they move about the playground (Pittsburgh Architects Workshop, 1979).

Equipment Offering a Variety of Uses

Some equipment defines its own use, because it has a singular purpose. Swings are for swinging and slides are for sliding. This equipment is usually not as useful as equipment that serves multiple functions. The playground designer should analyze each piece of apparatus to see if it provides for a variety of uses. For example, many different spatial experiences might be gained by a piece of apparatus that allows the child to crawl or climb under it, on it, through it, beside it, across it, above it, and around it. Ambiguous objects such as wooden climbing structures or rocks allow children to be creative and to use their imaginations.

Manipulation of Loose Parts

Closely related to the principle of offering a variety of uses is the idea of providing loose parts that the child can manipulate in a number of ways. Moore and his colleagues (1979) classify loose parts into three categories: (1) manufactured objects that are to be made into a specific product (e.g., a puzzle), (2) things that are manufactured but have a variable finished form (e.g., Tinkertoys), and (3) things found in the natural environment (e.g., old tires, boards, sand) that can be used in any variety of ways. The use of loose parts allows the child to have some control over his or her environment—to change it or to manipulate it. Adventure playgrounds are made up entirely of loose parts such as lumber, bricks, cardboard boxes, and old tires from which the children build whatever they desire. Moore and his colleagues state that the use of loose parts (including adventure playgrounds) has been successfully employed with children who have mental and physical disabilities. Furthermore, Roger Hart (1989), an internationally recognized expert on innovative design of children's play environments, has noted that *creating* playhouses and other play structures appears to be more important to children than playing in them once they are made.

Places and Spaces

Children need a variety of places to accommodate different types of play. Open spaces are required for group play and games. At least one third of the playground should be open space, according to Caesar (1999). Other places should be provided for play by a single child or a small group of children. While children require opportunities for group play, they also need places where they can gain privacy on the playground. Some small spaces need to be provided for solitary play or for just escaping. Small group play may be facilitated by designing areas where two to four children can play together. Sand and water areas or playhouses may be designed for this purpose.

Adapting Existing Playground Equipment

One means to begin ensuring adequate play areas for children with disabilities is to modify equipment on existing playgrounds. Specific suggestions have been offered by the Pittsburgh Architects Workshop (1979) on how to adapt traditional playground apparatus to make them usable by children with disabling conditions. The material that follows is based on the work of Pittsburgh Architects Workshop.

Slides

A soft ground surface may limit access to both conventional and timber slides. An initial improvement would be to provide a hard surface path to a surface pad (with a 6 ft. diameter) at the base of the steps or ramp leading to the top of the slide.

Conventional Slides Steps on conventional metal slides are too steep and too narrow for the use of children who are semiambulatory. The original steps may be replaced by ones adjusted to 45° or less. These new steps should be 2 ft. 6 in. to 3 ft. wide with a depth of 4 in. to 6 in. The space between steps should preferably be 4 in. and no more than 6 in. In replacing existing handrails on steps, ones approximately 3/4 in. in diameter should be used. At the top of the steps, a platform 2 ft. long (from front to back) and approximately 3 ft. wide should be constructed to allow space for the child to prepare to go down the slide. The sliding board should be 2 ft. 6 in. to 3 ft. 6 in. in width, rather than the standard 1 ft. 6 in. to 2 ft. 6 in. size, to accommodate children who have disabilities. A soft landing surface (6 ft. in diameter) should be provided at the bottom of the sliding board. Outside this landing area, a hard surface circulation path should be located for the use of semiambulatory children. Within the landing area, a short railing extending from either side of the bottom of the sliding board may be constructed to aid children with physical disabilities in getting up after coming off the end of the slide into the landing area. Finally, trees may be planted near the slide to provide shade to keep the sliding surface relatively cool on hot summer days.

Timber Slides Pipes are often placed on timber slides to be used as climbers to reach the platform. This access would be difficult for many children with disabilities, therefore alternatives may need to be employed to allow access to this apparatus. One means is to use either telephone poles or railroad ties cut at various lengths and placed on end to form stairs up the platform. Handholds may be placed on the support posts of the apparatus for use by children in gaining stability and pulling themselves up the stairs. Another alternative is to construct a ramp at least 4 ft. wide. As with any ramp, handrails should be placed on either side to facilitate movement by the children. Rubber coverings can be used on handrails and on the tops of support posts to cushion falls. On the platform, an elevated box can be constructed to allow children a gradual transfer to the surface of the sliding board. It is recommended that the box be 2 ft. long, 3 ft. wide, and 1 ft. to 1 ft. 6 in. high. As with a conventional metal slide, the sliding board and landing areas should be made to accommodate the needs of children with disabilities. (See the prior section on conventional slides for details.)

Swings

A surface path leading to a 6-ft.-diameter concrete pad directly under the swing offers the child who uses a wheelchair the opportunity to transfer to the seat of the swing. The path should come into the pad at a 45° angle so that there is a soft landing area directly in front of the swing. The placement of an inverted U-shaped metal pipe (1 in. to 1 1/2 in. in diameter and 2 ft. to 2 ft. 6 in. in height) in the concrete pad would enable users to stabilize themselves while getting seated. This railing should be set in the pad 10 in. to 12 in. from the path of the swing. (Even though this clearance is recommended by the Pittsburgh Architects Workshop, it seems highly important to make certain that the swing cannot strike the railing.)

Other modifications for an adapted swing include the addition of a back support, leg support, and safety belts. The back support should be at least 1 ft. 6 in. in height. The leg support should fold back under the wooden or metal seat when it is not needed by the child who has the ability to operate the swing without the device. When extended, the leg support should clear the ground by at least 6 in. to 8 in. The safety belts help ensure that the child with balance limitations will not fall from the swing. They are easily attached to the seat.

It is recommended by the Pittsburgh Architects Workshop (1979) that in each set of four swings, one swing should be adapted in the fashion indicated in this section. For those agencies that do not wish to modify existing swings,

commercial playground equipment manufacturers now offer molded plastic seats.

A Final Word on Playgrounds

It is not necessary or desirable to provide separate playgrounds for children with disabilities. Playgrounds can be designed with all children in mind. If play environments are well designed, the great majority of children with disabilities can join their peers without disabilities in healthful play experiences in our community parks, on our school grounds, or wherever playgrounds are provided. As of October 18, 2000, accessibility guidelines for the play areas are finalized by Access Board, but they are not yet standardized. Until they are standardized, tracking the status though Access Board (www.access-board.gov) is advisable.

APPLYING UNIVERSAL DESIGN FOR THE OPTIMAL RECREATION ENVIRONMENT

In designing an optimal recreation and playground environment for everyone, Universal Design is a concept that goes beyond the issues of accessibility for people with disabilities. The concept contains many innovative ideas that respond to the broad diversity of users including individuals with disabilities. Fundamentally, it is an approach that values and celebrates human diversity.

The phrase "Universal Design" is used interchangeably with "design for all," "barrier-free design," "trans-generational design," and "design for the broader average" (Sandhu, 2000). For some people, the phrase is considered a new politically correct term, connoting efforts that reflect "special features" for "special users," while for others, it is a more encompassing concept that addresses the needs of all potential users in society. It's clear that Universal Design does not mean politically correct behaviors or additional government mandates. Simply, it is, as Lusher and Mace (1989) put it, an approach to design that accommodates people of all ages, sizes, and abilities. Mace (1997) defined it as designs that considered the access needs of the broadest possible range of users. Steinfeld (1995) emphasized that Universal Design should be more an attitude than compliance to certain codes.

One can see the outcomes of Universal Design everywhere. With the passage of the ADA, curb cuts were designed to maximize accessibility for wheelchair users. However, from the perspective of Universal Design, the impact of the curb cuts can go beyond the wheelchair users. Many individuals without disabilities (e.g., parents with strollers, bicyclists, and delivery persons pushing hand trucks) can take full advantage of them. This inexpensive accommodation, initially designed for a relatively small segment of the population, benefits many. As this example shows, Universal Design is a design for a wide range of users.

Through a grant funded by the National Institute on Disability and Rehabilitation Research, a working group of professionals in various fields—such as architects, product designers, engineers, and environmental design researchers—collaborated to develop the Principles of Universal Design to help the public understand design disciplines that accommodate people of all ages, sizes, and abilities. Following are the seven Principles.

Principles for Universal Design

Principle 1: Equitable Use

The design is useful and marketable to people with diverse abilities.

Guidelines

1. Provide the same means of use for all users: identical whenever possible; equivalent when not.
2. Avoid segregating or stigmatizing any users.
3. Make provisions for privacy, security, and safety equally available to all users.
4. Make the design appealing to all users.

Principle 2: Flexibility in Use

The design accommodates a wide range of individual preferences and abilities.

Guidelines

1. Provide choice in methods of use.
2. Accommodate right- or left-handed access and use.

3. Facilitate the user's accuracy and precision.
4. Provide adaptability to the user's pace.

Principle 3: Simple and Intuitive Use

Use of the design is easy to understand, regardless of the user's experience, knowledge, language skills, or current concentration level.

Guidelines

1. Eliminate unnecessary complexity.
2. Be consistent with user expectations and intuition.
3. Accommodate a wide range of literacy and language skills.
4. Arrange information consistent with its importance.
5. Provide effective prompting and feedback during and after task completion.

Principle 4: Perceptible Information

The design communicates necessary information effectively to the user, regardless of ambient conditions or the user's sensory abilities.

Guidelines

1. Use the different modes (pictorial, verbal, tactile) for redundant presentation of essential information.
2. Maximize "legibility" of essential information.
3. Differentiate elements in ways that can be described (i.e., make it easy to give instructions or directions).
4. Provide compatibility with a variety of techniques or devices used by people with sensory limitations.

Principle 5: Tolerance for Error

The design minimizes hazards and the adverse consequences of accidental or unintended actions.

Guidelines

1. Arrange elements to minimize hazards and errors: most used elements, most accessible; hazardous elements eliminated, isolated, or shielded.
2. Provide warnings of hazards and errors.
3. Provide fail-safe features.

4. Discourage unconscious action in tasks that require vigilance.

Principle 6: Low Physical Effort

The design can be used efficiently and comfortably and with a minimum of fatigue.

Guidelines
1. Allow user to maintain a neutral body position.
2. Use reasonable operating forces.
3. Minimize repetitive actions.
4. Minimize sustained physical effort.

Principle 7: Size and Space for Approach and Use

Appropriate size and space is provided for approach, reach, manipulation, and use regardless of user's body size, posture, or mobility.

Guidelines
1. Provide a clear line of sight to important elements for any seated or standing user.

2. Make reach to all components comfortable for any seated or standing user.
3. Accommodate variations in hand and grip size.
4. Provide adequate space for the use of assistive devices or personal assistance. (Copyright 1997 NC State University, The Center for Universal Design)

These seven Principles can be applied to evaluate existing designs and to guide the design of products and environments for all users in society. While these Principles contain ideas that can be universally applied to all individuals, it should be noted that not all guidelines may be relevant to all designs. It is intended that the Principles of Universal Design address only universally usable design. Designers can flexibly consider other factors such as economic, engineering, cultural, gender, and environmental concerns in their design processes.

SUMMARY

This chapter dealt with concerns in designing appropriate recreation environments for all people, including those with disabilities. The chapter began with a discussion of terminology and legislation related to designing environments to meet the needs of individuals with disabilities. Following this introduction, the major portion of the chapter was devoted to guidelines and recommendations for creating usable recreation facilities. The final segments of the chapter covered the topic of designing playgrounds so that they will accommodate children who have disabilities and the Principles of Universal Design.

SUGGESTED LEARNING ACTIVITIES

1. Using Table 6.1, assess a local park or campus recreation facility. Several students may join together to assess a state, regional, or national park.
2. Drawing on the information from the section on playgrounds, assess a local playground for design criteria.
3. Using an actual playground, report how you would adapt existing equipment to meet the needs of all children, including those with disabilities.

4. Go to the home page of the Access Board on the Web. Evaluate its usefulness to students studying inclusive recreation. Report your findings in class.
5. Participate in a telephone lecture given by an authority on playground design for children with disabilities.
6. View an audiovisual presentation on facility or playground design for persons with disabilities.

REFERENCES

Architectural and Transportation Barriers Compliance Board. Americans with Disabilities Acts (ADA) Accessibility Guidelines for Buildings and Facilities; Play Areas (Final Rule). *Federal Register, 65*(202), 62498–69843, October 18, 2000.

Architectural and Transportation Barriers Compliance Board. Americans with Disabilities Acts (ADA) Accessibility Guidelines for Buildings and Facilities; Recreation Facilities (Final Rule). *Federal Register, 67*(170), 56352–56440, September 3, 2002.

Austin, D. R., & E. J. Hamilton. Assistive technology and recreation. In *Making the Technology Connection.* Indianapolis: Project ATTAIN, 1997.

Axelson, P. W., & D. Chelini. *Inventory and Computerized Mapping of Trails: The First Step Towards Access.* Santa Cruz, CA: Beneficial Designs, 1993.

Beckwith, J. Play environments for all children. *Leisure Today.* In *Journal of Physical Education, Recreation and Dance, 56*(5), 32–35, 1985.

Caesar, B. A matter of child's play. *Parks & Recreation, 34*(4), 66–73, 1999.

Christensen, K., & J. Morgan. To help children with disabilities, design by types of activities, not type of equipment. *Parks & Recreation, 38*(4), 50–53, 2003.

Colston, L. G. The expanding role of assistive technology in therapeutic recreation. *Leisure Today,* 39–41, April 1991.

Cook, A. M. Future directions in assistive technologies. In M. J. Scherer, Ed. *Assistive Technology: Matching Device and Consumer for Successful Rehabilitation.* Washington, DC: American Psychological Association 2002, pp. 269–280.

Federal Register, 56(144), July 26, 1991.

Frost, J. L., & B. L. Klein. *Children's Play and Playgrounds.* Boston: Allyn and Bacon, Inc., 1979.

Gilbert, A. Should a path be paved to the top of a mountain? Access to Heritage/parks areas. *Leisurability, 14*(1), 26–30, 1987.

Goltsman, S. M., T. A. Gilbert, & S. D. Wohlford. *The Accessibility Checklist: Vol. II Survey Form.* Berkeley, CA: MIG Communications, 1993a.

Goltsman, S. M., T. A. Gilbert, & S. D. Wohlford. *The Accessibility Checklist User's Guide* (2nd ed.). Berkeley, CA: MIG Communications, 1993b.

A Guide to Designing Accessible Outdoor Recreation Facilities. Ann Arbor, MI: Heritage Conservation and Recreation Service, U.S. Department of Interior, 1980.

Hamilton, E. J. *Beach Surface Accessibility Study: Final Report.* National Center on Accessibility, Indiana University School of Health, Physical Education and Recreation, Department of Recreation and Park Administration. Bloomington, IN: 2002.

Hamilton, E. J., K. Mispagel, & R. Bloomer. *Swimming Pool Accessibility: Final Report.* Bloomington, IN: National Center on Accessibility, Indiana University School of Health, Physical Education & Recreation, Department of Recreation and Park Administration, 1996.

Harrison, M. J. Customizing playgrounds. *Parks & Recreation, 28*(4), 42–45, 91, 1993.

Hart, R. Child development and the design of preschool play environments. Presentation to the College of Health and Human Development, Penn State University, February 2, 1989.

Henderson, W. Catching kids when they fall: Guidelines to choosing a playground surface. *Parks & Recreation, 32*(4), 85–92, 1997.

Hendy, T. The National Playground Safety Institute: The most commonly asked questions answered. *Parks & Recreation, 32*(4), 102–105, 1997.

Hudson, S. D., & D. Thompson. Are playgrounds still viable in the 21st century? *Parks & Recreation, 36*(4), 54–62, 2001.

Iverson, M. Soft contained playgrounds: A primer. *Parks & Recreation, 33*(4), 78–81, 1998.

Iverson, M. The staying power of soft contained playgrounds. *Parks & Recreation, 34*(4), 54–59, 1999.

Landscape Structures, Inc. *Playground Accessibility/ADA Compliance: Playguide Bulletin No. 2.* Delano, MN: Landscape Structures, Inc., 1997.

Lewis, R. B. Assistive technology and learning disabilities: Today's realities and tomorrow's promises. *Journal of Learning Disabilities 31*(1), 16–26, 1998.

Longmuir, P. E., & P. Axelson. Assistive technology for recreation. In J. C. Galvin and M. J. Scherer, Eds. *Evaluating, Selecting, and Using Appropriate*

Assistive Technology. Gaithersburg, MD: Aspen Publishers, Inc, 1996.

Lusher, R. H., & R. I. Mace. Design for physical and mental disabilities. In J. A. Wilkes & R. T. Packard, Eds. *Encyclopedia of Architecture.* New York: John Wiley & Sons, 1989, pp. 748–763.

Mace, R. The Center for *Universal Design.* [Online]. Available: http://www.design.ncsu.edu/cud/univ%5fdesign/princ%5foverview.htm, 1997.

Malkusak, T., J. Schappet, & L. Bruya. Turning accessible playgrounds into fully integrated playgrounds: Just add a little essence. *Parks & Recreation, 37*(4), 65–71, 2002.

McGovern, J. *The ADA Self-Evaluation: A Handbook for Compliance with the Americans with Disabilities Act by Parks and Recreation Agencies.* Arlington, VA: National Recreation and Park Association, 1992.

Moore, G. T., U. Cohen, J. Oerbel, & L. van Ryzin. *Designing Environments for Handicapped Children: A Design Guide and Case Study.* New York: Educational Facilities Laboratories, 1979.

National Center on Accessibility. *Beach Access: Assistive Devices and Surfaces.* Bloomington, IN: National Center on Accessibility, Indiana University School of Health, Physical Education & Recreation, Department of Recreation and Park Administration, 1994.

National Center on Accessibility. *Universal Trail Assessment Process.* [Online]. Available: http://www.indiana.edu/~nca/utap.htm, 1997.

Odom, S. L., P. S. Strain, M. A. Karger, & J. D. Smith. Using single and multiple peers to promote social interaction of preschool children with handicaps. *Journal of the Division of Early Childhood, 10*(1), 53–64, 1986.

Pittsburgh Architects Workshop. *Access to Play: Design Criteria for Adaptation of Existing Playground Equipment for Use by Handicapped Children.* Pittsburgh: Pittsburgh Architects Workshop, Inc., 1979.

PLAE, Inc. *Universal Access to Outdoor Recreation: A Design Guide.* Berkeley, CA: PLAE, Inc., 1993.

A Playground for All Children: Resource Book. Washington, DC: U.S. Government Printing Office, 1978.

Sandhu, J. S. Citizenship and universal design. *Ageing International, 25*(4), 80–89, 2000.

Schappet, J., A. Malkusak, & L. Bruya. Making surfacing a play asset: Considerations for truly integrated play structure. *Parks & Recreation, 38*(2), 60–62, 2003.

Schleien, S. J. Assess and inclusion in community leisure services. *Parks & Recreation, 28*(4), 66–72, 1993.

Smith, R. W. Personal communication. November 1981.

Smith, R. W. Plan of action: Reflections and recommendations. In D. Thompson and L. Bowers, Eds. *Where Our Children Play: Community Park Playground Equipment.* Reston, VA: American Alliance for Health, Physical Education, Recreation and Dance, 1989, pp. 85–97.

Spencer, A. Accessibility and your playground: A profile of facilities taking action. *Parks & Recreation, 38*(4), 40–49, 2003.

Steinfeld, E. Studio education through universal design. In P. Welch, Ed. *Strategies for Teaching Universal Design.* Boston, MA: Adaptive Environments Center, 1995, pp. 141–161.

Thompson, D., & L. Bowers, Eds. *Where Our Children Play: Community Park Playground Equipment.* Reston, VA: American Alliance for Health, Physical Education, Recreation and Dance, 1989.

The Universal Playground: A Planning Guide. Province of British Columbia: Ministry of Education, 1990.

Wadell, K. A. What is the minimum standard of care that the playground owner must provide? *Parks & Recreation, 36*(4), 80–86, 2001.

Wallach, F. Playground safety update. *Parks & Recreation, 32*(4), 95–99, 1997.

7

THE PLANNING PROCESS

(Courtesy of *VSA arts*, www.vsarts.org)

I f you were asked to conduct a three-day camp program for children with and without disabilities, would you immediately begin planning activities such as arts and crafts, a campfire program, and cooperative games, or would you attempt to find out more information before beginning your planning? If you answered "yes" to finding out more information before planning, you would be correct. Regardless of the setting, it is important that recreation professionals follow an organized approach when planning and providing recreational services. One example of a systematic approach involves a series of steps, including *assessment; planning mandates, policies, goals, and objectives; implementation;* and *evaluation.*

Throughout this planning process, recreation professionals should be aware of the strategies and techniques used to integrate persons with disabilities into their programs. This is important because changes in legislation and shifts in philosophy have resulted in increasing inclusion of persons with disabilities into life and regular community recreation programs (see chapters 2 and 3). All evidence points to this inclusionary trend continuing in the future. In the past, we assumed planning meant program planning and, more specifically, a special program such as a swimming program for children with physical disabilities or Special Olympics for a group of adults with developmental disabilities. However, we can no longer assume it is all right to develop yet another special program or search out an already existing special program (Wieck & Strully, 1991).

Furthermore, if this is the direction we are heading, then it is important to see planning in a new light. The goal of the planning process must be larger than the development of a program. Planning must be about engaging the broader community—with all its resources, opportunities, and, yes, programs—in the process of trying to understand what changes are needed in the

The authors would like to thank Christine Wilkinson for her extensive contributions to this chapter. Ms. Wilkinson, from Orillia, has work experience integrating persons with developmental disabilities into community recreation programs and is in the therapeutic recreation program at Georgian College. Ms. Wilkinson assisted with this chapter during her graduate study at The Pennsylvania State University.

community and in services to better meet the recreation and leisure needs of people with disabilities. In this sense, planning is about making a better community. The recreation literature calls this "community development," because as more and more people with disabilities join the community and more and more community settings struggle with learning to be more welcoming, the community becomes a better place (Hutchison & Nogradi, 1996; McKnight, 1995; O'Connell, 1990; Pedlar, 1996; Roeher Institute, 1997).

Finally, planning in the past may have fallen into the trap of focusing only on services and programs. For most people, thinking about leisure opportunities rather than leisure services may provide a broader and more useful context that better addresses the needs of people with disabilities. If a person with a disability wants to sing in a choir, then we need to understand this person's dreams and aspirations and find the best possible fit. We need to find a choir that is welcoming in the sense of being willing to accommodate, grow in its understanding of disability, and be in a relationship with the person. This is a very different picture than would have been created 20 years ago (McGill, 2000; Walker, 1999). And since the person with the disability is the only one who knows what he or she is dreaming about, that person must be at the front and center of any planning. Past approaches, where we have valued increased professionalism, including treating the recreation professional as the expert rather than the person with the disability, are being replaced by planning where citizens are full participants (Forester, 1993; Friedmann, 1992; Hutchison, 2000; Kuyek & Labonté, 1995; Sylvester, 1998).

Planning in this way provides a new approach to thinking about leisure, participation, and people with disabilities. It is based upon a social justice and rights framework discussed in chapter 3, and some believe it is possible to work toward social justice through inclusive leisure services (Zoerink & Rosegard, 1997). As we do this, Torjman (1997) says we will be reclaiming our humanity by creating a more civil or just society. Figure 7-1 illustrates the interrelationship of the planning process

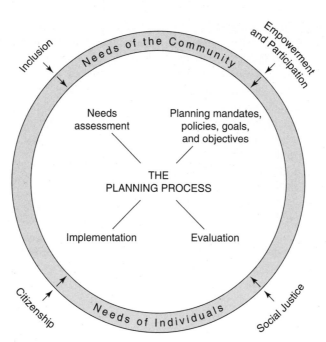

Figure 7-1   The Planning Process

with the overall goals of inclusion, empowerment and participation, social justice, and citizenship.

NEEDS ASSESSMENT

The number of persons with disabilities in the community or geographic area where leisure services exist or planning is to take place should be identified. Awareness that persons who have disabilities reside in the community will, in part, help justify leisure service planning. Some communities have conducted surveys to establish such information. The kind of information that might be useful includes age, sex, disabling condition, geographic location, and special considerations. Special considerations may include specific needs of the person related to transportation barriers; architectural barriers such as steps and curbs; the need for medication; and special kinds of assistance, such as transferring persons from their wheelchairs to the swimming pool.

There are two kinds of needs assessments to keep in mind. The first is to understand the needs

of people with disabilities within a broader community context, what we have referred to here as determining needs within a community. The second is to focus on identifying the needs, interests, and skills of individuals with disabilities through what is known as person centered planning.

Determining Needs within a Community

As previously mentioned in chapter 1, American and Canadian statistics indicate that 19.3% and 12.4% of the population, respectively, have some sort of disability (Statistics Canada, 2003; United States Census, 2003). It would be wise, therefore, for recreation providers to determine if their services and programs are meeting the needs of these individuals. Perrin, Wiele, Wilder, and Perrin (1992) suggested several methods for considering the recreational needs of persons with disabilities. Developing partnerships with persons with disabilities and their advocates is one method that may help determine how their needs can best be met (Bourne & Legg, 1998; Lord, 1998; McGill,

1998; Schleien, Rynders, Heyne, & Tabourne, 1995). Perrin and colleagues (1992) suggested forming partnerships with agencies that serve persons with disabilities. Schleien, Rynders, Heyne, and Tabourne (1995) suggest building partnerships with parents to encourage inclusion. Jones (2002) also reiterates the importance of the voice of parents in planning. These groups may offer suggestions about how best to include persons with specific disabilities into recreation programs. In their guidebook, Perrin and associates discuss the Burlington (Canada) Parks and Recreation Department's formation of a committee called "Recreation Ability Burlington," which has representatives from a variety of organizations serving persons with disabilities. This group provides guidance, information, resources, and feedback to the department through monthly meetings designed to determine the most effective ways to include persons with disabilities in Burlington's recreation programs. Lyons (1993) researched the importance of capitalizing on outreach recreation networks in Canada. In conclusion, Moon and colleagues (1994) suggest the following:

- Review current programs
- Determine which programs would be suitable for persons with disabilities
- Begin to eliminate segregated programs where appropriate
- Provide support and set a good example for agency staff
- Teach self-advocacy
- Make participation success-oriented
- Ensure that participation is inclusive
- Provide opportunities for freedom of choice
- Use naturally occurring environments as training sites
- Build on relationships

Individuals with disabilities are the best source of information about "what is not being done effectively," and they frequently can provide suggestions for change. The importance of including persons with disabilities in *all* aspects of the planning process cannot be overemphasized. Bedini and Henderson (1994), for example, used interviews to explore the lives of 30 women with disabilities to determine implications for parks, recreation, and leisure providers. These women "reported feeling that they did not have opportunities or support to express their needs and interests concerning recreation and leisure" (p. 28). Moreover, many of these women emphasized that recreation providers need to be proactive in seeking the opinions of persons with disabilities. One woman advised:

> It would be very empowering for [persons with disabilities] to say what it is that they want as opposed to being told by a recreation department these are the things we have available for you. . . . I would probably pose a question, "What would you like to experiment with that you have not been able to do on your own?" . . . and we'll brainstorm and come up with a way to make it possible . . . lots of times they [parks and recreation planners] make plans for you that you can't use. So they give you ideas that they think are feasible and . . . when people with disabilities get there, they can't use it. (pp. 28–29)

Focus group techniques are an excellent way to encourage persons with disabilities to express their opinions and relate their personal experiences (Anderson & Heyne, 2000; Heyne, McAvoy, & Schleien, 1994). Focus groups typically include 7 to 10 participants in a carefully planned discussion designed to obtain perceptions on an area of interest in a nonthreatening way (Kruger & Casey, 2000). Focus groups often attempt to involve a range of stakeholders. Heyne et al. note that focus groups enable recreation service providers to "stay in touch with needs of individuals with disabilities and their families, give them an opportunity to voice their opinions, encourage collaboration between diverse groups, and ensure increased understanding and an enhanced quality of life for all people" (p. 24).

Identifying the Needs, Interests, and Skills of Individuals

Now that we have heard about assessment of the broader community, it is time to focus on the individual. The person-centered approach to assessing personal needs is gathering recognition in leisure settings and beyond (Bradley, Ashbaugh, & Blaney, 1994; Bullock & Mahon, 2000; Cipriano, 1998). You may have heard about the individual program plan (IEP) that has been used for years, particularly in educational settings. There are some similarities here, although the differences are what makes this new approach more powerful. An IEP is a plan completed on an individual by a team, such as teachers, other professionals, often parents, and sometimes the person. It is usually more professionally dominated and controlled compared to person-centered planning. Person-centered planning often includes the individual, parents, other family members, friends or circle members, and any other significant persons who are able to offer important information related to participation. The person with the disability is not only the center of the process. There is always an assumption that the person is highly valued and his or her views are central. The person has control over who is invited, what will be discussed, and the outcome of the planning process. Only a few selected professionals who are trusted by the person and/or family are invited. Often a planning process such as MAPS or PATH is used, which is grounded in the dreams and hopes of the person (Galambos, 1995; O'Brien & Pearpoint, 2002).

Person-centered planning is seen as an ongoing process that identifies needs, interests, skills, gifts, capacities, and contributions of the person. It is most useful because the content of the planning is not limited to any one aspect of the person's life, such as school, work, or recreation, but can relate to other important areas such as relationships and friendships (Mount, 1995; O'Brien & O'Brien, 1998; Pedlar, Haworth, Hutchison, Taylor, & Dunn, 1999). Recently, the importance of friendships and other close relationships has come to the awareness of the recreation profession (Heyne, Schleien, & McAvoy, 1993; Lyons, Sullivan, & Ritvo, 1995; Mahon, Mactavish, & Bockstael, 2000). People with disabilities, like all other persons, need a range of close friends (Grenot-Scheyer, Staub, Schwartz, & Peck, 1998). Person-centered planning recognizes that real friendships cannot be replaced by professionals or volunteers. Recreation planning, which fails to recognize the importance of real friends and the potential of leisure settings for friendship development, cannot be considered person-centered. A detailed examination of seven approaches for recreationists to promote friendship development within a person-centered framework—from reconnecting, 1:1 matching, bridging, social networks, circles, to leisure identities—is provided (Hutchison & McGill, 1998).

Now how does all this relate to needs assessment, which is where we started this section? Person-centered planning helps us understand that assessment of individuals has to be more than surveys or questionnaires. Community planning and person-centered planning come together because it is person-centered planning that gets us beyond generalities and stereotypes about people with disabilities. It helps communities get to know persons with disabilities for what they really are and what they have to offer the community. It ensures that any plans by recreation services are grounded in the real needs of people. The development of the community and its services can be a bottom-up approach where person-centered plans create an awareness of what kind of services are needed for people to be able to live their dreams. For example, if a person has an interest in yoga, then building relationships with yoga clubs and finding the most suitable and welcoming setting is pursued. Or if one goal is to gradually begin to eliminate many special programs, person-centered planning is important because it enables people to create a new vision of life that is separate from the service system and is inclusive. Community planning remains important because it enables a community to address system and service issues. The growth in person-centered planning is beginning to influence the issues that community planning may face.

PLANNING MANDATES, POLICIES, GOALS, AND OBJECTIVES

When the needs and interests of the community and persons with disabilities have been assessed, the information gained can now be used in planning mandates, policies, goals, and objectives. Developing an agency *mandate* based on the inclusive philosophy and creating follow-up policies can go a long way toward making persons with disabilities feel welcome at programs (Dattilo, 2002; Perrin, 1992). Moon and colleagues (1994) suggest that educating yourself about current practices and recent legislation affecting the inclusion of individuals with disabilities in community leisure and recreation activities and programs is the first step. In addition, one needs to approach changes in philosophy and practices within an organization cautiously. Lyons (1994) discussed the trend toward municipal recreation departments having a mission statement regarding their overall ideology and commitment to recreation services "for all," including persons with disabilities. In the front entrance of a local YMCA, their mission statement is engraved on a beautiful large plaque, stating in part:

Y MISSION

The YMCA of Kitchener-Waterloo is a charitable association, creating opportunities to develop individuals, families, and communities.

CORE VALUES

ACCEPTANCE:	Welcoming and open to *all*
BALANCE:	Developing people in spirit, mind, and body
CARING:	Responding to the needs of others
GIVING:	Contribution of time, skills, and money
RESPONSIBILITY:	Accountable for yourself, others, and the world we live in

Policies usually refer to a set of statements that define the roles, rules, and procedures of a recreation organization (Lyons, 1991; 1994). It is important that there is consistency between values and policy (Peck, 1991; Pedlar, 1991). It is important that policies are created that reflect recent trends toward inclusion and diversity (Allison & Schneider, 2000; Ash, 1994; Frazee, 2002–03; Victorian YMCA, 2001).

Because of the potential impact of changes in the mandate and policies of a service or program, key stakeholders who have been involved as partners during the community assessment process will need to be involved here. It is important that people with disabilities themselves play a key role in these stakeholder organizations and play a major role during the planning of policies, thereby avoiding more professionalized partnerships (Lord, 1998). Connolly and Law (1999) conducted a recent study on the role of people with disabilities shaping municipal inclusion and access policy. In their study, they also found that Participatory Action Research (PAR) is an extremely useful tool for encouraging inclusion during planning, evaluation, and research. The policy recommendations included that an ongoing Resource Group be formed consisting of people with disabilities, families, and advocates to monitor these new policies; that the municipal human resources department coordinate training of key municipal staff; that the municipality act as facilitator with liaisons to informal recreation providers such as sport organizations; that the municipality use the Canadian Standards and Guidelines for Barrier Free Design; that the access symbols be included in all program information; and that registration fees for volunteer assistants be waived in municipal programs.

Lyons (1991) said there are many reasons why municipalities should develop policies for persons with disabilities: to help make recreation a credible municipal service; because of the prevalence of disability; because of the leisure and lifestyle effects of disability; because of the health and social costs of not providing recreation services; to support the need for specialized services, including policy; and to comply with human rights legislation and avoid litigation. Examples of policy questions include:

- Does the department assist community agencies on recreation issues related to persons with a disability?
- Does the department help with transportation?
- Are persons with a disability excluded from publicly operated programs because of inability to pay?

- Will the department jointly sponsor a skill upgrading program with a community agency?
- Does the department have a plan for increasing physical accessibility in publicly funded facilities?

This report goes on to say that policies should be simple and understandable, operationally feasible, flexible, capable of directing change, consistent with regard to ideology and practice, responsive to individual and group needs, directly relevant to leisure constraints, clear in defining roles and responsibilities, fiscally reasonable, consistent with general policies of the department, and supported by key community agencies. Detailed descriptions of how-tos for each stage of policy development are discussed (Lyons, 1991). Here is one of the numerous examples of policies provided:

> The Department of Tourism, Recreation and Parks will play a significant role in bringing concerned individuals, including those with a disability, and community groups together to address key issues related to the provision of leisure services for persons with a disability— St. John's. (p. 16)

Once broader mandates and policies are established, recreation providers can then plan for more specific goals and objectives. The achievement of these goals and objectives should mean the satisfaction of needs and interests of the participants and community. A detailed description of the process involved in writing goals and objectives is beyond the scope of this book, and readers seeking further information are directed to the sources listed at the end of this chapter. A brief overview of this element of program planning is included here.

The terms *goals* and *objectives* are often used interchangeably, therefore it is important to distinguish between the two. Goals are general statements of intent while objectives are more specific outcomes described in terms that are measurable. Both goals and objectives answer the question, Where are we going?

The purpose of recreation programming is to provide opportunities for fun, enjoyment, satisfac-

tion, and self-improvement. The formulation of recreation goals should reflect these purposes and should be based on the strengths, interests, and skills of the individuals participating, including those persons who have disabilities. Peterson and Gunn (1984) provide examples of recreation participation goals that state the intent of the program:

1. To facilitate participation in previously acquired *leisure skills*
2. To facilitate *self-expression* through leisure
3. To provide opportunities for *social interaction*
4. To provide an environment for the *integration* of diverse physical, mental, social, and emotional skills
5. To provide opportunities for *creative and self-directed* leisure involvement

Following the establishment of goals such as those listed, the recreation professional should be able to reduce these goal statements into behavioral objectives (Mager & Pipe, 1970). An example of a behavioral objective for goal 5 could be: "At the completion of the three-session craft program, 90% of the participants will have completed a project of their choosing." Regardless of the setting, it is up to the leaders of the program to establish goals and objectives that they feel are in keeping with the abilities and interests of the participants and are in line with the nature and purpose of the program. In some instances, recreation leaders may work in a goal-free environment. That is, rather than writing objectives, the leaders observe outcomes of participation in leisure programs.

IMPLEMENTATION

Having completed the needs assessment and planned mandates, policies, goals, and objectives, we are now ready to discuss implementation. Everyone plays a key role in implementing inclusion (Germ & Schleien, 1997). To implement inclusive programs, it is essential to adopt a positive attitude toward inclusion, prepare the proper foundation for inclusion, structure activities to promote inclusion, and effectively manage problem behavior.

Positive Attitude toward Inclusion

For inclusion to be successful, recreation professionals need to adopt a positive attitude toward inclusion. Moreover, this attitude must be apparent to everyone involved in the process, including participants, parents, staff, and volunteers. The words and behaviors of the recreation professionals need to demonstrate that he or she *values* inclusion and is dedicated to making a difference in the recreational lives of community residents, with and without disabilities. This is essential because negative attitudes from staff and other program participants are often identified by people with disabilities as barriers to successful participation (Bedini, 2000; Schleien, Ray, & Green, 1997).

For many recreation professionals who do not have prior experience with persons who have disabilities, the first step toward adopting a positive attitude may be overcoming their fears. It is "normal" to be afraid of unfamiliar circumstances; however, giving into fears associated with inclusion will, ultimately, undermine the integrity of a program by denying appropriate services to people with disabilities. Pearpoint and Forest (1999) observed that being afraid of interacting with persons who have disabilities is instilled by our society's culture, but that it can be overcome. They stated:

> The answer is that we must face the fear and do it anyway (i.e., include everyone). This will be uncomfortable, even terrifying for a few moments, but fears pass. When we face our fears, and proceed regardless, they immediately diminish and come into perspective. We have had conversations with hundreds of "inclusion survivors." . . . They endured a few weeks of "Tylenol therapy" and then as if by magic, the terror passed. In interviewing people about that period, there is an overwhelming pattern. Every single person remembers being terrified. No one can remember what they were afraid of . . . just that they were afraid and it passed.

Displaying a positive attitude toward inclusion also means that recreation professionals must embrace change. Old ways of doing things (i.e., segregated programming) are no longer viable.

Godbey (1989) wrote, "Change is the one 'constant' of our emerging profession. We will either change of our own accord, be forced to change or disappear. It is time to rethink, experiment and go in some new directions" (p. 1). He added that "leisure services must be prepared to both respond to and initiate change" (p. 87). This message remains important today. Persons with disabilities are increasingly active in demanding inclusion in all aspects of society. Recreation professionals must respond to this demand, and the appropriate response is to initiate inclusive recreation services.

Overcoming fears and embracing changes associated with inclusion allows recreation professionals to display a positive attitude toward the inclusion process. As noted, this attitude is reflected in everything the recreation professional says and does. Having a positive attitude toward inclusion means:

- Showing you genuinely care for all participants, including those with disabilities.
- Using appropriate terminology (see chapter 2).
- Being flexible and willing to adapt activities to meet the individual needs of participants.
- Working with participants, parents, staff, and volunteers to provide the most appropriate environment for each participant.
- Striving to eliminate *all* barriers to recreation participation (see chapter 5).
- Insisting that all participants be treated with respect and dignity.
- Learning about disabling conditions and their implications for recreation participation (see chapter 4).
- Emphasizing similarities among participants, while acknowledging and making allowances for individual differences.

Prepare the Foundation for Inclusion

Careful advance planning is required to provide the foundation for successful inclusion. Needs assessment and planning mandates, policies, goals, and objectives, described earlier in this chapter, are part of this preparation; however, more is needed to ensure successful inclusion. Orientation or preservices activities should be designed to provide staff with skills for effective inclusion. In-service activities should also be structured to facilitate the inclusion process. Paid staff and volunteer support may be needed to ensure that persons with disabilities can maximize their involvement in recreational activities. Finally, people with disabilities play an important role in promoting social acceptance in inclusive settings (Devine & Lashua, 2002).

People who work or volunteer in recreation settings usually take part in some type of orientation or preservice training designed to help them carry out the functions of their job more effectively. Part of this training should be devoted to developing the skills and positive attitudes that will assist persons with disabilities to participate successfully in the recreation programs offered. McGill (1984) makes the case that inadequate staff training decreases the likelihood of successful inclusion of persons with disabilities. A variety of topics should be covered in such a training program. First and foremost, the agency must make its commitment to inclusion well known to the staff and must attempt to foster a welcoming attitude toward persons with disabilities. This may be done by using preprepared training packages that focus on dispelling myths about persons with disabilities and by making staff feel more at ease in including these individuals in their programs. Examples of these training packages include "All Ways Welcome," from the Ontario Ministry of Tourism and Recreation, and "Disability Awareness Training," developed by the Canadian Rehabilitation Council for the Disabled. Information on obtaining these and other training packages is included at the end of this chapter. Regardless of what type of training is given, it should include an overview of the methods used by the agency to support individuals with disabilities. The agency's training program may also include some leadership hints and tips for working with people with particular disabilities, such as persons with visual impairments or brain injuries (see chapter 4). Methods of analyzing and adapting activities, which will be outlined later in this chapter, could also be a useful part of the training process.

To be most effective, the training program should involve a variety of training methods, such as videos, printed material, discussions, problem solving, hands-on experiences, and presentations. The training can be implemented using a number of sources. Someone within the agency who has the appropriate background may initiate the training program, or departments may wish to hire an inclusive recreation specialist as a consultant to conduct this training (Schleien, Ray, & Green, 1997). Professionals from agencies that serve persons with disabilities can also be a good source of information, and could be active participants in the education process (Burt Perrin Associates, 1989). If possible, staff training should include the involvement of persons with disabilities. They have firsthand experience with what works and what doesn't (Hutchison & McGill, 1998).

Training and education should not be limited to a formal program conducted upon hiring. Staff should have open access to printed resources that may be of assistance, to further training programs as they are made available, and to ongoing support that may be needed to help solve problems as they arise. Sable (1992), for example, described using biweekly group sessions and individual supervision meetings with staff to facilitate integration in a residential camp. Timely and effective staff training will go a long way toward ensuring the successful inclusion of persons with disabilities.

A well-trained staff alone, however, may not be enough to ensure optimal participation by all persons who have disabilities. For some individuals with disabilities additional supports may be required during the program to allow them to take part. Many recreation departments and agencies have implemented one or a number of such support services. The following paragraphs highlight some methods of support used throughout the United States and Canada.

Paid Support

Some agencies or parks and recreation departments hire an individual to act as a special needs coordinator or integration specialist. This person is usually responsible for ensuring that the needs of persons with disabilities are being met by the programs offered, and he or she also oversees any additional support services that are provided. Some agencies that serve persons with disabilities employ what Dattilo and St. Peter (1991) term a leisure coach. The leisure coach is available to teach persons with disabilities those skills necessary for participation in recreational activities, to provide inclusion information and support to the recreation staff, and to offer assistance to the participant with a disability during the activity, if needed. Recreation providers can assist in this process by allowing the person with a disability and the coach to observe or try a number of different activities to gain exposure, and by providing tours and information about programs and facilities, as requested.

Volunteers

Volunteers are used in many agencies and recreation departments to assist in the inclusion of persons with disabilities. Names such as Leisure Buddy, Leisure Link, or Volunteer Advocate denote programs where an individual without a disability is matched with an individual with a disability, and the two of them participate in a community recreation program together. The Montgomery County (Maryland) Mainstreaming Initiative, for example, uses this approach to ensure that programs are open to all county residents (see chapter 8). Rynders and Fahnestock (1997) also discussed the importance of using peers without disabilities (i.e., buddies or companions) to promote inclusion. They note, however, that the ages of the peers among children should vary according to the goal of the activity. If the primary purpose of an activity is to promote social interaction, same age peers are best. If the activity is intended to promote skill development, older children should be used as tutors. Rynders and Fahnestock noted that *both* social interaction and skill development may be enhanced if "an older peer without a disability tutors a younger peer with a disability while a peer without a disability of the same age as the child with a disability serves as a social companion" (p. 108).

It is important that volunteers who assist in recreation programs also receive appropriate training so that the participant with a disability and the volunteer have the best possible experience. Volunteers should be made aware of what type of assistance may be needed (information that is best provided by the person with the disability), and should encourage the participant to do as much for him- or herself as possible.

While there are many benefits to these accompaniment programs, there are also some limitations. Normally these programs do not lead to friendships because of the way they are structured. This is a limitation when we consider the importance of opportunities for friendship building discussed earlier. Furthermore, the relationship is often limited to the two persons, the individual and the buddy. Other approaches to friendship building have greater potential for building a broader network of friends, such as the social network approach. Finally, friendship is often not a goal of these programs; the emphasis is more on accompaniment. The bottom line here is that people with disabilities need a strong network of friends in their lives, that cannot be replaced by volunteers or staff (Gold, 1988; Hutchison & McGill, 1998).

It should come as no surprise that the person with the disability does not always have to be at the receiving end of the volunteer service. With the trend toward inclusion and encouraging people with disabilities to be in valuing roles, the role of volunteer is gaining recognition (Roker, Player, & Coleman, 1998). The benefits that accrue from volunteering include feelings of self-worth by the volunteer because of making a contribution to the creation of stronger, better resourced communities (Hall, McKeown, Roberts, 2001; Hamilton & Hussain, 1998). These benefits are no different whether the person has a disability or not (Graff & Vedell, 2000; Miller, Schleien, Rider, Hall, Roche, & Worsley, 2002). Despite this awareness of the benefits of volunteering to both the individual and society, there is some controversy about whether or not volunteering should replace work. Some believe this is not the case for most working-age adults and therefore should not be encouraged with individuals with disabilities. However, others argue that if work is menial and low-paid, there should be less pressure on individuals with disabilities to feel they have to find employment (Hutchison, 1994). Regardless, we know that supported volunteering is on the rise.

Group Support

In light of the limitations raised about leisure buddies, a variety of other options are increasing in popularity. Social support is important because many people with disabilities are isolated, so building networks contributes to social support. Social support is also a determinant of health because when people have other people in their lives, they are healthier (Lord & Hutchison, 1998; Van Dreunen, 1996). Therefore, social support is essential to the inclusion process (Lee, McCormick, & Austin, 2001).

In one approach to building social support, the idea is that a group of people without disabilities form a natural support system around a person.

Sometimes referred to as a "circle of friends," other times simply "friends," the people without disabilities become friends, support the person in making other friends, and develop strategies for overcoming barriers that might prevent acceptance and participation (Bedini, 1993; Gold, 1999; Falvey, Forest, Pearpoint, & Rosenburg, 1994; Schleien, 1993; Staub, 1998). Acceptance is very important for reversing negative images of people with disabilities (Harlan-Simmons, Holtz, Todd, & Mooney, 2001).

Selecting and Modifying Activities

In selecting activities for participation, the recreation leader should keep in mind the information gained during the assessment phase and also the goals and objectives of the planning phase.

Occasionally, it is necessary to modify activities to meet the needs of those being served. There are several reasons why activities may need to be adapted. First, adaptations may be necessary to

Activity analysis may clarify the need to modify an activity to meet the needs of participants with disabilities.
(Courtesy of Courage Center, Golden Valley, MN)

allow everyone to participate. For example, in skiing, a participant who is blind may use a sighted guide, and a person with a lower limb amputation may make use of an outrigger (a ski-like attachment to a pole). Both of these adaptations allow individuals with disabilities to take part in a sport that would otherwise be difficult for them to participate in.

A second reason for adapting an activity may be to enhance achievement of the program's goals and objectives. For example, if one of the goals of the program was to "provide opportunities for social interaction," the leader might modify an activity like T-shirt painting, which is traditionally done alone, by requesting that all projects be done in pairs. This way, individuals with and without disabilities would have to work together to complete the task.

A third reason for adapting activities is to accommodate any operational concerns that the leader may have. Insufficient staff, facilities, participants, or equipment may make it difficult or dangerous to perform an activity the way it was meant to be performed. For example, if a woodworking program were being offered but there were not enough staff to supervise the machinery, the activity may need to be modified so that the participants only do the sanding and finishing on their projects; thus, their safety is not put in jeopardy.

Guidelines for Modification

The rationale for the adaptations cited here is not meant to give the impression that activities should be altered with little thought to the implications of the modifications. A point that Labanowich (1978) made about wheelchair sports is that we need to be careful not to slant recreational activities toward an air of "temporariness," particularly for children and youth. According to Labanowich, such activities may "fail to convey a sense of realism for the participant projected against their utility as later life pastimes" (p. 12). Keeping in mind that activities should be beneficial or meaningful to the individual, the leader should ask the question: "Will modifying or adapting the activity be unfair

and/or detract from the meaningfulness of the activity for the individual?" The following are some guidelines that should be considered when selecting and modifying activities for persons who have disabilities.

1. Change as little as necessary. For example, try to keep the structure and the rules of a game as close as possible to the existing game. It is better to undermodify to challenge the individual and to provide normalized experiences.

2. Where possible, involve the person in the selection and activity modification process. Many times, the user is a good source of information. The rules for wheelchair basketball are based on this phenomenon. All rule modifications of the National Wheelchair Basketball Association need the approval of participants.

3. Don't make assumptions about an individual based on his or her disability. No two persons with the same disability have the exact same modification needs. Get to know the person before deciding on any needed modifications.

4. There may be elements of competition to consider when working with groups of children and adults. In more competitive settings, for instance, past performance, age, and sex of the participant are usually taken into consideration when pitting one person against another.

5. Where possible, activities should have common denominators, especially if they are modified. For example, in wheelchair basketball or sledge hockey, everyone plays in a wheelchair or sleigh and follows the same rules, which ensures equality in participation.

6. In many instances, the person with a disability is cast in the role of spectator. The authors of this text strongly feel that individuals should be provided opportunities to participate in, and be encouraged to join, participant-based programs. If full and active

participation is not possible, then the person with the disability should be provided with opportunities for partial participation.

7. Start at the level where the participants are currently functioning. This does *not* mean starting at the lowest level.

8. Individuals should be given opportunities for free choice. This may enhance the feeling of control and reduce feelings of "learned helplessness."

Keeping the aforementioned guidelines for modification in mind, there are several types of adaptations that could be used, if needed, to facilitate the inclusion of persons with disabilities. These modifications fall into one of the following four categories:

1. *Procedural/operational adaptations:* These are changes or alterations in the operation of play that achieve the same purpose as the original activity. This may involve modifications to the rules (e.g., shortening the length of time a game is played to accommodate short attention spans), changes in the procedures for action (e.g., having participants walk instead of run during an activity), changes in the roles of the participants (e.g., using the buddy system in the outfield in baseball if a participant with a disability needs assistance), or changes in the social interaction requirements of an activity (e.g., allowing two people to answer questions together in a trivia quiz).

2. *Environmental adaptations:* This involves adaptations directly related to the environment in which the activity is taking place. For example, if a participant has a mobility impairment, the leader could use barriers around the group to decrease the distance that the ball rolls. Or, if a participant has a visual impairment, arrangements could be made to ensure that the lighting does not hamper that person's ability to track objects.

3. *Equipment adaptations:* There are two types of equipment adaptations. The first type, aids to existing equipment, allows individuals to use standard equipment. Examples of such aids include card holders for people unable to hold playing cards and vises to hold craft projects for people who have use of one hand. The second type of equipment modification, specialized equipment, involves changes to standard equipment or the creation of new equipment to allow activity participation. Examples of specialized equipment include four-holed scissors, with which an instructor can physically help a person cut something; talking books for people unable to read regular books; and sledges, used in an adapted form of ice hockey played by persons with and without a physical impairment.

4. *Human intervention:* This involves a leader, volunteer, or peer assisting with an individual's participation in an activity. This may take the form of passive assistance (providing verbal prompting, encouragement, or praise), or more active assistance (providing physical prompts, hand-over-hand assistance, or moving with the individual). In either case, the individual with the disability should be allowed to do as much for him- or herself as possible.

Recreation professionals should be encouraged to use creativity and flexibility in trying to accommodate all individuals in programs. The use of innovative adaptations allows participation in a particular activity by many people who would otherwise find it difficult or impossible. And it goes without saying that holding programs in facilities that are as barrier-free as possible, or making adaptations to program facilities, can also help facilitate the participation of people with disabilities in community programs (Bedini & McCann, 1992).

Structure Activities to Promote Inclusion

Activity modification can enable a person who has a disability to participate in a given activity, but it does not, within itself, ensure effective inclusion. Activities need to be carefully structured to promote inclusion.

Probably the best and most important way to promote inclusion is to provide activities that offer a *climate of cooperation.* This means structuring activities to encourage positive peer interaction and the development of interpersonal skills and friendships among participants.

Although persons with disabilities should be given the opportunity to participate in competitive activities if desired, competition can create situations where the person with a disability does not succeed. By eliminating the focus on winning and dominance, cooperative activities create an atmosphere that allows participants to express themselves more freely and support one another (LeFevre, 1988). Removing anxiety about performance creates an atmosphere of interdependence, and the result will most likely be positive social interactions among persons with and without disabilities (Rynders & Schleien, 1991).

Rynders and Fahnestock (1997) have cautioned about the use of competition. They stated that "if a setting is not structured for cooperative learning experiences, then negative competition is likely to emerge and may actually socialize children without disabilities to reject peers who have a disability" (p. 104). Sometimes, however, participants, including those with disabilities, request a competitive structure. If a competitive structure is selected, leaders should still facilitate a climate of cooperation. One way to do this is to be aware of the abilities of participants and consider altering the activity to facilitate inclusion. If an activity is by nature one in which individuals compete against each other, the activity could be altered so that people compete against themselves by trying to improve their performance. In bowling, for example, rather than competing for the highest score, individuals could try to beat their own average, with the person scoring the most pins over average being declared the winner. This structure gives all participants an opportunity to succeed.

Another way to structure competitive activities that allow individuals with disabilities equal opportunities for succeeding and developing peer friendships is to structure activities that create an - interdependence among team members. With this structure, every member's contribution to the task is what determines "winning" (Rynders & Schleien, 1991). For example, in a group chili-making contest, the rules could state that each member of the group must perform a given number of tasks in the preparation of the chili. Moreover, the rules could state that each participant must do "blind taste tests" to help determine the winners. In this way, persons with and without disabilities are equal partners in influencing the outcome of their group's efforts.

When planning group activities, leaders should give consideration to the most appropriate size for the group. Johnson and Johnson (1980) have indicated that, to best facilitate integration, the decision for group size should be based on several factors. Usually, the younger the group, the more complex the task, the weaker the cooperative skills of the group members, and the shorter the time available to complete the task, the smaller the group should be. Also, offering a progression from small-group to large-group activities may facilitate social integration.

Some additional suggestions for implementing activities that promote inclusion are:

- Empower participants with disabilities by encouraging optimal independence, providing opportunities to make appropriate choices, and facilitating perceptions of freedom.
- Offer age-appropriate activities.
- Encourage development of skills that can be transferred to other community activities.
- If appropriate, use technology to facilitate inclusion; however, be aware that inappropriate or excessive use of technology may impede inclusion.
- Structure group activities so that each member must make contributions toward the goal.
- Provide a variety of appropriate materials for use by participants, and ensure that they are convenient to persons with disabilities.
- Identify "high status" members of a group and enlist their assistance in the inclusion process (e.g., use as buddies).
- Provide participants with disabilities enough practice with important skills to ensure success.

Creating a climate of cooperation encourages positive interaction among persons with and without disabilities. (Courtesy of *VSA arts*, www.vsarts.org)

Managing Problem Behavior

When implementing programs, recreation leaders must occasionally deal with problem behavior exhibited by one or more participants. Managing such problem behavior is a difficult and frustrating task that requires patience and skill. In general, behavior management techniques that are effective for the general population are also effective for persons who have disabilities. The following list of simple strategies,[1] although far from a cure-all, may help to increase appropriate behavior among participants whose behavior is difficult to manage.

1. *Reinforce desirable behavior.* It is usually much easier to establish desirable behavior patterns than to alter problem behavior after it has started. A smile, gesture, or brief word of support is frequently all that is necessary to encourage a participant to maintain or to increase acceptable behavior.

2. *Clearly state privileges as well as rules.* Tell participants what they may do; too many "don'ts" violate strategy 1. If participants clearly understand what is permitted, they will not need to test to determine acceptable limits. Participant involvement in establishing rules may help as well.

3. *Tolerate some annoying behavior.* Too much attention to annoying behavior may not only interfere with an activity's effectiveness, but may serve to reinforce undesirable actions. Also, certain annoying behaviors may be

[1]Modified from "A Camp Director's 10: A List of Strategies for Managing Problem Behavior of Young Campers" by Ralph W. Smith, in *Camping Magazine*, June 1980, Vol. 52, No. 7, p. 7. Reprinted with permission from the American Camping Association, Inc. Copyright © 1980 American Camping Association, Inc.

typical for a young person's developmental stage.

4. *Use nonverbal cues.* Eye contact, accompanied by a frown or gesture, may control undesirable behavior without the possibility of embarrassing the participant in front of his or her peers.

5. *Consider redirection to a different task or activity.* The challenges of any activity should be consistent with the participant's skill development, so plan for varying levels of skill and try to individualize tasks to each person's abilities. Many behavior problems result from activity dissatisfaction or boredom and may be eliminated by redirecting the person to another task or activity.

NOTE: Despite careful attention to the above strategies, problem behaviors may occur that require immediate intervention. Any disciplinary action should be fair, consistent, and administered in an understanding manner. The next strategies may be helpful when intervention is required.

6. *Clarify consequences of unacceptable behavior.* A participant should clearly understand the personal impact of his or her behavior, such as anticipated disciplinary action. It also may be advisable to encourage young participants to clarify the consequences of his or her own actions by asking, "What things do you think will happen if you continue to act this way?" When clarifying consequences, avoid using a threatening tone of voice and, above all, the recreation professional must be prepared to follow through if the undesirable behavior continues.

7. *Clarify benefits of acceptable behavior.* This is the corollary to strategy 6, and may be useful in concert with it. Pointing out the benefits of acceptable behavior will be most effective if it occurs immediately after desirable behavior (strategy 1).

8. *Use time-out procedures.* It may be necessary to temporarily remove a disruptive person from the situation in which problem behavior is occurring and place him or her in a location where little or no enjoyable stimulation is received. Once removed, the person should be allowed to return after a short time, but it is important that this return be contingent on appropriate behavior.

9. *Punishment, if used, should be a last resort.* Punishment of any kind does not allow the person to avoid the consequences by exhibiting acceptable behavior. Thus, attention is directed to the punishment, rather than to the problem and alternative forms of behavior. Any form of punishment should be appropriate to the situation and must conform to agency policies.

10. *If in doubt, seek help.* This strategy should be used whenever the recreation leader feels incapable of coping with a particular situation or behavioral problem. Seeking help is not a sign of defeat or inadequacy. No one, regardless of experience, has all the answers to handling behavior problems. If the participant is a child, remember parents are an important resource.

One source of help, especially with severe behavior problems, is the Professional Crisis Management Association, 4321 N.W. 93 Way, Sunrise, FL 33351 (website: http://www.pcma.com). This organization provides various levels of training in crisis management that emphasize human dignity and freedom of choice. On a similar note, McGee and his colleagues founded the Gentle Teaching Approach (McGee, Menolascino, Hobbs, & Menousek, 1987).

EVALUATION

Evaluation is the final component of the planning process. Kendrick (1991) has some important reflections about service evaluation.

Most people who work in human services programs have a perception, from time to time, that they are not doing as good a job as they should. . . . It is clear that "services" are not merely the personal interactions between the "served" and the "server." Services are greatly influenced by a massive historical process of professionals, ideologies, laws, agencies, social movements, economics, politics and culture. This "context-of-service" deeply influences what service becomes. . . . It is important to think of evaluation as a process whereby we develop in ourselves the ability to be uneasy with the way we do things. (pp. 14–15)

Here are a few examples of questions Kendrick (1991) believes we should be asking ourselves in order to begin to think more critically about services:

1. What is difficult for us to consistently do well?
2. To what extent do we provide services in a way that benefits others more than the client?
3. Do we have a different or lower standard for how clients should be treated than ourselves?
4. Do we do, say, think, or acquiesce to things that stigmatize or devalue the client?
5. Are there things we're assuming about clients or our programs that are simply not true or accurate?
6. Are there things missing from the client's lives that we do little about?
7. Are we doing things that don't really do much of importance for the client?
8. Is the person served really the reason the program looks the way it does?
9. What do we actually believe about people given what we actually do?
10. Do we have a focus in how we serve people?
11. What do we really want (deep down) for our clients and how hard will we work on it?
12. Do we live up to our principles?
13. Are we afraid to talk about our weaknesses, limitations, and shortcomings?
14. Where do we excel and what does this say about who we serve and who we don't?
15. Would I like to be a client of this service? (Kendrick, 1991, pp 19–20)

It is these kinds of critical questions that are being used to evaluate many special programs and, as a result of long and thoughtful evaluation, eliminate many of these services. These critical questions are also very useful for evaluation in inclusive settings. They are based on the assumption that people with disabilities have rights and are entitled to quality services afforded citizens without disabilities. These questions reiterate the importance of values in the planning process and ground evaluation in the lives of individuals with disabilities as well as community change.

Reasons for Evaluation

Why should professional recreators evaluate their programs? There are a multitude of reasons. The following are a few examples.

- To determine if program objectives have been accomplished
- To discover the impact the program had on the participants
- To decide if the program was cost-effective
- To provide information for future program planning and modification
- To obtain key information necessary to justify future financial support for the program
- To obtain information for formal reports to the board, planning committees, and other target audiences
- To provide information necessary to market the program to potential clients, decision makers, and program sponsors

Types of Evaluation

Recreation boards and commissions, administrators, the public, and clients like to see hard evidence that recreation services are effective. It is important to clarify what we mean by success in your efforts. As one example, quantitative information helps track the number of participants in a recreation program. Over time, comparisons can be made to determine whether the number of participants with disabilities increased, decreased, or stayed about the same. Knowing information about the number of people may reflect interest in recreation programs, particularly if individuals return to engage in other activities.

Qualitative information is also important. As pointed out by Schleien and Ray (1988), "The successful (or unsuccessful) social integration of participants may be determined by observing certain behaviors between participants with and without disabilities. These behaviors may include initiating social interactions, eye contact between peers, physical proximity, appropriate physical contact, sharing" (p. 91).

What is assessed in program evaluation should pertain to the mission, policies, goals, and objectives of the agency. Deciding on the most appropriate approach will be the challenge. There are several approaches used in conducting evaluations. The following are some typical examples of the types of evaluation that could be used.

- Casual impressions, including comments from participants
- Self-checking or feedback exercises, including simple reaction forms and verbal feedback from participants
- Do-it-yourself evaluations, including follow-up surveys or simple phone surveys
- Impact studies, including carefully designed evaluation studies
- Experimental research, including rigorous studies using standard research designs that control errors
- Participatory Action Research (PAR)
- Accreditation

To illustrate one type of evaluation from this list, one that is least known but growing in popularity is Participatory Action Research (PAR) or action research (Barnsley & Ellis, 1992; Park, 1993; Whyte, 1991). Recently PAR has been used in leisure research as well as disability research and evaluation (Haasen, Hornibrook, & Pedlar, 1998; Connolly & Law, 1999; Pedlar, 1995; Van Dreunen, 1996). The benefits of PAR include its scientific rigor, yet practical relevance; individuals with disabilities participate directly in defining, analyzing,

and solving problems, resulting in a more authentic analysis of the issues; learning-as-you-go; empowerment; supportive relationships that serve to diminish power imbalances between the leisure research community and citizens; and the improvement of quality of life for people with disabilities (Balcazar, Keys, Kaplan, & Suarez-Balcazar, 1998; Krogh, 1998; Nelson, Ochocka, Griffin, & Lord, 1998; Pedlar & Hutchison, 1999; Taylor & Botschner, 1998).

Another type of evaluation that may need further explanation is the last one on the list. The Council on Quality and Leadership (2003) is an organization that was created 30 years ago to devise opportunities for people with disabilities to lead lives they choose and to improve the quality of services and supports. It is based on person-centered solutions at all levels from national to local and supports both professional and self-advocates organizations in the United States and beyond. It emphasizes value-based supports, individualized planning, and personal outcomes as the basis of the accreditation review process. In addition to accreditation services, it provides organization assessment, consultation, and technical assistance; third-party evaluation; and research. There are 25 outcome-based performance measures under categories such as personal goals, choice, social inclusion, relationships, rights, dignity and respect, health, environment, security, and satisfaction (Accreditation Council of Ontario, 2003). An example under choice would be "People choose how to use their free time." Under social inclusion, "People participate in the life of the community." In each of the 25 measures, there is also the opportunity to determine if there is support from the service to meet the outcomes. The assumption is "informed choice," so if they say a person is happy, the evaluators ask "What are those indicators?" "What options, choice, and exposure has the person had to be able to make that informed choice?"

Program Evaluation Steps

As stated earlier, evaluation planning starts when service planning starts, and evaluation is a key step of the program planning process. Each time recreation leaders plan a program or service, they should (1) decide on the objectives the program is designed to accomplish, (2) establish a plan of action to meet the objectives, (3) decide which level of evaluation is appropriate, and (4) design an evaluation instrument to accomplish this goal.

There are many approaches to an evaluation with each having a number of steps. The following is one example of steps to accomplish a program evaluation:

Before Recreation Program Is Implemented

- Select program to be evaluated and audience from which to gather information
- Identify the audience with whom the evaluation information will be shared
- Decide why this particular program needs to be evaluated
- List and review program objectives
- Decide which level of evaluation is appropriate and feasible
- Decide how the information will be collected
- Develop or obtain the evaluation instrument(s)

After Recreation Program Is Implemented

- Conduct the evaluation (collect data on participants)
- Analyze, summarize, and study results
- Revise future programs accordingly
- Prepare written reports and disseminate results and recommendations

The process of program or service evaluation is a continuous one. The goal of the evaluation process is to provide better leisure opportunities and to seek ways to improve various aspects of program features. As mentioned, there are many approaches to the various kinds of evaluation procedures and a multitude of evaluation tools to measure the different phenomena. Records such as attendance sheets can answer questions pertaining to the number of participants and can offer comparisons that reflect any increases or decreases. Schleien and Ray (1988) give examples of skill acquisition forms, social interaction tools,

peer acceptance evaluations, and measures of self-concept that can be used with persons with disabilities.

Sample Evaluation Tools

There are several evaluation tools that have been used within the recreation fields, particularly with persons with disabilities. In this section, the Recreation Inventory for Inclusive Participation, the Benefits-Based Management Activity Planning Model, and the Importance-Performance Analysis will be cited. In addition, a listing of other tools is given, wherein a Peer Acceptance Survey and a typical sociogram are described.

The Recreation Inventory for Inclusive Participation

The Recreation Inventory for Inclusive Participation (RIPP) was designed to provide the community recreation professional and others with instructional content and the information needed to make viable leisure education instructional decisions (Schleien et al., 1993). The inventory identifies needs of individuals with disabilities and provides a starting point from which to consider necessary program modifications to enhance successful participation. Thus, using this inventory would provide recreation professionals with a systematic approach of involving persons with disabilities within a variety of community settings, including school-based programs (Schleien et al., 1997).

The inventory approach can help recreators develop detailed descriptions of recreation activities. As such descriptions are generated by observing peers without disabilities, the necessary skills for successful participation can be compared with performance criteria exhibited by individuals with disabilities. Schleien and his colleagues (1997) suggest people with disabilities should be taught functional, age-appropriate leisure skills that are comparable to those used by individuals without disabilities and that can lead to successful performance in inclusive community recreation settings. The inventory sections are listed here. For more detailed information, refer to Schleien et al. (1997).

- Part I: (A) Appropriateness of Recreation Activity/Setting
- Part I: (B) General Program and Participant Information
- Part II: Activity/Discrepancy Analysis
- Part III: Specific Activity Requirements
- Part IV: Further Activity Considerations

Benefits-Based Management

A hot topic in recent years has been Benefits-Based Management (BBM). In an article by Allen and McGovern (1997), the BBM Activity Planning Model is described and examples are highlighted.

The National Recreation and Park Association funded demonstration projects to implement a benefits-based recreation program model to illustrate the impact recreation programs can have on participants. The first section of the model requires the identification of measurable outcomes. As Allen and McGovern (1997) point out, target issues relate to the long-term impact of the recreation experience. For example, target goals may include "identification of the protective factors that will be developed through the series of activities provided over the length of the program" (p. 48). The second section of the activity planning model relates to the development and implementation of purposive recreation programs. The content and structure of these programs, according to Allen and McGovern, must be specific to the stated target issues and target goals for a specific group. For each session, there is a listing of measurable performance outcomes with criteria for measuring successful completion of the objective, and they are related to the target goals. Some examples of performance objectives include the following.

- Eighty percent of participants will be able to swim across the swimming pool.
- Fifty percent of participants will demonstrate how to tie a knot within three minutes.
- Seventy percent of participant will be able to identify the primary colors.

Based on the model, once the performance objectives are stated, the experiences must be developed in a manner to maximize the probability of achieving the performance objective(s) and the target goals. According to Allen and McGovern (1997) it is important to give participants an opportunity to process the experience; that is, to reflect on the day's activities.

The third component involves the assessment of benefit outcomes that relate to the target issue and the target goals. This would necessitate the development of an evaluation plan and is viewed as an imperative feature of the model. For more detailed information including specific examples, refer to Allen and McGovern (1997).

Importance-Performance Analysis

Obtaining participant input is a primary ingredient in the development and improvement of recreation programs and services. Empirical research has demonstrated that client satisfaction is a function of *expectations* related to certain important attributes and judgment of attribute *performance* (Meyers & Alpers, 1968; Swan & Coombs, 1976).

Guadagnolo (1985) has applied importance-performance analysis to the recreation and parks field. There has been success in using this approach to market and evaluate programs for adults who were mentally retarded (Guadagnolo, et al., 1984), for persons with physical disabilities (Kennedy, 1986), and for the elderly (Gillespie, Kennedy, & Soble, 1989). In all instances, the respective audiences have been willing and able to complete forms and to demonstrate the necessary understanding of the process.

The first step in importance-performance analysis is determining what specific program features are important to measure. The features list should reflect those items over which an agency has some degree of control. The quality of the information collected is dependent on the program features list; therefore, ample time should be devoted to its development.

Various qualitative research techniques such as focus groups and unstructured interviews have been used to identify important program features. In a

	Importance Scale				
Feature	**Not Important**		**Somewhat Important**		**Very Important**
Safety	1	2	3	4	5
Family involvement	1	2	3	4	5

	Performance or Satisfaction Scale				
Feature	**Not Satisfied (Poor Performance)**		**Somewhat Satisfied (Average Performance)**		**Very Satisfied (Excellent Performance)**
Safety	1	2	3	4	5
Family involvement	1	2	3	4	5

Figure 7-2   Importance Scale

swim program, for example, the features list could be initiated by the recreation staff. Once the features list is drafted, staff members could talk with two or three potential participants or to parents of children with disabilities, if appropriate. Based on these conversations, a features list can be finalized. A list for a swim program might look like the following:

Safety	Family involvement
Privacy	Length of swim session
Transportation	Temperature of the water
Program location	Ratio of staff to participants
Pool accessibility	Instructor's teaching skill

Once the features list is developed, the next step is the development of the importance-performance (I-P) scale. The I-P scale usually consists of two Likert scales, one measuring importance and the other, performance. The features are rated on a scale ranging from "not important" to "very important." Similarly, performance or satisfaction is rated. In the example provided, a 5-point scale is used. However, shorter scales (3 points) and longer ones (7 points) can be used. Also, faces depicting feelings have been used with young children and adults with mental retardation.

The I-P scale is usually handed out to participants at the completion of the program. Each person is instructed on how to fill out the form. After the individuals fill out the I-P scale, average scores are calculated for each pair of importance and performance features. The features are then plotted on a two-dimensional, four-quadrant grid. Figure 7-3 gives an example of an importance-performance analysis grid used to evaluate a swimming program. The caption in the upper right quadrant reads "Keep up the good work." Features in this quadrant represent items that are not only important to the participant, but are also given high marks on performance. The lower right quadrant, labeled "Concentrate here," includes features that the participant views as important, but for which the agency receives low ratings on performance or satisfaction. It is this quadrant that provides the agency staff with information to improve the program. The last two quadrants, labeled "Low priority" and "Better than necessary," reflect low importance ratings by participants, and low and high performance, respectively.

Knowing about client expectations and how a given program performs will help staff improve program offerings. Agency officials are usually limited by such factors as budget restrictions, space limitations, and personnel capabilities,

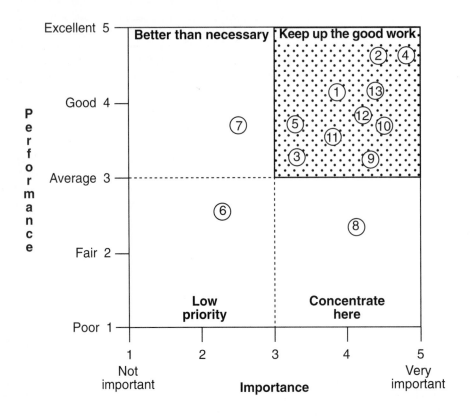

Figure 7-3   Sample Importance-Performance Analysis Grid

1=Safety   5=Instructor's teaching skills   10=Privacy
2=Pool accessibility   6=Ratio of staff to client   11=Family involvement
3=Program location   7=Accessibility of locker room   12=Frequency of sessions
4=Equipment   8=Length of swim session   13=Cost of program
                          9=Transportation

therefore the information gained by such an evaluation (accompanied by other information) can help to prioritize where resources should be allocated. Furthermore, such efforts could promote participation in activities and, ultimately, meet the needs and interests of the clients.

Assessment Tools

On a therapeutic recreation directory website (1999) a number of individuals were asked what assessment tools they used. While the responses appeared to relate to clinical settings, many may be used within a community recreation environment. The following are some examples of the listings.

- Custom-made activity assessment form
- Farrington Leisure Assessment
- Functional Abilities Scale
- Walker-McConnell Assessment to evaluate behaviors of school children before and after implementation of an intervention called the

Living Skills Club in which anger management, friendship, cooperation, and esteem-based issues are addressed.

- Leisure Diagnostic Battery
- Leisure Activities Survey
- Leisure Activities Blank
- Peirs Harris Self-Concept Scale
- Jesness Inventory, a measure of adolescent deliquent behavior
- Comprehensive Evaluation in Recreational Therapy, (CERT)

As pointed out by Schleien et al. (1997), there are a number of areas or domains that can be assessed and evaluated in a recreation activity or program. The initial questions pertain to whether the individual knows how to use equipment and facilities in an appropriate manner. Assuming objectives are written, evaluating leisure skills requires some sort of task analytic assessment according to Schleien (1993).

Some time ago, Farrell and Lundegren (1978) suggested that those who work in the recreation and parks field should use sociometry to look at social structures of individuals in group situations. With regard to inclusive recreation, friendships should be fostered. Bishop, Jubala, Stainback, and Stainback (1996) discuss strategies that have been helpful to parents, educators, and others in facilitating friendships, specifically between students with disabilities and their peers without disabilities. Creating an awareness of friendship and respect for diversity is highlighted by the authors. An example of a sixth-grade class in which a unit on friendship was developed is discussed. For more information, see Bishop et al. Schleien and colleagues suggest that sociometry can be used to evaluate the emotional climate of a group and the attitudes of participants within a group toward each other as well as to identify any friendships that are being established. These features are usually put into what has been referred to as a sociogram. See Schleien et al. (1997) for examples. Figure 7-4 shows a typical sociogram form.

Voeltz (1980) developed the Peer Acceptance Survey, which measures children's attitudes toward persons with disabilities who are peers. Schleien et al. (1997) offer a modified version in

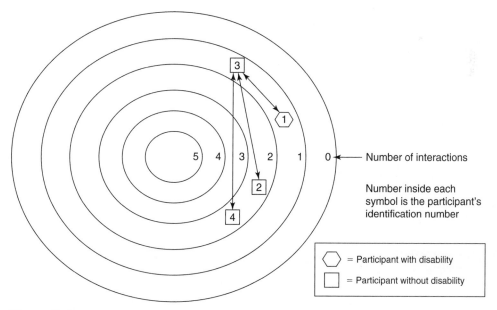

Figure 7-4   Typical Sociogram Evaluation Graphing Form

their text. It is a listing of 20 statements with an agree-disagree format. The following are a couple of examples of possible questions and format.

- People who have physical disabilities should not come to the park for activities.

    ❏ Agree   ❏ Disagree   ❏ Undecided

- I have talked to people who are in wheelchairs.

    ❏ Agree   ❏ Disagree   ❏ Undecided

This section dealing with assessment discussed examples of standardized and non-standardized tools, including task analysis, socio-metrics, and peer acceptance tools, and the list from the Therapeutic Recreation Directory web-site. However, many other tools do exist. The recreator should explore more fully what approaches and tools work best given the clientele and goals of the recreative experience.

SUMMARY

This chapter has dealt with the planning process. Discussion focused on four steps involved in this process: assessment; planning mandates, policies, goals, and objectives; implementation; and evaluation. Information was included about how each of these phases can facilitate the involvement of persons with disabilities in recreation programs.

During the *assessment* phase, information is gathered from the community and people with disabilities to determine the needs and interests of persons with disabilities. Based on this information, informed decisions are made about how best to meet these needs. The section on *planning* mandates, policies, goals, and objectives took a broad approach to the planning process. Just remember, Dr. Martin Luther King, Jr., said, "I have a dream." He did not say, "I have goals and objectives." Success during the *implementation* phase depends not only on effective preparation and education of staff, but also on providing any appropriate support that an individual may require. Several forms of support and education were outlined in this section. After implementation, recreation programs should be evaluated. Reasons for performing this *evaluation* were identified, along with what should be assessed. Examples of program evaluation steps were given and importance-performance analysis was highlighted as an example of a participant feedback approach. Readers interested in more informa-

tion on preprepared staff training programs are encouraged to consult the following resources:

"Community Recreation for Handicapped Persons: Inservice Education Program." Office on Community Recreation for Handicapped Persons, Division of Community Resources, Bureau of Recreation, New Jersey Department of Community Affairs, Trenton, NJ.

"Disability Awareness Training." Canadian Rehabilitation Council for the Disabled, 45 Sheppard Avenue East, Suite 801, Toronto, Ontario M2N 5W9.

"LIFE Resource and Training Manual." University of North Carolina, Chapel Hill, NC.

"Mainstreaming: A Total Perspective." Montgomery County Department of Recreation, Silver Spring, MD.

"Open for Business." Ontario Ministry of Tourism, Culture and Recreation, 77 Bloor Street West, 8th Floor, Toronto, Ontario M7A 2R9.

"WE CAN DO IT! A Training Manual for Integrating Disabled People into Recreation Programs." Bay Area Outreach Recreation Program, Inc., Berkeley, CA.

Inclusion Press. www.inclusionpress.com

SUGGESTED LEARNING ACTIVITIES

1. Develop a one-page questionnaire that could be used to identify the recreational interests and support needs of individuals with disabilities in your community.

2. Assume that you are the director of your local parks and recreation department. Write a policy that demonstrates your commitment to including persons with disabilities in your programs.

3. Contact an agency that serves persons with disabilities (e.g., Association for Community Living, Association for Retarded Citizens, etc.) and obtain the agency's philosophy and mandate regarding recreation opportunities in the community for individuals it serves.

4. Using the four categories of modification outlined in the chapter, discuss how you could adapt the activity of baseball to allow a wheelchair-using person with left-sided paralysis to participate in an integrated program.

5. Contact your local parks and recreation department (or other recreation provider) and find out what types of supports they have available to allow persons with disabilities to participate in their programs.

6. List five ways the Web could be used to assist the planning process.

7. Select a service and decide what you would like to evaluate about it. Then select or devise an instrument or tool to measure the processes and outcomes.

SOURCES OF INFORMATION

Active Living Alliance for Canadians with a Disability. Opening Doors: Keys to inclusive recreation policy for persons with a disability. [Online]. Available: Leisure Information Network, 1995.

Centre for Research and Education in Human Services 73 King St. W., Suite 202, Kitchener, ON N2G1A7 phone: 519-741-1318   fax: 519-741-8262 general@crehs.on.ca   http://www.crehs.on.ca/

The Council on Quality and Leadership (www.thecouncil.org/) and the National Center on Outcomes Resources (www.ncor.org/) 100 West Road, Suite 406, Towson, MD 21204 phone (410) 583-0060   fax (410) 583-0063.

Independent Sector. *Giving and Volunteering in the United States 2001: Key Findings.* [Online]. Available: http://www.independentsector.org/PDFs/ GV01keyfind.pdf, 2001.

National Recreation and Park Association. *Position Statement on Inclusion,* 1999. [Online]. Available: http://www.nrpa.org/branches/ntrs/inclusion/htm, March 18, 2001.

Perspectives on Social Inclusion: Children's Agenda/ Working Paper Series. www.laidlawfdn.org, 2002–2003.

REFERENCES

Accreditation Ontario. [Online]. Available: www.accreditationontario.com, October 20, 2003.

Allen, L. R., & T. D. McGovern. BBM: It's working! *Parks and Recreation, 32*(8), 48–55, 1997.

Allison, M. T., & I. E. Schneider. *Diversity and the Recreation Profession: Organizational Perspectives.* State College, PA: Venture, 2000.

Anderson, L., C. Brown, & P. Soli. *Inclusion: Strategies for Including People with Disabilities in Parks and Recreation Opportunities.* North Dakota: North Dakota Parks and Recreation Department, 1996.

Anderson, L., & L. Heyne. A state-wide needs assessment using focus groups: Perceived challenges and goals in providing inclusive recreation services in rural communities. *Journal of Park and Recreation Administration, 18*(4), 17–37, 2000.

Ash, E. Canadian Parks and Recreation Association policy development initiative for leisure services and persons with disabilities. *Journal of Leisurability, 21*(3),16–28, 1994.

Avedon, E. M. *Therapeutic Recreation Service: An Applied Behavioral Science Approach.* Englewood Cliffs, NJ: Prentice-Hall, 1974.

Balcazar, F., C. Keys, D. Kaplan, & Y. Suarez-Balcazar. Participatory action research and people with disabilities: Principles and challenges. *Canadian Journal of Rehabilitation, 12*(2), 105–112, 1998.

Barnsley, J., & D. Ellis. *Research for Change: Participatory Action Research for Community Groups.* Vancouver, BC: The Women's Research Centre, 1992.

Bedini, L. Transition and integration in leisure for people with disabilities. *Parks & Recreation, 28*(11), 20–24, 1993.

Bedini, L., & C. McCann. Tearing down the shameful wall of exclusion. *Parks & Recreation, 27*(4), 40–44, 1992.

Bedini, L. A. "Just sit down so we can talk": Perceived stigma and community recreation pursuits by people with disabilities. *Therapeutic Recreation Journal, 34,* 55–68, 2000.

Bedini, L. A., & K. A. Henderson. Women with disabilities and the challenges to leisure service providers. *Journal of Park and Recreation Administration, 12,* 17–34, 1994.

Bishop, K. D., K. A. Jubala, W. Stainback, & S. Stainback. Facilitating friendships. In S. Stainback & W. Stainback, Eds. *Inclusion: A Guide for Educators.* Baltimore: Brookes Publishing, 1996.

Bourne, C., & D. Legg. Linking to the community: The Active Living Alliance for Canadians with a Disability. *Journal of Leisurability, 25*(3), 11–16, 1998.

Bradley, V. J., J. W. Ashbaugh, & B. C. Blaney, Eds. *Creating Individual Supports for People with Developmental Disabilities. A Mandate for Change at Many Levels.* Baltimore, MD: Paul H. Brookes Publishing Co., 1994.

Bullock, C., & M. Mahon. *Introduction to Recreation Services for People with Disabilities* (2nd ed.). Champaign, IL: Sagamore Publishing, 2000.

Burt Perrin Associates. *Leisure: A Key to Community Integration.* Toronto: Author, 1989.

Cipriano, R. E. An individualized person-centered approach to therapeutic recreation services. *TASH Newsletter, 23*(4), 6–7, 1998.

Compton, D., & P. A. Witt. *The Leisure Diagnostic Battery: Background, Conceptualization and Structure.* Denton, TX: North Texas State University, June 1981.

Connolly, K., & M. Law. Collective voices: People with disabilities shaping municipal policy, *Journal of Leisurability, 26*(1), 16–24, 1999.

The Council on Quality and Leadership www.thecouncil.org/ and the National Center on Outcomes Resources www.ncor.org/ Towson, MD.

Cunconan-Lahr, R., & M. Brotherson. Advocacy in disability policy: Parents and consumers as advocates. *Mental Retardation, 34*(6), 352–358. 1996.

Darrah, J., J. Magill-Evans, & R. Adkins. How well are we doing? Families of adolescents or young adults with cerebral palsy share their perceptions of service delivery. *Disability and Rehabilitation, 24,* 542–549, 2002.

Dattilo, J. *Inclusive Leisure Services: Responding to the Rights of People with Disabilities.* State College, PA: Venture Publishing, 2000.

Dattilo, J., & S. St. Peter. A model for including leisure education in transition services for young adults with mental retardation. *Education and Training in Mental Retardation, 26*(4), 420–432, 1991.

Devine, M. A., & B. Lashua. Constructing social acceptance in inclusive leisure contexts: The role of individuals with disabilities. *Therapeutic Recreation Journal, 36,* 65–83, 2002.

Falvey, M., M. Forest, J. Pearpoint, & R. Rosenburg. *All My Life's a Circle.* Toronto, ON: Inclusion Press, 1994.

Forester, J. *Critical Theory, Public Policy, and Planning Practice: Toward a Critical Pragmatism.* Albany, NY: State University of New York Press, 1993.

Frazee, C. Thumbs up! Inclusion, rights and equality as experienced by youth with disabilities. *Perspectives on Social Inclusion: Working Paper Series* (pp. 1–20). Toronto: Laidlaw Foundation, 2002–03.

Friedmann, J. *Empowerment: The Politics of Alternative Development.* Cambridge, MA: Blackwell, 1992.

Galambos, D. *Planning. . . . to Have a Life.* Toronto, ON: Sheridan College, 1995.

Germ, P. A., & S. J. Schleien. Inclusive community leisure services: Responsibilities of key players. *Therapeutic Recreation Journal, 31*(1), 22–37, 1997.

Gillespie, K. A., D. W. Kennedy, & K. Soble. Utilizing importance-performance analysis in the evaluation and marketing of activity programs in geriatric settings. *Activities, Adaptation, & Aging, 13*(1/2), 77–89, 1989.

Godbey, G. C. *The Future of Leisure Services: Thriving on Change.* State College, PA: Venture, 1989.

Gold, D. A look at Leisure Buddy programs. In D. Gold & J. McGill, Eds. *The Pursuit of Leisure.* Toronto, ON: Roeher Institute, 1988, pp. 81–89.

Gold, D. Friendship, leisure, and support: The purpose of "Circles of friends" of young people. *Journal of Leisurability, 26*(3), 10–21, 1999.

Graff, L. L., & J. A. Vedell. Opportunities for all: The potential for supported volunteering in community agencies. *The Journal of Volunteer Administration, 18*(2), 10–16, 2000.

Grenot-Scheyer, M., S. Staub, L. Schwartz, & C. Peck. Reciprocity in friendships. Listening to the voices of children with and without disabilities. In L. H. Meyer, H. S. Park, M. Grenot-Scheyer, I. S. Schwartz, & B. Harry, Eds. *Making Friends: The Influences of Culture and Development.* Baltimore: Paul H. Brookes, 1998, pp. 149–167.

Gronlund, N. E. *Stating Behavioral Objectives for Classroom Instruction.* London: The Macmillan Co., 1970.

Guadagnolo, F. B. The importance-performance analysis: An evaluation and marketing tool. *Journal of Park and Recreation Administration, 2*(1), 4–16, 1985.

Guadagnolo, F. B., G. C. Godbey, D. L. Kerstetter, D. W. Kennedy, P. Farrell, & R. B. Warnick. *An Evaluation of Program Services Offered by Essex County Department of Parks, Recreation, and Cultural Affairs.* Unpublished report, Venture, Inc., State College, PA, 1984.

Haasen, B., T. Hornibrook, & A. Pedlar. Researcher and practitioner perspectives on a research partnership. *Journal of Leisurability, 25*(3), 25–32, 1998.

Hall, M., L. McKeown, K. Roberts. *Caring Canadians, Involved Canadians: Highlights from the 2000 National Survey of Giving, Volunteering, and Participating* (Catalogue No. 71-542-XIE). Ottawa: Ministry of Industry, 2001.

Hamilton, M., & A. Hussain. *America's Teenage Volunteers.* Washington, DC: Independent Sector, 1998.

Harlan-Simmons, J. E., P. Holtz, J. Todd, & M. F. Mooney. Building social relationships through valued roles: Three older adults and the community membership project. *Mental Retardation, 39,* 171–180, 2001.

Heyne, L. A., L. H. McAvoy, & S. J. Schleien. Focus groups . . . bringing people together in therapeutic recreation. *Palaestra, 10*(2), 19–24, 1994.

Heyne, L., S. Schleien, & L. McAvoy. *Making Friends: Using Recreation Activities to Promote Friendship between Children with and without Disabilities.* Minneapolis, MN: Institute on Community Integration, University of Minnesota, 1993.

Hubert, E. *Leisure Interest Inventory.* Master's thesis, University of North Carolina, Chapel Hill, 1969.

Hutchison, P. Work and leisure: Paradoxes and dilemmas for people with developmental disabilities. *Journal on Developmental Disabilities, 3*(1), 1–15, 1994.

Hutchison, P. The evolution of integration research: Celebrating 25 years of the Journal of Leisurability. *Journal of Leisurability. 27*(4), 32–43, 2000.

Hutchison, P., & J. McGill. *Leisure, Integration and Community* (2nd ed.). Toronto, ON: Leisurability, 1998.

Hutchison, P., & G. Nogradi. The concept and nature of community development in recreation and leisure services. *Journal of Applied Recreation Research, 21*(2), 93–130, 1996.

International Center for the Disabled. *The ICD Survey of Disabled Americans: Bringing Disabled Americans into the Mainstream.* New York: Louis Harris and Associates, 1986.

Johnson, D. W., & R. T. Johnson. Integrating handicapped students into the mainstream. *Exceptional Children, 47*(2), 90–92, 1980.

Jones, D. B. Parents' perspectives on recreation programs in Maine for their children with disabilities. *MRPA Today 2*(3), 8–9, 2002.

Kendrick, M. Values: The foundation of evaluation. *Journal of Leisurability, 18*(3), 14–21, 1991.

Kennedy, D. W. Importance-performance analysis in marketing and evaluating therapeutic recreation services. *Therapeutic Recreation Journal, 20*(3), 30–36, 1986.

Kennedy, D. W., & H. M. Lundegren. Application of the discrepancy evaluation model in therapeutic recreation. *Therapeutic Recreation Journal, 15*(1), 24–34, 1981.

Krogh, K. A conceptual framework of community partnerships: Perspectives of people with disabilities on power, beliefs and values. *Canadian Journal of Rehabilitation, 12*(2), 123–134, 1998.

Kruger, R., & M. A. Casey. *Focus Groups: A Practical Guide for Applied Research* (3rd ed.). Newbury Park, CA: Sage, 2000.

Kuyek, J., & R. Labonté. *From Power-Over to Power-With: Transforming Professional Practice.*

Saskatoon, SK: Prairie Region Health Promotion Research Centre, 1995.

Labanowich, S. The psychology of wheelchair sports. *Therapeutic Recreation Journal, 12*(1), 11–77, 1978.

Lee, Y., B. McCormick, & D. Austin. Toward an engagement in social support: A key to community integration in rehabilitation. *World Leisure Journal, 43*(3), 25–30, 2001.

LeFevre, D. *New Games for the Whole Family.* New York: Perigee Books, 1988.

Lord, J. Building genuine partnerships: Potential, principles, and problems. *Journal of Leisurability, 25*(3), 3–10, 1998.

Lord, J., & P. Hutchison. Living with a disability in Canada: Toward autonomy and integration. *Determinants of Health: Settings and Issues.* Papers commissioned by the National Forum on Health. Ottawa: Les Editions MultiMondes, 1998, pp. 375–431.

Lyons, R. Municipal government policy guidelines: Recreation services for persons with a disability. Ottawa: Canadian Parks and Recreation Association, 1991.

Lyons, R. F. Meaningful activity and disability: Capitalizing upon the potential of outreach recreation networks in Canada. *Canadian Journal of Rehabilitation, 6*(4), 256–265, 1993.

Lyons, R. Recreation policy and disability: Where to from here? *Journal of Leisurability, 21*(3), 3–11, 1994.

Lyons, R., M. Sullivan, & P. Ritvo. *Relationships, Chronic Illness and Disability.* Newbury Park, CA: Sage, 1995.

Mager, R. F. *Preparing Instructional Objectives.* Palo Alto, CA: Fearon Publishers, 1962.

Mager, R. F., & P. Pipe. *Analyzing Performance Problems* or *"You Really Oughta Wanna."* Palo Alto, CA: Fearon Publishers, 1970.

Mahon, M., J. Mactavish, & E. Bockstael. Making friends through recreation: Social integration, leisure and individuals with intellectual disability. *Parks and Recreation,* 25–40, April 2000.

McDowell, F., Jr. Toward a healthy leisure mode: Leisure counseling. *Therapeutic Recreation Journal, 8*(3), 96–104, 1974.

McGee, J., F. Menolascino, D. Hobbs, & P. Menousek. *Gentle Teaching: A Non-Aversive Approach to*

Helping Persons with Mental Retardation. New York: Human Sciences Press, 1987.

McGill, J. A retrospective: Twenty-five years of practice in the field of leisure and persons with disabilities. *Journal of Leisurability, 27*(4), 9–31, 2000.

McGill, J. Leisure Connections Facilitator Training Initiative. *Journal of Leisurability, 25*(3), 17–24, 1998.

McGill, J. Training for integration: Are blindfolds really enough? *Journal of Leisurability, 11*(2), 12–15, 1984.

McKechnie, G. E. Psychological foundations of leisure counseling: An empirical strategy. *Therapeutic Recreation Journal, 8*(1), 4–16, 1974.

McKnight, J. *The Careless Society: Community and Its Counterfeits.* New York: Basic Books, 1995.

Meyers, J. H., & M. I. Alpers. Determining attributes: Meaning and measurement. *Journal of Marketing, 32*(4), 13–20, 1968.

Miller, K. D., S. J. Schleien, C. Rider, C. Hall, M. Roche, & J. Worsley. Inclusive volunteering: Benefits to participants and community. *Therapeutic Recreation Journal, 36*(3), 247–259, 2002.

Mirenda, J. *Mirenda Leisure Interest Finder.* Milwaukee, WI: Milwaukee Public Schools, Dept. of Municipal Recreation and Adult Education, 1973.

Moon, M. S., C. L. Stierer, P. J. Brown, D. Hart, C. Komissar, & R. Friedlander. Strategies for successful inclusion in recreation programs. In M. S. Moon, Ed. *Making School and Community Recreation Fun for Everyone: Places and Ways to Integrate.* Baltimore: Brookes Publishing, 1994.

Mount, B. *Capacity Works: Finding Windows for Change Using Personal Futures Planning.* New York, NY: Graphic Futures, 1995.

Nelson, G., J. Ochocka, K. Griffin, & J. Lord. Nothing about me without me: Participatory action research with self-help/mutual aid organizations for psychiatric consumer/survivors. *American Journal of Community Psychology, 26I,* 881–912, 1998.

O'Brien, J., & C. L. O'Brien. *Implementing Person-Centered Planning: Voices of Experience.* Toronto: Inclusion Press. 1998.

O'Brien, J., & J. Pearpoint. *Person-Centered Planning with MAPS and PATH: A Workbook for Facilitators.* Toronto: Inclusion Press, 2002.

O'Connell, M. *Community Building in Logan Square: How a Community Grew Stronger with the*

Contributions of People with Disabilities. Evanston, IL: Center for Urban Affairs and Policy Research, 1990.

Overs, R. P. A model for avocational counseling. *Journal of Health, Physical Education and Recreation, 41*(2), 36–38, 1970.

Park, P. What is participatory research? A theoretical and methodological perspective. In P. Park, M. Brydon-Miller, B. Hall, & T. Jackson, Eds. *Voices of Change.* Westport, CT: Bergain & Garvey, 1993.

Pearpoint, J., & M. Forest. Inclusion! Its about change! [Online]. Available: http://www.inclusion.com, 1999.

Peck, C. A. Linking values and science in social policy decisions affecting citizens with severe disabilities. In L. H. Meyer, C. A. Peck, & L. Brown, Eds. *Critical Issues in the Lives of People with Severe Disabilities.* Baltimore: Paul H. Brookes, 1991, pp. 1–15.

Pedlar, A. Supportive communities: The gap between ideology and social policy. *Environments, 1*(2), 1–7, 1991.

Pedlar, A. Relevance and action research. *Leisure Sciences, 17,* 133–140, 1995.

Pedlar, A. Community development: What does it mean for recreation and leisure. *Journal of Applied Recreation Research, 21I* (1), 5–24, 1996.

Pedlar, A., L. Haworth, P. Hutchison, A. Taylor, & P. Dunn. *A Textured Life: Empowerment and Adults with Developmental Disabilities.* Waterloo, ON: Wilfrid Laurier University Press, 1999.

Pedlar, A., & P. Hutchison. Maximizing participatory processes in leisure research: Moving the social agenda forward. *CCLR 9 Conference on Leisure, Politics and Power: Driving the Social Agenda into the 21st Century.* Wolfville, NS: 1999.

Perrin, B. Community recreation for all: How to include persons with disabilities in regular leisure and recreation. *Journal of Leisurability, 19*(4), 28–36, 1992.

Perrin, B., K. Wiele, S. Wilder, & A. Perrin. *Sharing the Fun: A Guide to Including Persons with Disabilities in Leisure and Recreation.* Toronto: Canadian Rehabilitation Council for the Disabled, 1992.

Peterson, C. A. *State of the Art Activity Analysis. Leisure Activity Participation and Handicapped Populations: Assessment of Research Needs.*

Arlington, VA: National Recreation and Park Association and Bureau of Education for the Handicapped, U.S. Office of Education, April, 1976.

Peterson, C. A., & S. L. Gunn. *Therapeutic Recreation Program Design: Principles and Procedures* (2nd ed.). Englewood Cliffs, NJ: Prentice-Hall, 1984.

Roeher Institute. *Community Development and Social Change: Strategies and Actions for Human Rights and People with Disabilities.* North York, ON: 1997.

Roker, D., K. Player, & J. Coleman. Challenging the image: The involvement of young people with disabilities in volunteering and campaigning. *Disability & Society, 13*(5), 725–741, 1998.

Rynders, J. E., & M. F. Fahnestock. Intervention strategies for inclusive recreation. In S. Schleien, M. T. Ray, & F. P. Green, Eds. *Community Recreation and People with Disabilities: Strategies for Inclusion* (2nd ed.). Baltimore: Paul H. Brookes, 1997, pp. 101–128.

Rynders, J. E., & S. J. Schleien. *Together Successfully.* Arlington, TX: Association for Retarded Citizens of the United States, 1991.

Sable, J. Collaborating to create an integrated camping program: Design and evaluation. *Therapeutic Recreation Journal, 26*(3), 38–48, 1992.

Schleien, S., F. Green, & L. Heyne. Integrated community recreation. In M. Snell Ed. *Instruction of Students with Severe Disabilities* (4th ed.). Columbus, OH: Charles E. Merrill Publishing, 1993, pp. 526–555.

Schleien, S. J. Access and inclusion in community leisure services. *Parks and Recreation, 28*(4), 66–72, 1993.

Schleien, S. J., J. E. Rynders, L. A. Heyne, & C. E. S. Tabourne, Eds. *Powerful Partnerships: Parents and Professionals Building Inclusive Recreation Programs Together.* Minneapolis, MN: University of Minnesota, 1995.

Schleien, S. J., M. T. Ray, & F. P. Green. *Community Recreation and People with Disabilities: Strategies for Inclusion* (2nd ed.). Baltimore: Brookes Publishing, 1997.

Statistics Canada. *A Profile of Disability in Canada.* Ottawa: Human Resources Development Canada, 2001.

Statistics Canada. Retrieved July 9, 2003, from *http://www.statcan.ca/start.html* and http://www.statcan.ca/english/freepub/ 89-577-XIE/Canada.htm

Staub, D. *Delicate Threads: Friendships Between Children With and Without Special Needs in Inclusive Settings.* Bethesda, MD: Woodbine House, 1998.

Swan, J. G., & L. J. Coombs. Product performance and consumer satisfaction: A new concept. *Journal of Marketing, 40*(2), 25–33, 1976.

Sylvester, C. Careers, callings, and the professionalism of therapeutic recreation. *Journal of Leisurability, 25*(2), 3–13, 1998.

Taylor, A., & J. Botschner. *Evaluation Handbook.* Toronto, ON: Ontario Community Support Association, 1998.

Therapeutic Recreation Directory. [Online]. Available: http://www.recreationtherapy.com/, 1999.

Turnbull, A., & H. Turnbull. *Families, Professionals, and Exceptionality: A Special Partnership.* Columbus, OH: Merrill, 1990.

United States Census 2000. US Department of Commerce, Economics and Statistics Administration, U.S. Census Bureau, Washington, DC, 2003.

Van Dreunen, E. Common houses . . . A community strategy for accessing leisure and social support activities. *Journal of Leisurability, 23*(1), 33–41, 1996.

Victorian YMCA *Welcoming Diversity: Access and Inclusion Policy.* Melbourne, VIC: The Association, 2001.

Voeltz, L. M. Children's attitudes toward handicapped peers. *American Journal of Mental Deficiency, 84,* 455–464, 1980.

Walker, P. From community presence to sense of place: Community experiences of adults with developmental disabilities. *Journal of the Association for Persons with Severe Handicaps, 24*(1), 23–32, 1999.

Whyte, W. F., Ed. *Participatory Action Research.* Thousand Oaks, CA: Sage Publications, 1991.

Wieck, C., & J. Strully. What's wrong with the continuum? A metaphorical analysis. In L. Meyer, C. Peck, & L. Brown, Eds. *Critical Issues in the Lives of People with Severe Disabilities.* Baltimore, MD: Paul H. Brookes, 1991, pp. 229–234.

Zoerink, D. A., & E. J. Rosegard. Social justice through inclusive leisure services. In D. M. Compton, Ed. *Issues in Therapeutic Recreation: Toward the New Millennium* (2nd ed.). Champaign, IL: Sagamore Publishing, 1997, pp. 17–37.

8 SELECTIVE EXAMPLES OF COMMUNITY SERVICES

(Courtesy of *Sports 'n Spokes*/Paralyzed Veterans of America)

The American Park & Recreation Society (APRS) and the National Therapeutic Recreation Society (NTRS), two branches of the National Recreation and Park Association (NRPA), surveyed 221 parks and recreation agencies in 1996 to determine:

1. to what degree recreation *inclusion* is happening;
2. what problems have been found in implementing inclusion;
3. what training needs have been identified; and
4. which organizations should provide training or technical assistance.

Some highlights of findings include:

- In describing their program and service opportunities, the most frequent response was that people with disabilities were permitted to register for any program they choose and participate alongside people without disabilities.
- In describing the response from people with disabilities to inclusive recreation programs, the most frequent response was that a small number of people with disabilities have requested registration in programs with people without disabilities.
- In describing the organization's approach to funding inclusive recreation programs, the most frequent response was that there was no change to the existing funding policy.
- In describing the response by the community to the inclusion of people with disabilities into general recreation programs, it was viewed as positive. (APRS & NTRS, 1997)

The results of this study indicate that the road to inclusion is a slow process. If a small number of people with disabilities show an interest in registering in inclusive programs, we must look at what we are doing as recreationists. Have people been so segregated that this is all they know? Are we as professionals encouraging segregation by the number of special programs we still offer? If individual supports for integration are not provided, then people may feel more comfortable choosing a special program. And why do we need to stigmatize community-based services by referring to them as "therapeutic" or "special," as you will see from some of the examples that follow, when those very services claim to be promoting inclusion or compliance with the ADA? Ultimately, we are searching for "best practices" (Wolf-Klitzing, 2002).

This chapter presents eight examples of community services for individuals who have disabilities. They represent a variety of services and structures. They were chosen from different states and provinces across the United States and Canada. It is hoped that by learning what kinds of programs and services exist in different areas, readers will be better prepared to organize their own services and programs.

CINCINNATI RECREATION COMMISSION, DIVISION OF THERAPEUTIC RECREATION*

Introduction and Background

In 1968, the Cincinnati Recreation Commission (CRC) established the Division of Therapeutic Recreation to offer a variety of community recreation programs to children, teens, and adults with disabilities. Concern for meeting the individual needs of program participants prompted the development of a program skill level continuum. This continuum consisted of four levels ranging from programs for persons with disabilities who required one-to-one contact to those that focused on independent integration. The Division of Therapeutic Recreation has developed a more inclusionary approach and has hired *"inclusion specialists,"* who have therapeutic recreation as well as general recreation backgrounds.

Philosophy and Guiding Principles

In their program materials, CRC describes their philosophy on recreation for people with disabilities

---

*Information about the Cincinnati Recreation Commission, Division of Therapeutic Recreation program was obtained from program materials.

as follows: Participating in recreation activities is an important part of everyone's life. The benefits of participating are many, including fitness, socialization, self-expression, and personal enjoyment. Historically, individuals with disabilities have had fewer opportunities to participate in community recreation programs. The programs available were typically "special" programs that tended to segregate and limit opportunities for individual choice.

If individuals with disabilities are to become valued members of society, they must have access to the same community experiences as their peers without disabilities. Through participation in community recreation programs, individuals with disabilities have the opportunity to develop friendships and age-appropriate skills. Inclusive programs benefit everyone. In addition to the benefits to those with disabilities, inclusive programs help everyone to become more sensitive to individual differences. It is hoped that this awareness and sensitivity to individual differences will lead to attitudes of acceptance that carryover to all areas of life. The goals of the CRC program are to assist individuals with disabilities in personal growth, to contribute to the quality of life, and to enhance a leisure lifestyle.

Programs and Services

An important aspect of the strategic plan of the CRC program for individuals with disabilities is the expansion of citizen inclusiveness. It is advocated that all participants are listened to and to include as many people as possible in CRC issues that affect them. Other points include implementing a public relations effort to inform and educate citizens about CRC issues, create opportunities for dialogue on public issues related to CRC programs and services, develop tools for shared decision making, and work closely with program and center-based advisory councils on the planning, implementation, and evaluation of programs and services.

The Cincinnati program guides identify recreation and leisure activities that have been developed

with the intention of providing something of interest to everyone. While some programs can accommodate participants of varying levels of ability, other programs have specific skill requirements because of the nature of the activities. Programs designed specifically for participants with physical disabilities (mobility impairments, wheelchair users, etc.) have a wheelchair symbol within the program guide listings.

The following are a few examples of program offerings: *Adapted Bowling, Climbing Club, Lakers Basketball, Wheelchair Sports Club, Sit Aerobics and Weight Training, Dolan Method Instructional Swim, Friday Night Socials, Outdoor Adventures,* and *WOW (Winners on Wheels).* The Cincinnati Recreation Commission has been active in wheelchair sports over the years and publishes a Wheelchair Sports Newsletter for the greater Cincinnati area.

CITY OF MIAMI DEPARTMENT OF RECREATION, PROGRAMS FOR PERSONS WITH DISABILITIES*

Introduction and Background

With the thought that it is the responsibility of municipal government to provide services to citizens who are disabled, the City of Miami has developed a comprehensive system to serve persons with disabilities. Programs for Persons with Disabilities was formed in 1973.

The City of Miami has been a national leader in obtaining funding from outside sources to support special recreation services. Monies were obtained, for example, from the U.S. Department of Education Office of Special Education and Rehabilitation Services for Project STAR (Staff Training for Adapted Recreation). The purpose of Project STAR was to develop an in-service training model to be used by public park and recreation departments to prepare their staff to include citizens

*Information in this section was taken from materials furnished by the City of Miami, Department of Recreation, Programs for Persons with Disabilities.

with disabilities as participants in their programs. City of Miami recreation staff members were able to benefit from training provided through Project STAR.

Another example of a project funded by an outside source was Project CARE (Continuum of Adapted Recreation Education). Project CARE was designed to address leisure education needs of citizens with disabilities who live in the greater Miami area. This project, too, was funded by a grant from the U.S. Department of Education Office of Special Education and Rehabilitation Services.

Philosophy and Guiding Principles

Project CARE was based on a full-spectrum participation philosophy. According to this philo-sophical position, no member of society, including the estimated 60,000 citizens with disabilities residing in Miami, should be denied the right to participate in and benefit from a full range of leisure education experiences. Monitoring the city's compliance with the Rehabilitation Act of 1973, as amended by the ADA, and other state, federal, and local legislation that impacts the city's services and coordinating city services that relate to the community's people with special needs is important, as is co-ordinating city services that re-late to the community's people with special needs.

Programs and Services

The following are five types of services provided by the Programs for Persons with Disabilities:

1. *Barrier-Free Design*—Assist with the development of plans for the removal of architectural barriers from the community's park and governmental facilities. Acquire funds to complete this work.
2. *Leisure Services*—Provision of leisure services and special events to citizens with disabilities who are not able to become involved in programs with the general population.
3. *Work-Oriented Activity Center*—Activities in self-help skills, prevocational aptitude, academics, and supported employment to improve the independence of previously institutionalized citizens and those living at home or in sheltered living arrangements.
4. *Community Relations*—Information source for community members in areas related to various groups with special needs.
5. *Training for Adapted Recreation*—The in-service training of general recreation staff to recognize the attitudinal and architectural barriers that prohibit the delivery of equal services to persons with disabilities in a recreational setting.

The City of Miami developed a continuum flow pattern for appropriate placement in leisure and education programs. The level of advance-ment begins with the Leisure on Wheels program in the homes of individuals who are homebound. Leisure on Wheels focuses on participants who are not in an organized program because of behavioral problems or functional level. This homebound program serves the individual for two hours per day, two days per week. A parent or guardian of the homebound individual is encouraged to become involved with the program on a regular basis.

The next phase of the flow pattern is the Tran-sitional Training Program. This segment is de-signed to transfer the homebound participant into a more involved community skills program designed to expand the participant's successful inclusion into the general community. The final phase in the flow pattern, prior to total integration into the main-stream of the community, is the general recreation program offered by Programs for Persons with Dis-abilities. Components of this program include, but are not limited to, activities such as creative arts, sports and fitness, outdoor education, aquatics, and special events.

As can be readily surmised, the City of Miami Programs for Persons with Disabilities has many thrusts. The primary focus, however, remains that of providing citizens with special needs in the Miami area with equal access to recreation services.

NORTHERN SUBURBAN SPECIAL RECREATION ASSOCIATION COOPERATIVE OF THE PARK DISTRICTS*

Introduction and Background

The Northern Suburban Special Recreation Association (NSSRA) in Illinois was formed in 1970 as the first special recreation association in the country. This partnership was created when neighboring small park districts, serving from 3,000 to 40,000 residents, recognized that if they joined together they could eliminate duplicative supervisory cost while retaining more resources for programs. Over the years, NSSRA has been the model for laws that allow park districts and cities to join efforts to provide leisure services for people with disabilities. Today, Illinois has 26 special recreation associations made up of 142 park districts and 24 municipalities, serving a gross population of 221,000. The association has grown from serving a few children with mental retardation in its early years, to serving more than 4,000 registrants with disabilities annually.

Funding for NSSRA programs comes from property taxes received by the partner park districts and municipalities, program fees, and donations from private sources. For the owner of a $500,000 home in the NSSRA communities, the annual property tax cost averages $9.

Philosophy and Guiding Principles

Whether a participant wants to join one of the specially designed programs, recreate in a park district or recreation department program with people who do not have a disability, or partake in a leisure activity directly in his or her home, NSSRA provides assistance. Inclusion is a key element of the NSSRA program. Inclusion looks at the needs, interests, and abilities of people instead of focusing on their disabilities. Inclusion supports the

*Information in this section was taken from materials furnished by the Northern Suburban Special Recreation Association (NSSRA).

process of preparing, learning, experiencing, and growing with each person, each family, and each recreation staff. NSSRA supports personal growth and achievement through recreation, friendship, relaxation, and fun.

Programs and Services

To include people with disabilities in their local park district or city recreation centers, NSSRA provides support in the form of extra staff, sign language interpreters, adapted rules and policies, behavior management support, disability awareness training, and other important services. The key to the success of NSSRA programs is the quality of its staff. Professionals well-prepared in recreation and disability issues are the planners and managers at NSSRA. These critical people are the link to the participants and their families. Certified Therapeutic Recreation Specialists with a background in community recreation are preferred. Almost 80 percent of NSSRA programs are directly supervised by a full-time therapeutic recreation specialist. NSSRA has 14 full-time employees, 10 of whom are therapeutic recreators. This is one of the key benefits to the partnership. No single NSSRA community, ranging in size from 3,000 to 50,000 could hire 10 therapeutic recreators. But in the partnership that is NSSRA, each has the benefit of 10 therapeutic recreators.

NSSRA provides year-round recreation programs for the residents of its 12-partner communities who have any type of disability. Programs include cultural, sport, social, physical, outdoor, and special event activities. These programs offer the same type of experiences available for people without disabilities in the park district or reception department setting.

Over 300 programs are offered throughout the year. These programs are planned and conducted by full-time staff trained in recreation for people with disabilities. Programs include extensive involvement in Special Olympics, after school activities for children, evening programs for adults, weekend programs for all ages, special events, extended trips, and social activities.

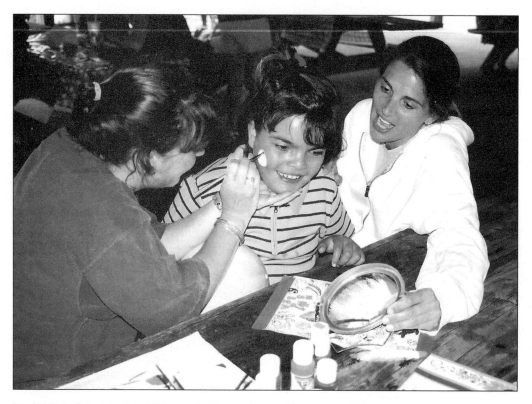

The Northern Suburban Special Recreation Association provides extra staff and other support services to facilitate inclusion in their park district and city recreation centers.
(Courtesy of Northern Suburban Special Recreation Association)

RCH, INC., SAN FRANCISCO, CALIFORNIA*

Introduction and Background

RCH, Inc., (formerly Recreation Center for the Handicapped, Inc.) established in 1952 by Janet Pomeroy, is recognized nationally and internationally as a pioneer program and a model in developing community recreation for persons with disabilities. The center was founded with private funds in one room of an old pool building owned by the San Francisco Recreation and Park Department, with six teenagers with physical disabilities enrolled and with only volunteer help. When the center moved

*Information in this section was taken from materials furnished by RCH, Inc.

into a newly constructed facility in 1973, enrollment had increased to 650 children, teens, and adults with a wide range of disabilities, served by a paid professional staff of 80 and a corps of 120 volunteers. Today the center is a major provider of services to persons with disabilities in the City and County of San Francisco, with an enrollment of more than 2,000 community residents of all ages with 77 types of disabling conditions and nearly 200 professional staff with 350 volunteers.

A large proportion of the operating budget is raised annually by the board of directors through personal solicitation of individuals, service clubs, and groups; by letter solicitation of individuals; and by working with groups who conduct benefits for the center. Fund-raising events such as horse shows, luncheons, and bazaars are conducted annually by these groups. Parents of participants and some persons with disabilities assist the board in all fund-raising events. For example, one major contribution made by parents is a yearly donation of a bus as a result of fund-raising activities.

Philosophy and Guiding Principles

From the beginning, the center has changed and evolved to keep pace with changing conditions and community needs. The center is a community-based facility that serves individuals of all ages and disabilities. The mission statement of RCH, Inc. is "To open door of opportunity for children and adults with disabilities through programs and services in therapeutic recreation, vocational rehabilitation and education, child and adult development, respite care and transportation."

Programs and Services

In 1970, the center initiated an Outreach Program to serve the needs of children, teens, and adults who could not participate in programs at the center. Social recreation programs are offered to persons in their own homes, in board and care homes for individuals with mental retardation, and in residential care homes. These include "travel groups" designed to integrate groups into the community and "Project 1:1," which provides volunteers on a 1:1 basis for those who are homebound. The center's "Playtime" program offers services to children with chronic and terminal illnesses in home and hospital settings.

The center is located on 5 1/2 wooded acres adjacent to a lake, near the ocean and the San Francisco Zoo. Accessible facilities include a large main hall and stage that is home to "Theatre Unlimited," the center's famous mainstreamed theater company. Related facilities include a full-service kitchen, arts-and-crafts-room, and four multipurpose rooms. The center also has an indoor therapeutic swimming pool heated to 95° and measuring 25 ft. × 75 ft., as well as a full-size gymnasium and wooded day camp area. The center uses a variety of community facilities, including a YMCA

Camp in the Santa Cruz Mountains, which plays host to the center's Residential Camp Program for children and adults. Their Outdoor Environmental Education Program also uses such natural resources as national parks and forests for senior retreats and adventure trips.

Primary day, evening, and weekend programs are offered through five departments providing direct service to center participants. Those departments include Adult Development, Children and Teens, Community Leisure Training, Leisure/Outreach, and Adult Behavior. Support services are provided by Aquatics/PE, Social Services, and Transportation. The center owns and operates 26 vehicles, including lift vans providing services to more than 300 participants on a regular basis. Department programs include such therapeutic recreation activities as nutrition education, music, and sports and games adapted for participants of all ages and abilities.

Their new Children's Annex, dedicated in April, 1989, provides preschool, infant, and respite-care programs. The preschool program serves children ages 3 to 5 in a mainstreamed setting, with infant care for those with special needs. The respite-care program offers 24-hour services in four beautifully designed respite-care rooms. The annex was built through the charitable contributions of several foundations and individuals who were interested in helping the Center achieve its goal of "meeting the needs of the community."

RCH, Inc., has many unique programs that have not been discussed. One such program, Theatre Unlimited, is discussed in considerable detail in chapter 10. Also, the center has been dynamic and progressive throughout the years. As Janet Pomeroy indicates in the 45th anniversary report,

> Opening Doors of Opportunity—the theme of the 45th Anniversary Report—is dedicated to the individuals *empowered* by the Center since 1952 to safely and successfully live, work, and enjoy full *inclusion* in the community. These participants and their families continue to shape our future through determination, enthusiasm, courage and love. (Anniversary Report, 1997) [emphasis added]

ACTIVE LIVING ALLIANCE FOR CANADIANS WITH A DISABILITY*

Introduction and Background

It was in 1986, at the Jasper Talks—a national symposium on physical activity and disability—that people involved in disability and fitness issues asserted that physical activity must be an integral part of the daily lives of Canadians with disabilities. A focal point for the active living movement in Canada is the Active Living Alliance for Canadians with a Disability. It is an alliance of individuals, agencies, and national associations that facilitates and coordinates partnerships among the members of its network. Any organization, community, or individual who embraces their principles and goals is welcome to join the Alliance network. The network has grown to more than 500,000 contacts.

Philosophy and Guiding Principles

The *vision* of the Active Living Alliance for Canadians with a Disability is a society where all Canadians lead active and healthy lives, including Canadians with disabilities. Central to each goal is the belief that the individual must be considered first when developing any program or service, and that the rights and dignity of the individual must always be respected.

Goal 1: To facilitate the growth of self-empowerment through awareness, education, and support. Often, Canadians with disabilities are not aware of programs and services that are available to them. With encouragement, support, and opportunities to accept more responsibility, people with disabilities can be empowered to set personal goals, to control everyday events, and to choose and maintain an active way of living.

Goal 2: To develop quality networks and delivery systems with clearly defined roles, responsibilities, and communication links at all levels. There is a lack of coordinated effort among organizations developing physical activity programs and services, so the program delivery systems tend to be fragmented and disjointed.

Goal 3: To enhance organizational planning and policy development by providing resources and support mechanisms. Organizations need to examine their plans and policies to ensure that participation opportunities for all Canadians are an integral part of every program, service, or policy being developed.

Goal 4: To identify, develop, and promote effective programs and services at the national, provincial, and local levels. Many inactive Canadians with disabilities say they do not participate in physical activities because they are physically unable to do so. People with disabilities also cite fear of injury and lack of skills as barriers to increased activity substantially more often than those without disabilities. These barriers sometimes result from traditional interpretations of fitness, which placed more emphasis on structured or athletically challenging activities such as organized sports, aerobics, or running.

Goal 5: To develop and promote leadership by providing programs and support. Canadians with disabilities can be more effectively served by a thoughtful leadership system that recognizes them as leaders, promotes coordination among existing agencies, and develops new leadership programs that realize the many roles leaders play in facilitating physical activity.

Goal 6: To develop public awareness through promotional strategies involving community action and public education. Too frequently, service and program providers who want to accommodate access requests by people with disabilities lack the information that can enable them to do so. We need effective campaigns on the rights, needs, and interests of Canadians with disabilities.

Goal 7: To identify, promote, and support research priorities and to disseminate state-of-the-art

*Information about Active Living Alliance for Canadians with a Disability in this section came from the website www.ala.ca

Note: For your information, a comparable organization can be found in the United States called the National Centre on Physical Activity and Disability; contact www.ncpad.org

information. Ensuring that active living opportunities are available, accessible, and inclusive for Canadians with disabilities requires a strong knowledge base. Because it is through research that such a knowledge base is developed and maintained, it is essential to continue to support and encourage a wide spectrum of research initiatives and develop a better way to distribute existing research findings.

Programs and Services

- *Activate Yourself.* Finding the opportunities, equipment, and even motivation to become involved in physical activities can be a challenge. Here, Canadians with a disability can learn about others who have addressed the challenges of getting and staying active and about how they can do the same.
- *Health Matters.* Health professionals have an enormous impact on the lives of Canadians with disabilities. Here are a few tools to help them continue to positively influence their patients and clients to be active—because health does matter!
- *Active Youth.* Kids are active—naturally! Sometimes grown-ups need a little more knowledge and support to make sure that youth with disabilities are active too. In this section are information and resources to help include everyone in all active living situations— physical education classes, community recreation programs, and anywhere else we may find active youth!
- *Community Leaders.* All across Canada, there are some great ideas being implemented by those leaders in the community who are responsible for facilitating active leisure, recreation, and sport opportunities for the entire community, regardless of a person's ability. This section will provide those with a stake in program provision with strategies, resources, contacts, and insight to help make inclusive programs a reality.

REACH FOR THE RAINBOW*

Introduction and Background

Reach for the Rainbow is a registered charity serving children and young adults with a range of support requirements, including those with complex and challenging needs, from across Ontario. In 1987, Reach for the Rainbow introduced integrated summer camps to Ontario. Rather than design a whole new system of camps, Reach for the Rainbow worked to support established camps to provide integrated opportunities for children with disabilities. In 1987, Reach for the Rainbow partnered with one camp and integrated 20 campers with disabilities. The 2003 camping season saw an estimated 600 participants attending 50 integrated camps with 1:1 support.

Philosophy and Guiding Principles

The vision of Reach for the Rainbow is a world where *all* children belong, are equal in their right to fully participate in activities within the community, and have the opportunity to do so in the company of their peers. This goal is achieved through the provision of integrated programming, training, and active resource support to camp personnel and recreational staff at participating regular camps. Administered under the auspices of *Project Rainbow,* the program wing of the agency, programs provide an opportunity for children and youth with physical and/or developmental disabilities living at home to participate in integrated summer camps and community programs.

Programs and Services

Project Rainbow works within existing recreational programs in the community and with selected summer camps across the province to

---

*Information about Reach for the Rainbow in this section came from the website www.reach.on.ca/who.htm and www.reach.on.ca/partnersinintegration.htm. Recently, a qualitative study examining the inclusion process at a residential camp affiliated with Project Rainbow was completed (Mecke, 2003).

provide integrated opportunities for children and youth with disabilities.

- *Partners in Integration.* Summer camps throughout Ontario choose to form partnerships with Project Rainbow to foster successful integrated experiences. Working with Project Rainbow provides camps with coordination of participants; training opportunities for all levels of camp staff; camper profiles; consultative resource visits to each camp to build relationships with staff and provide strategies to overcome challenges; 24-hour on-call pager service; and reimbursement for 1:1 counselor salaries.
- *Referral Sources.* Associations for Community Living, Autism Societies, Children's Aid Societies, Day Cares, Down Syndrome Associations, Extend-a-Family, Geneva Centre, Hospital for Sick Children, Integration Action Group, Jewish Family Support Services, MCSS, ODSP, Parent Referrals, Rehabilitation Centers, School Boards.
- *Program Options.* Project Rainbow achieves its mandate through partnerships with existing summer camps and other recreational community programs. In terms of residential summer camps, there are locations across Ontario for campers age 7 and up; one- and two-week sessions are available; and the camps have a variety of outdoor activities like swimming, canoeing, arts and crafts, camping, and out-trips. For the summer day camps, there are campers age 6 through 13; junior camps for ages 3 to 5 in some areas; and one- and two-week sessions with a variety of programs such as sports, aquatics, and outdoor adventure. Finally, year-round services include integrated recreational opportunities at selected community centers, sports programs, and YMCAs in the Greater Toronto Area.
- *1:1 Support.* Partnering camps and recreational programs hire the 1:1 staff that forms the backbone of the program. The role of these staff is tailored to meet the unique needs of each participant. These counselors facilitate safety and supervision, independence

and increased self-reliance, enriched skill development, positive peer interactions, and full participation in programs.
- *Loan Cupboard.* Adapted equipment is available to participating camps and affiliate programs. All-terrain wheelchairs (Terra-Treks and joggers) make sandy or rugged areas more accessible to individuals with physical disabilities. Camp Resource Visits include an opportunity for partners in integration to use cooperative games and adapted craft supplies from program boxes. These make for activities that everyone can get involved in!
- *Volunteers with Support.* Project Rainbow offers volunteer positions in various camp staff roles for individuals with disabilities who have grown beyond camper age. These volunteers attend camp with 1:1 support in age-appropriate roles and form part of the staff team. Roles include kitchen assistance, land/maintenance workers, and activity assistants. Spaces are limited for registrants over the age of 16, with priority given to returning participants who reside at home.
- *Training Opportunities.* A well-trained staff is instrumental in providing children and youth with successful integrated experiences. Project Rainbow offers the Annual Project Rainbow Conference, coordinator training, pre-camp training (on-site), director training, and Gift of Belonging summer workshops designed for Leaders in Training. Project Rainbow also partners with the Ontario Camp Leadership Workshop and the Ontario Camping Association Counselor Day training events.

RECREATION INTEGRATION VICTORIA*

Introduction and Background

Recreation Integration Victoria (RIV), located in British Columbia, is a unique partnership between

*Information in this section was taken from materials furnished by Recreation Integration Victoria and from the website http://www. islandnet.com/--riv.

Integrated Recreation Services and the Victoria Integration Society. Their vision is for all people to have equal opportunities to participate in community activities.

Integrated Recreation Services is designed to assist people with disabilities in the Greater Victoria area to pursue active lifestyles. Active living is more than living actively. Active living contributes to the social, mental, and emotional well-being of persons with disabilities. Integrated Recreation Services is funded by the Municipalities of Oak Bay, Esquimalt, Saanich, Victoria, and the Peninsula Recreation Commission.

The Victoria Integration Society has been incorporated since September 1983, and provides recreation services to people with physical, mental, and/or neurosensory disabilities. The Society's continued advocacy for recreation integration opportunities has resulted in improved access to programs, facilities, and services in the area. The partnership with Integrated Recreation Services is an example of the ongoing commitment to participation in inclusive community recreation and leisure participation. The Victoria Integrated Society is funded by the Ministry of Children and Families, Human Resources Development Canada, and private donations.

Philosophy and Guiding Principles

Recreation Integration Victoria provides services that facilitate inclusive recreation and leisure opportunities for people with disabilities. As an affiliate partner of the Active Living Alliance for Canadians Living with a Disability, RIV has adopted the following principles:

Principle 1 Quality of life is a fundamental right. Active living is an important and essential component in the quality of life of *all* people, and quality of life is among the fundamental rights of Canadians. Active living increases overall well-being by providing physical, intellectual, emotional, social and spiritual benefits. Active living allows all of us to carry out activities of daily

living with less fatigue and frustration, greater safety and more self-confidence.

Principle 2 Empowerment is the key. The empowered individual is the core of any successful program or service. As society's awareness of people with disabilities has increased, so has the realization of the importance of self-determination—the opportunity to take charge of one's life. People with disabilities have a right to be involved in planning programs, choosing activities of interest, and initiating change when required. Self-empowerment does not mean, however, that individuals are left to act on their own. We live in a society that aims to promote interdependence, where people collaborate with others and receive support for acts of self-determination.

Principle 3 Every community should be involved. Programs and services are best delivered at the community level. Since individuals are the core of any successful program or service, it follows that these programs and services should be implemented at the local level. This principle also implies that these community programs and services should be fully accessible to allow for maximum participation.

Principle 4 Equal access must be guaranteed. All individuals should have an equal opportunity to participate in physical activities regardless of age, gender, language, ethnic background, economics or ability. This principle stresses that opportunities to participate in active living should focus on inclusion rather than exclusion; the individual rather than the statistical norm; and current needs and interests rather than historical precedence. There is a need to enhance organizational planning and policy development to be inclusive, and to continue efforts to eliminate discrimination within the system.

Principle 5 Respect and dignity are the foundation. Preserving the respect and

dignity of all individuals is fundamental to
the success of the active living movement.
The principles of dignity of risk, age
appropriateness, personal satisfaction and
freedom of choice are fundamental to
providing programs and services for, by and to
people with disabilities. Participation options
should be available which are personally
challenging and demanding, they should be
geared to the participants' age group, and they
should be varied enough that individuals can
choose from a wide range of activities.

Programs and Services

Recreation Integration Victoria assists people with
disabilities in accessing their recreation and leisure
interests through community-based opportunities.
This is accomplished through four principle
services:

1. *Leisure Planning and Referral.* One-to-one
   assistance to the individual in identifying
   their leisure and recreation interests and
   where they can pursue them in their local
   community.
2. *Leisure Assistance.* One-to-one volunteer
   assistance that facilitates the inclusion of
   people who otherwise would not be able to
   participate in community-based opportunities.
3. *Training and Education.* Opportunities for
   consumers, recreation and parks staff, and
   the general public to learn about Recreation
   Integration, how people with disabilities
   participate, and how to facilitate this
   participation in community recreation and
   leisure services.
4. *Community Partnerships.* Assistance to
   organizations that provide recreation and
   leisure services to people with disabilities.

Recreation Integration Victoria also provides other
programs and services, including the following:

- *Leisure Assistance Pass.* This pass is issued by
  RIV and allows an individual providing leisure
  assistance to a person with a disability
  free admission to all municipal recreation
  facilities and some private sector venues. The
  pass is issued to the person with the disability.
- *Outdoor Explorations.* This program introduces
  people with disabilities to outdoor recreation
  opportunities that are new to them and in many
  cases have not been considered accessible to
  people with disabilities. Outdoor explorations
  have included surfing, kayaking, sailing, hang
  gliding, fishing, and more.
- *Recreation Integration Victoria News. RIV
  News* is a quarterly newsletter that highlights
  upcoming recreation and leisure opportunities
  available in the local communities and provides
  some thought provoking editorials that relate to
  people with disabilities and community
  inclusion.
- *Summer Leisure Assistance Program.* With
  summer placement program funding from
  Human Resources Development Canada, RIV
  facilitates at no cost to the family, the inclusion of
  children and teens with disabilities into summer
  community parks and recreation programs and
  services through the use of trained staff.
- *Leisure Inclusion For Empowerment (LIFE).*
  This is a demonstration project with the
  Ministry for Children and Families, Services
  for Community Living Branch, which is
  piloting a one-to-one leisure education model
  for youths with multiple disabilities.
- *Community Respite Service for Families.* In
  conjunction with the Queen Alexandra Centre
  for Children's Health and the Ministry for
  Children and Families, this ongoing service
  provides trained community respite workers to
  families with children with disabilities and
  allows parents an opportunity for respite while
  the children pursue community recreation and
  leisure activities.
- *Parks and Recreation Staff Training.* RIV
  provides an interactive workshop on recreation
  integration and the role of an inclusion
  facilitator in a community-based program.
  These workshops are conducted throughout the
  Greater Victoria region.

INDIVIDUALIZED FUNDING AND BROKERAGE: IMPERIAL COUNTIES SELF-DETERMINATION PROJECT, SAN DIEGO, CALIFORNIA, AND VELA MICROBOARD ASSOCIATION, BRITISH COLUMBIA

A worldwide paradigm shift is occurring in the disability field toward an emphasis on self-determination. A dominant assumption has been that the best way to provide disability supports is for government to give money to agencies, rather than individuals. The dilemma of agency-directed services is that the disability supports are generally developed by their paid staff, limiting self-determination by individuals with disabilities and input from families (Lord & Hutchison, 2003). In response to these concerns, person-centered planning and individualized funding are emerging (Dowson & Salisbury, 2000; O'Brien, 2001; Stainton, 2000). "The most recent effort to individualize support comes through direct individual funding, with funds being transferred directly to the control of the individual and/or his or her family, so that they may purchase services directly from service providers, as they so choose" (Pedlar, Haworth, Hutchison, Dunn, & Taylor, 1999, p. 21). Many individualized funding programs promote a holistic view of quality of life, looking at employment supports, community living, leisure pursuits, and relationship building (Glover, 1999; Pedlar & Hutchison, 2000; Pedlar et al., 1999). Finally, this innovative approach to meeting the needs of individuals is taking hold in many countries such as England, Australia, the United States, and Canada (Lord & Hutchison, 2003). Two such projects are shared here. Even though it might appear that these examples are outside the bounds of recreation, it is important that recreationists be aware of this trend and begin to think about ways to incorporate these ideas into future planning.

Imperial Counties Self-Determination Project, San Diego, California*

Introduction and Background

The Imperial Counties Self-Determination Project uses individualized funding sponsored by the San Diego Regional Center for the Developmentally Disabled in San Diego. Regional centers were originally started as pilot projects in San Francisco and Los Angeles to assist persons with mental retardation and their families in locating and developing services and programs that provide the maximum opportunity to participate in everyday living experiences that permit development to the highest potential.

Philosophy and Guiding Principles

- *Choice:* Individuals have the right to choose how they will live their lives, where, and with whom. When they need help, it is friends and family closest to them who assist in broadening their experiences and exercising their right to choose. It is essential that each person have a circle of support chosen by them and that they have options in their lives.
- *Contribution and Community:* Everyone has the ability to contribute to his or her community in a meaningful way. The giving of self helps people establish a sense of belonging and identity. Community membership and full citizenship include having an opportunity to be employed, to live in a home of one's own, to be truly involved in community life, and to make a difference in the lives of others.
- *Responsibilities:* Individuals, as they take greater control and authority over their lives and resources, assume greater responsibility for their decisions and actions. They can be

*Information about the Self-Determination Project came from the website www.sdrc.org and the video "MY LIFE . . . MY WAY" SELF DETERMINATION.

PILOT PROJECT, Mosaic Connections, 1-866-461-2760.

assisted in creating more meaningful relationships by linking them with needed supports, removing barriers, developing safety networks, and ensuring that dreams come true.

- *Fiscal Responsibility:* Making things happen does not always require money. Alternatives to paid support should always be considered. When support must be purchased, individuals will get what they need, pay only for what they get, make real investments, spend money wisely, and make adjustments when they are needed. To find the best quality for the most reasonable price, people are free to purchase in and out of the "system."

- *Relationships:* The relationships a person has with others are like precious gems. A relationship must be reassured, nurtured, and protected. Those with whom the individual has real relationships provide the strength, assistance, and security that ensure each person's well-being.

- *Control:* Individuals have the power to make decisions and truly control their own lives. This includes gaining authority over financial resources and determining what supports are needed, how they will be implemented, and by whom. Individuals control the hiring of those who provide support.

- *Dreaming:* All persons have hopes and dreams that guide the actions they take and are most meaningful to them. A commitment to helping individuals determine their dreams, respecting those dreams, and helping to make their dreams come true is essential.

- *Dignity and Respect:* Every person has an inherent right to be treated with dignity and to be respected as a whole person. Some of life's greatest lessons are learned by making choices that are later realized to have been mistakes. All people have the right to the dignity of risk. A network of support makes risk possible by weaving a safety net that supports growth.

- *Whatever It Takes:* Those who work in the system become barrier removers. The attitude "nothing is impossible" is required. "No, we can't" as an answer is replaced by "How can we make this happen?" Clear, simple, streamlined solutions will be sought.

Programs and Services

Self-determination is not a program, a mechanism, or a new technology. It is not a new way of "doing business." Self-determination is both a concept and an end goal. If you are motivated by a desire to enable people with disabilities to reach their full potential, enjoy a better quality of life, receive fair and equal treatment, and be treated with dignity and respect, then you have already begun to embrace the underpinnings of self-determination. Self-determination begins with individuals—individuals who express an interest in defining for themselves how they will participate in their community, how they will form friendships and with whom, and how they will spend their day and what they will choose to learn.

Individualized funding is a separate, but critically related, concept. Individualized funding simply means enabling individuals to make the decisions about funds available to them, to establish their own budget, and to support their chosen lifestyle. The idea of supporting people with disabilities to become more self-determined through the use of individualized funding first took shape in British Columbia in the mid-1970s. On January 1, 1999, Senate Bill 1038 authorized a three-year pilot of self-determination projects in California. The Self-Determination Project represents the diversity of individuals receiving services from the San Diego Regional Center. Participation in the project is voluntary.

Participants have the option if they so desire to use a *service broker* for the design and development of the Self-Determination Plan and a *fiscal intermediary* to handle the money involved in implementing a plan. If the consumer/family desires to use a service broker, they select one from a list of six brokers. The service broker meets with the consumer/family getting to know their wants, needs, and dreams. Together they design and develop a Self-Determination Plan and accompanying budget. The service broker researches community resources and identifies those appropriate for the plan. Once the plan has been written, it is submitted to the San Diego Regional Center for review and approval. The consumer/family can amend the plan and budget as they identify new needs and dreams.

Individualized Funding and Microboards, British Columbia*

Introduction and Background

In the mid-1970s, direct or individualized funding was mandated by the legislature in British Columbia. The Community Brokerage Services Society and microboards have emerged as a result. In 1989, a nonprofit organization in British Columbia named the Vela Housing Society, which had been offering subsidized housing to people with developmental challenges, started a pilot project with three microboards (Vela Microboard Association, 2000). Responsibility for microboards originally fell to the Ministry of Health, but has since shifted to the Ministry of Social Services. Under the provincial Society Act, a minimum of five people may form a nonprofit society or microboard. These boards consist of a small group of individuals (family and friends) who work together to address the support needs of a person with challenges. Vela facilitators also help to link up individuals who are not involved with family and friends with others who would be interested in participating in a microboard. Microboards have the option of overseeing any hiring needed in the provision of support services, and Vela provides support to the microboard for this employer role. Microboards are able to access funding because they are registered societies similar to the Associations for Community Living (Vela Microboard Association, 2000).

There are now over 150 microboards in British Columbia. A recent study of support services across Canada published in the book *A Textured Life* affirms the uniqueness of British

Columbia compared to other provinces (Pedlar et al., 1999). A survey was sent to provincial government ministries responsible for services to adults with developmental disabilities and to provincial Associations for Community Living. The results indicated that agencies serving 10 or fewer individuals, which included microboards, were numerous in British Columbia (n = 126) compared to all other provinces (e.g., Manitoba n = 17; Ontario n = 10; Nova Scotia n = 7). More importantly, this book shows how family, home, work, leisure, and relationship outcomes for people receiving support through the microboard approach differ from more traditional models.

Philosophy and Guiding Principles

Microboards are for people with "challenges" and their friends and families, including those who are unable to self-direct their support services (Vela Microboard Association, 2000). Microboards are grounded in a belief that empowerment is only possible when there is a shift in the power relationships between the person with a disability/family, the community, and social and political spheres (Pedlar et al., 1999). The primary focus of microboards is to provide support for an individual and a mechanism for individualized funding. The Community Brokerage Service Society, through service brokers or planners, offers unencumbered planning supports as well as assistance with negotiating individualized funding. Vela's guiding principles include:

- Microboard members must have a personal relationship with the person.
- All people are assumed to have the capacity for self-determination.
- All services developed or contracted are based on the person's needs, not availability of services.
- Staff who work with a person through their microboard are not attached to the buildings in which the person lives, works, volunteers, or recreates. They work for the person, not an agency or business. (Vela Microboard Association, 2000)

---

*Information about the microboards in British Columbia came from Lord, Zupko, and Hutchison (2000).

Programs and Services

A microboard, with support from Vela, develops a plan and a proposal for funding. The proposal is then approved by the Ministry of Social Services (Vela Microboard Association, 2000). What is most important here is that funding goes directly to the person and the microboard, not an agency like other types of funding. In addition to planning and informal support, the microboard has the fiscal resources to obtain any needed formal supports and services (Pedlar et al., 1999). Not unlike any other service, the microboard must comply with government regulations around bylaws and constitution, budgeting, employment forms, bookkeeping, banking, Workmen's Compensation, and an annual general meeting. Keeping microboard planning separate from direct services is important in British Columbia. There are several ways this happens (Vela Microboard Association, 2000). First, microboards have the mandate to do their own planning and support separate from Vela or anyone else. Second, Vela formed a separate Vela Microboard Association. Third, individuals with disabilities/families have assistance from independent brokers.

Individual microboards cannot operate without support. In British Columbia, that support primarily comes from the Vela Microboard Association. Vela provides an annual microboard conference, enables members to stay connected through the microboard webpage, provides support and technical assistance to microboards, and, if requested, continues to provide facilitator support as long as needed.

Microboards facilitate a wide variety of community experiences in order to ensure the person has the best quality of life possible including social, recreational, educational, and employment opportunities. Sometimes, those opportunities are readily available in the community and the microboard easily accesses them; other times, the microboard may decide that the opportunities needed are not available and they need to provide direct service. They then hire staff and become employers. Microboards provide people with more choice, stronger connections with the community, stronger relationships, the chance to live out their dreams, the technical supports they require, greater flexibility and creativity in providing support, and the option of hiring their own staff. "Individualized funding *along with* a microboard service model seemed most promising in terms of fostering empowerment-in-community and the realization of texture in people's lives. We doubt that either one of these approaches . . . would function particularly well without the other" (Pedlar et al., 1999, p. 124).

SUMMARY

By briefly reviewing different examples of recreation services, it should be apparent that similarities and differences exist between programs. For example, philosophically all programs tend to aim toward integrating individuals with disabilities into the mainstream. Yet, some programs offer fewer segregated activities than others or none at all. The emphasis on therapeutic effects also tends to vary from program to program. While some programs focus almost exclusively on the recreative experience, others give more emphasis to therapeutic benefits, and more programs stress inclusion. Interagency cooperation was specifically illustrated in most program descriptions. Such cooperation is important to the success of community recreation services.

Programs like the ones discussed in this chapter have set the tone for new and improved programs and services for the new millennium. For individuals who desire further information, the addresses for the services referenced in this chapter are as follows:

- Cincinnati Recreation Commission
  Division of Therapeutic Recreation
  2 Centennial Plaza Suite 800
  Cincinnati, OH 45202
  Phone: (513) 352-4028
  Website: www.cincyrec.org
- City of Miami
  Programs for People with Disabilities
  Department of Leisure Services
  2600 South Bayshore Drive

Miami, FL 33133
Phone: (305) 461-7201
Website: www.ci.miami.fl.us

- Northern Suburban Special
Recreation Association
7 Happ Road
P.O. Box 8437
Northfield, IL 60093–8437
Phone: (847) 501-4332
Website: www.communityresources.net/nssra.html

- RCH, Inc.
207 Skyline Boulevard
San Francisco, CA 94132
Phone: (415) 665-4100
Website: rchinc.org

- Active Living Alliance for Canadians with a
Disability
720 Belfast Road, Suite 104
Ottawa, Ontario K1G 0Z5
Phone: 1-800-771-0663 or (613) 244-0052
E-mail: info@ala.ca
Website: www.ala.ca

- Reach for the Rainbow
20 Torlake Crescent

Toronto, Ontario
M8Z 1B3
Phone: (416) 503-0088
E-mail: projectrainbow@reach.on.ca.
Website: reach@reach.on.ca

- Recreation Integration Victoria
4135 Lambrick Way
Victoria, B.C. Canada V8N 5R3
Phone: (251) 477-6314
Website: www.islandnet.com

- Imperial Counties Self-Determination Project
Head Office, 4355 Ruffin Rd., Suite 200
San Diego, CA 92123
Phone: (858) 576-2996
Hotline: (858) 503-4409
Website: www.sdrc.org

- Vela Microboard Association
100-17564 56 A Avenue
Surrey, BC V3S 1G3
Phone: (604) 575-2588
Email: info@microboard.org
Website: www.microboard.org

SUGGESTED LEARNING ACTIVITIES

1. Obtain information about community-based recreation programs for individuals with disabilities in your own community, and present your findings orally or in writing. This should include mission, goals, programs and services and funding.

2. Given specific demographic factors in your community, indicate how you would implement an inclusive recreation program for persons with disabilities.

3. Invite local recreation personnel into class to discuss their program philosophy, goals, and activities. Then compare their offerings and themes to those outlined in this chapter.

4. Select one of the website addresses above. Go to the website. Identify two features of the website that you consider a problem and suggest changes.

REFERENCES

APRS and NTRS. Recreation for People with Disabilities Survey. Unpublished report, 1997. (Mary Ann Devine, student at the University of Georgia, analyzed results.)

Dowson, S., & B. Salisbury, Eds. *Foundations for Freedom: International Perspectives on Self-Determination and Individualized Funding*. Seattle: The First International Conference on Self-Determination and Individualized Funding, 2000.

Glover, T. Funding the individual: An idea that spans the ideological spectrum. *Journal of Leisurability, 26* (4), 3–9, 1999.

Lord, J., & P. Hutchison. Individualized support and funding: Building blocks for capacity building and inclusion. *Disability and Society, 18*(1), 71–86, 2003.

Lord, J., B. Zupko, & P. Hutchison. *More Choice and Control for People with Disabilities: Individualized*

Supports and Funding. Toronto: Ontario Federation for Cerebral Palsy, 2000.

Mecke, T. A Qualitative Study of the Inclusion Process at a Residential Summer Camp. Master's thesis, Brock University, St. Catharines, ON, 2003.

O'Brien, J. *Paying Customers Are Not Enough: The Dynamics of Individualized Funding.* Atlanta: Responsive Systems Associates, 2001.

Pedlar, A., L. Haworth, P. Hutchison, A. Taylor, & P. Dunn. *A Textured Life: Empowerment and Adults with Developmental Disabilities.* Waterloo, ON: Wilfrid Laurier University Press, 1999.

Pedlar, A., & P. Hutchison. Restructuring human services in Canada: Commodification of disability. *Disability and Society, 15,* 637–651, 2000.

Stainton, T. *What Is Self-Determination?* Paper presented at the First International Conference on Self-Determination and Individualized Funding, Seattle, WA, July 2000.

Vela Microboard Association. [Online]. Available: www.microboard.org, 2000.

Wilson, B. Personal Communication. 1990. Recreation Integration Victoria. [Online]: Available: http://www.islandnet.com/--riv, 1999.

Wolf-Klitzing, S. The best practices for successful inclusion. *Parks and Recreation, 37*(5), 60–65, 2002.

PART

III

Inclusive and Special Recreation Program Areas

(Courtesy of Courage Center, Golden Valley, MN)

The following section highlights activities and successful programs that enable people with disabilities to pursue their recreational interests. Chapter 9, Camping and Wilderness-Adventure Experiences, describes actual and potential contributions that organized camping and wilderness experiences offer to people who have disabilities. The importance of qualified and enthusiastic leadership is stressed, and a detailed presentation on wilderness-adventure programs is included. Chapter 10, The Arts—for Everyone, outlines the benefits of arts participation for everyone. A special section features information on *VSA arts*. The chapter concludes with two examples that emphasize the deep, personal meaning that comes from participation in the arts. Selected sports programs for people with disabilities are covered in chapter 11, Competitive Sports. The pros and cons of competitive sports programs are discussed, and detailed information on wheelchair sports, the Special Olympics, the Barrie Integrated Baseball Association, and bocce is provided.

The emphasis of part III is on the benefits to people with disabilities of well-organized and professionally directed recreation activities. Most of the activities presented are easily incorporated into inclusive programs. Some of these activities, however, such as wheelchair sports and Special Olympics, restrict participation to people with disabilities. Including such examples in no way implies that we advocate segregated programming for most people who have disabilities. To the contrary, we feel that each person with a disability should participate in the least restrictive recreational environment. We have highlighted some segregated recreation programs solely because they allow us to identify more clearly the benefits of a given recreational activity for all people with disabilities.

9 CAMPING AND WILDERNESS-ADVENTURE EXPERIENCES

(Courtesy of The League: Serving People with Physical Disabilities, Inc., Baltimore, MD)

If you ask a group of people to define *camping,* you might get as many definitions as there are people in the group. To one person, camping might mean backpacking through California's High Sierras. To another, it may bring back memories of childhood scouting trips to lakeside woods. Yet another person may picture himself or herself sitting in an elaborate recreational vehicle parked in a neatly arranged campground. The word camping has come to refer to a wide variety of outdoor experiences. The equipment may range from simple to sophisticated; the surroundings, primitive to developed; and the activities, nature based to indoor oriented. Camping means many things to many people. This chapter, however, is concerned with *organized* camping programs and their potential for benefiting individuals with disabilities.

As the term implies, *organized camping* refers to outdoor living experiences that are carefully structured and supervised. The American Camping Association (ACA), a nationwide organization dedicated to organized camping, provides the following definition:

> [Camping is] a sustained experience which provides a creative, recreational and educational opportunity in group living in the outdoors. It utilizes trained leadership and the resources of the natural surroundings to contribute to each camper's mental, physical, social and spiritual growth. (American Camping Association, 2003)

Camping as referred to in this textbook does not pertain to "escaping" urban living in recreation vehicles with all the comforts of home, nor does it apply to the solo backpacker who sets out on an extended hiking expedition. Each of these activities may meet the needs of its participants, but neither contains all of the essential components of an organized camping experience. Betty Lyle (1947) wrote that five components are common to any definition of organized camping, including (1) out-of-doors, (2) recreation, (3) group living, (4) education, and (5) social adjustment. Despite that her observation was made more than 50 years ago, the similarity between her remarks and the current

ACA definition is striking. Adding one critical component to Lyle's list, trained leadership, provides an understanding of how organized camping differs from casual outdoor experiences. It is a *directed* experience that combines the unique properties of nature with the developmental potential of human group interaction. As an editorial in *Camping Magazine* (American Camping Association, 1985) stated:

> [Organized camping] is living in a community of people. It is face-to-face contact with the ebb and flow of human life—it is the civilizing, socializing, humanizing process of people working and playing and living together, closely, intimately. It is experimenting with hopes and aspirations, joys and sorrows, laughter and tears, successes and failures, moods and temperaments, and all humanity. It is *group* living—strong, virile, robust living together in the realm of people. Minus this human element, it is not organized camping. (p. 22)

Camping is fun, but equally important, it offers unlimited opportunities for human interaction and personal growth. Each year, thousands of campers go to summer camps expecting to become more comfortable with nature; most return more comfortable with themselves.

CAMPING AND PEOPLE WITH DISABILITIES

At one time, most camping opportunities for persons with disabilities were confined to segregated experiences. Camps were designed and built to accommodate the unique needs of children and adults with disabilities; moreover, programs were developed to facilitate each camper's personal growth within the "protected" social environment of peers with similar disabilities. Legislation, however, especially the Individuals with Disabilities Education Act (IDEA) and the Americans with Disabilities Act (ADA) (see chapter 3), helped to expand inclusive camping opportunities for people with disabilities.

Segregated Camping Programs

Camping for people with special needs is traced to the 1880s, but it was not until the 1930s that a concerted effort was made to provide segregated camping opportunities for large numbers of people with disabilities. At first, these programs focused on therapy and treatment for children, but the camp environment's potential to aid personal growth of the *total* individual was eventually recognized by camp leaders. Since the 1960s, most camps for people with disabilities have closely paralleled camps for the general population. Their goals, objectives, activities, and organizational structures are similar. Although the camper-staff ratio may vary (segregated camps for individuals with disabilities usually have fewer campers per counselor), the emphasis is the same: development of the total person through enjoyment of the out-of-doors.

The similarity between most camps for people with disabilities and so-called regular camps can be detected in the following general concepts listed by a National Easter Seal Society task force:

1. Persons with special needs should be afforded the same rewarding experiences that are available to [campers without disabilities].
2. Special programs can play a major role in the rehabilitation or habilitation of persons with special needs.
3. The sociorecreational values to be derived from association with nature through camping are inherently therapeutic without regard to any concomitant medical or paramedical benefits that may accrue.
4. Group living and working or playing situations provide social and psychological opportunities not available in the clinical or educational setting. (Hardt, 1968, p. 2)

Clearly, the unique value of a segregated camping experience is enhanced because the camp's leadership accepts a holistic view of the individual (Robinson & Skinner, 1985). All aspects of the person's life, from eating habits to activity selection, contribute to his or her personal

fulfillment. Therefore, camps should provide quality opportunities in as many aspects of life as possible if the potential of a camping experience is to be fully realized. The girl who receives extensive physical therapy at camp undoubtedly benefits from the therapy. Does she, however, receive maximum benefit from all that camping has to offer? One longtime leader in the field of camping for persons with disabilities, Jeanne Feeley from Pennsylvania, emphasized the importance of camping—not therapy—in her personal philosophy statement. Her words summarize the underlying theme of this chapter.

> I believe every person, handicapped [*sic*] or not, should have at least one camp experience. . . . I believe in the intrinsic value of camping. We need to preserve these values for our children and our children's children. Let all people whether mildly, moderately, or severely handicapped know what good camping is. (Feeley, 1972, pp. 44–45)

Feeley did add one warning that should be kept in mind, however: Not everyone will enjoy camping. Some individuals will discover that outdoor activities and group living are perfectly suited to them; others will learn that the out-of-doors is not for them. The important thing is that everyone, whether having a disability or not, has the *opportunity* to experience camping. Only through personal experience can one discover the potential benefits of a camp experience. As one teenaged camper remarked, "I can't believe it! I didn't even want to go on this [camping] trip; now I wish I could *live* in the woods!" Opportunity enables discovery. Unfortunately, the percentage of children and adults with disabilities who have experienced camping appears to be small; and those who have had camping opportunities were usually provided those experiences at segregated camps designed specifically for individuals with disabilities. Historically, the importance and value of segregated camps is undeniable; moreover, they continue to provide valuable opportunities for children and adults who are, for whatever reason, not prepared for inclusion into regular camping programs. Nevertheless, we agree with Havens's (1992) statement that inclusive experiences "should be the priority in most cases and segregated experiences considered an alternative, or 'stepping stone'" (p. 16).

Inclusive Camping Programs

Historically, few camps have promoted inclusion of persons with disabilities into their regular camping programs (Sable, 1992); moreover, integrated camping opportunities for persons with severe disabilities have been rare (Rynders, Schleien, & Mustonen, 1990). This situation is changing, however, as more camps are offering inclusive camping experiences (Keung & DeGraaf, 1999). As noted by Sable, "Although in its infancy, it is encouraging to see private camp directors, youth service agencies, and parents creating inclusionary environments for children. Such environments prevent parents from being faced with the dilemma of returning to a segregated summer program for their child after intensely advocating for the integration of their child within the school program" (p. 39).

The importance of inclusion was recently noted in a study by the National Inclusive Camp Practices (NICP) Project (Arick, Brannan, Fullerton, & Harris, 2003), which conducted the first national outcomes-based study of inclusive resident camps and outdoor schools serving youth with and without disabilities. The purpose of the study was to examine mainstream (traditional) camps and outdoor schools, and to identify their inclusive practices and effects on the growth and development of the youth. Over a 3-year period, using both quantitative and qualitative methods, the study examined youth from 14 mainstream resident camps and outdoor sites across 12 states. The participants in the study were 743 youth, including 76 youth who were part of a case study. In each case study, interviews were conducted with parents and counselors to gather information in nine developmental areas: social interactions, communication with others, taking responsibility, self-reliance, self-esteem, participation in recreation, skill achievement, self-help, and respect for others.

The study found that campers and students, with and without disabilities, demonstrated growth in all nine developmental areas as a result of their inclusive experience. Both groups positively viewed their integrated experiences, while youth without disabilities had increased respect and awareness for their peers with disabilities. Parents of youth with and without disabilities also benefited by learning about their children's developmental growth (i.e., self-reliance) and perhaps gained a more accurate understanding of their child's abilities, resulting in more realistic expectations of their child.

> As the counselor . . . reported about a boy with autism and ADHD, "At the beginning of the week, I would have to put soap in his hands and shampoo in his hair when showering. After three days, he got the soap and shampoo himself. He also has become very good at keeping himself occupied during free time." Later his mother said, "He has become more self-reliant since returning from camp. For example, he now puts dishes in the sink after meals. He shows continued growth in keeping himself busy with his own free-time activities." (Arick, Brannan, Fullerton, & Harris, 2003, p. 228)

As a result of the inclusive experience, camp directors and counselors alike noted an enhanced sense of community within their programs including increased tolerance, caring, creativity, and quality of leadership. Overall, the NICP study's findings build on the findings in an earlier study by Sable (1992), who also found positive outcomes for individuals involved in an integrated camping experience.

Keung and DeGraff (1999) have described a model program called TREATS, a camping program designed to offer an inclusive environment. TREATS serves over 12,750 children and youth in Hong Kong, and serves as an example of what can be accomplished if a program is committed to inclusion. This commitment includes:

1. Knocking down barriers and roadblocks so that all children, regardless of ability or background feel welcome.

2. Having staff and volunteers who are aware, trained, and ready to facilitate an inclusive program.
3. Promoting a process in which each child is seen and respected as an individual with strengths and abilities.
4. Encouraging both physical and social inclusion in all aspects of camp life.
5. Creating a supportive environment where everyone feels both physically and psychologically safe to participate. (Keung & DeGraaf, p. 24)

As camp directors fulfill their legal mandate to provide programs that are accessible to persons with disabilities, inclusive camp environments will undoubtedly expand. With this expansion will come increased awareness of the benefits that inclusion offers to *all* campers.

Camp Objectives

Each camp, whether segregated or inclusive, should establish its own general objectives. These objectives are used to guide staff decision making in all aspects of the camp, including activity selection, food preparation, discipline techniques, personnel policies, and administrative procedures. The philosophy of the camp's governing body is usually reflected in the list of general objectives. It is important, therefore, that all objectives be clearly stated in writing. Wilkinson (1981) provided a list of six general objectives that reflect a holistic view of a camp's purpose. These general objectives, developed by the American Camping Association, are appropriate for most camps, no matter how many of their campers have special needs:

1. To provide each camper with the opportunity for wholesome fun and adventure in a safe and supervised outdoor program.
2. To help develop a concept of safe and healthful living by stressing wholesome daily health habits; by stressing safety in camp skills; by offering a change for increasing strength, vitality, and endurance; and by fostering freedom from mental tensions.

3. To contribute to the development of "at-home-ness" in the natural world by imparting an understanding of and appreciation for the world of nature, by fostering an understanding of human dependency on nature and a sense of responsibility for conservation of natural resources, and by increasing the ability to use basic camping skills.
4. To increase a camper's concept of spiritual meaning and values through encouraging the development of a kinship with the security in an orderly universe, and through gaining an understanding of and appreciation for persons of other religions, cultures, nationalities, and races.
5. To encourage the development of skills and knowledge that can contribute to wholesome recreation during later years.
6. To contribute to the development of the individual through adjustment to group living in a democratic setting by instilling in him a sense of worth of each individual, by helping him to function effectively in a democratic society, and by helping him to develop a sense of social understanding and responsibility. (pp. 10–12)

Robinson and Skinner (1985) also provide some general objectives that give direction for camps that integrate campers with disabilities into traditional camp programs. These include developing positive relationships, promoting camper independence, encouraging social integration, teaching leisure skills, and having fun.

The preceding list of general objectives may not be ideal for all camps. Also, each camp should develop specific objectives that are more limited in scope and easier to measure than general objectives. Many camps are organized by sponsoring organizations to use the outdoor setting as a way of promoting specific special interests or outcomes. Religious camps, weight-control camps, and computer camps are a few examples of special-interest camps. General and specific objectives also may vary according to the type of camp. Day camps, resident camps, wilderness-adventure camps, trip

One goal of most organized camping programs is to provide group living experiences that enhance social understanding and responsibility. Camp is an ideal setting for cooperative activities that promote "togetherness" among campers with and without disabilities.
(Courtesy of City of Las Vegas Parks & Leisure Activities/Adaptive Recreation)

camps, and family camps are examples of different camp types. Each type has its own advantages, and these should be emphasized within the written objectives.

Properly written and publicized camp objectives are exceedingly important because they serve two purposes. First, as stated earlier, they provide direction to all camp staff members. Thus, consistency and quality of services are more easily maintained. Second, written objectives provide essential information to parents and campers. If maximum enjoyment is to occur, the programs and operations of the camp must be well suited to the camper's individual interests. Written objectives help provide a basis for selecting the most appropriate camp. Vinton, Hawkins, Pantzer, and Farley (1978) provide five basic principles for camps serving children. The principles should help any

camp create an appropriate atmosphere for achieving its objectives. They are

- Emphasize what the [child with a disability] can do rather than what he or she cannot do. Provide programs that are within range of abilities of the child.
- Stress both the fun and the educational potential of each experience equally.
- Provide a flexible program that is geared to the needs of each individual child.
- Provide a situation that is as normal as possible, deviating or adapting only when necessary.
- Stress participation in the democratic processes. Environmental education and camping should be a doing process, involving the child in all levels of planning and implementing the program. (p. 8)

Camp Leadership

Objectives provide direction in any camp program, but the camp's staff has responsibility for achieving these objectives. Anyone who has attended or worked in an organized camp can testify to the importance of a competent and enthusiastic staff. This is especially true in a camp that has campers with disabilities. It is easy for a counselor to become frustrated if the pace of camp is slowed by campers with physical disabilities or if maintaining discipline becomes difficult because of behavioral disorders among campers. How counselors deal with these frustrations helps determine their job effectiveness, and effective counselors are critical to a camp's success.

Fullerton (2003) lists 10 inclusive practices used by counselors that provide individualized support to youth. Counselors can use these techniques as appropriate to help the campers (with and without disabilities) achieve their goals and promote inclusion.

Practice 1: Provide encouragement and motivation.

Practice 2: Model how to complete activities.

Practice 3: Provide more time to complete an activity.

Practice 4: Arrange for peers to provide assistance.

Practice 5: Provide physical assistance.

Practice 6: Break task down into smaller steps.

Practice 7: Provide alternative ways to do an activity.

Practice 8: Provide extra practice.

Practice 9: Provide alternative ways to communicate.

Practice 10: Provide special equipment.

Whether working with children or adults, the qualities, or personality traits, of an ideal camp counselor are almost endless. Some, however, are more important than others. Kimball (1980) emphasized "flexibility, a high degree of perseverance and tolerance for frustration, an ability to empathize, and a sense of humor" (p. 31). Creativity is certainly another vital characteristic, as is good judgment. Knowledge of how to manage the special needs of campers is essential when a camp includes campers with moderate to severe disabilities. However, the most important characteristic for any camp counselor is a genuine interest in and love for the campers. When counselors are "into" their campers, the camp's atmosphere is alive and exciting for everyone, and possibilities for personal fulfillment abound.

One experienced director of a camp for children with disabilities confided that he and his administrative staff once sat around a campfire discussing the attributes of previous counselors. "We selected an 'all-star' staff made up of the best counselors we had seen during the preceding 10 years," he said. "Afterwards, we tried to identify what qualities made them so exceptional. Their ages and personalities varied, but one characteristic was common to all—they *loved* being with the campers." These counselors showed their love in a variety of ways; they put the campers' needs above their own desires, they asked for the campers' ideas and tried to implement them, they were alert to risks but never overprotected the campers, and, above all, they established an atmosphere of sharing between themselves and the campers. "They all stayed a few summers and then moved on," the director said, "but their campers will never forget them." After a brief pause, he added, "And I know they will never forget their campers!"

Good counselors enable a camp to fulfill its potential. They serve as role models for the campers and promote personal growth within their group. Successful camps select their counselors wisely, and they provide them with the best possible training. As most camp directors acknowledge, a camp is only as good as its counselors.

Staff Training

Staff training is of vital importance to the success of any camp program. Each training program should do the following: include some "hands-on" experience, provide practical tips and information,

Effective camp counselors enable a camp to achieve its objectives. Counselors who are dedicated to the well-being of their campers provide experiences that foster personal growth and self-discovery.
(Courtesy of The League: Serving People with Physical Disabilities, Inc., Baltimore, MD)

specify policies and procedures, stress safety and health, and clarify program philosophy. In short, camp training must prepare staff members for all aspects of their jobs. Of primary importance, however, is preparation for being with the campers.

There is no single approach to preparing to be with the campers. Fullerton (2003) described three different approaches to training that might help counselors to understand better how inclusion and its philosophy might appear in practice. The three approaches include the use of scenarios, role-play, and strategy identification to psychologically prepare counselors for the arrival of their campers.

Scenarios. In this approach, one staff member reads a scenario while the other staff make noise and flip the lights on and off. Then the counselors are given a test about the scenario's content. This activity brings to focus how distractions affect a person's

ability to remember, which leads into a discussion about children with ADHD. The needs of these campers are then discussed and strategies for helping campers with ADHD to refocus and attend are identified. This approach might also help to create an awareness for working with children with memory problems, autism, brain injury, and/or learning disabilities. Other scenarios can be created for campers with different disabilities.

Role-Play. Another training approach might be to role-play whereby two "training counselors" play the role of a counselor and camper. The two counselors would then act out a challenging situation, one that might typically occur at camp. The two counselors would elicit appropriate responses to the situation from other counselors and act them out and then discuss. The training counselors would conclude the role-play by offering guidelines on how to best deal with the situation based on previous experience.

Strategy Identification. This approach involves describing the accommodations and support strategies that have worked with campers in the past. Returning staff share stories and experiences that they have had and describe how they handled the situation and what was unsuccessful and successful. Returning staff also share what they learned over time and from talking to parents about strategies that are helpful. The idea with this approach is to encourage counselors to be flexible, collaborate, and be creative in order to promote a successful inclusive environment.

Although each of these approaches may help to prepare counselors for situations that they may encounter when working with campers with varying abilities, it is equally important not to emphasize differences between individuals with and without disabilities in the process. Doing so creates a sense of separateness in the minds of the counselors, instead of inclusiveness, which is what is desired. It is also important not to exaggerate characteristics of the disabling conditions to "scare" the counselors into thinking that they are going to be working with "monsters." The idea behind these approaches is, instead, to learn ways to promote togetherness when challenging situations arise.

Formal staff training should also include leadership opportunities for persons with disabilities. For example, at the University of Indiana's Bradford Woods Outdoor Education, Recreation, and Camping Center, formal camp-related leadership training is provided to people with disabilities. Robb and Shepley (1988) note that leadership development programs for people with disabilities have lagged behind similar training in traditional residential and other camp settings. They emphasize: "Leadership begins with recognizing the intrinsic value of each person, and with that recognition comes the equality and integration of all people" (p. 21).

Proper training refines the skills and attitudes of all camp staff members and enables them to offer the best possible experience to all campers, including those with disabilities. If campers are to receive the maximum benefit from their stay at camp, a well-trained staff is essential.

Benefits of Organized Camping

Camping offers many potential benefits to individuals with disabilities. Parents and health professionals agree that the camp environment offers a unique setting for personal growth. Many individuals with disabilities have limited life experiences because of the barriers they face. Camp, however, gives a chance for exploration of oneself and the environment. It allows the flexibility to express creativity, yet provides sufficient structure for feelings of security. Above all, it offers a chance for independence of thought and action to individuals who are, regretfully, too often forced to assume a dependency role.

Advocates attribute numerous benefits to an organized camping experience. McCormick, White, and McGuire (1992), for example used a statistical procedure (factor analysis) to assess the benefits that parents perceived camping offered to their children with mental retardation. Their results revealed "six dimensions of benefits of an ideal summer camp program" (p. 32). These dimensions are social skill development, social competence, respite care, cognitive development, expressive development, and physical competence. They added, "Overall, the most important benefit of summer camp, as perceived by parents of campers with mental retardation, appears to be social growth" (p. 34).

It is hoped that camp's many benefits interact to help campers with disabilities increase their own feelings of self-worth. Thus, their self-concepts are strengthened. Lundegren (1976) observed that an individual's self-concept is influenced by interaction with others (especially significant others) and by interaction with the environment. A number of self-concept studies have supported Lundegren's contention (Hourcade, 1977; Robb, 1971; Sable,

1995; Sessoms, 1979; Shasby, Heuchert, & Gansneder, 1984), but the evidence is far from conclusive. Nevertheless, the skills and activities available in camping activities are ideally suited to self-concept improvement. Camps offer new skills to novice campers and almost unlimited opportunities for skill improvement among experienced campers. As noted by Iso-Ahola, LaVerde, and Graefe (1988), skill development and continued skill enhancement appear to be fundamental to improvements in self-concept.

Unfortunately, most of the benefits claimed by camping enthusiasts have only limited research support. Weaknesses in research methodology and use of questionable measures have limited the results of many camping studies. Also, some authorities doubt that short camp sessions, with young and often inexperienced counselors, could produce significant changes in campers. Still others caution that returning from camp to an institution may have negative consequences, particularly for those with psychological disorders (Polenz & Rubitz, 1977; Ryan & Johnson, 1972).

There is still much research that needs to be done, but almost everyone who has worked in camps with individuals who have disabilities can cite examples of personal growth among campers. They are convinced, as we are, that organized camping programs offer many benefits to campers, irrespective of disabilities or special needs. As Bedini (1995) concluded, "camps are the perfect arena for education and change" (p. 21).

WILDERNESS-ADVENTURE PROGRAMS

One of the most exciting developments in camping and outdoor-related activities for people with disabilities has been the emphasis on wilderness-adventure programs. These programs provide a challenging experience for any action-oriented individual, irrespective of disabling condition (Dattilo & Murphy, 1987). They also offer participants many opportunities for physical expression and personal achievement that are *not* based on

complex language skills or abstract thinking processes. Wilderness-adventure programs include challenges that can be understood in concrete terms, and they take place in an outdoor environment that maximizes feelings of personal freedom. It is precisely these qualities that make wilderness-adventure programs the ideal leisure experience for many people with disabilities.

While wilderness-adventure programs vary in format and techniques, most have been adapted from the model established by the Outward Bound program (Hollenhorst & Ewert, 1985). In the early 1960s, Outward Bound opened this program to people with special needs by incorporating "delinquent" youth into the program. By the 1980s, Outward Bound was offering challenging outdoor experiences to many individuals with disabilities. People with cerebral palsy, paraplegia, multiple sclerosis, amputations, muscular dystrophy, and many other disabilities were being given the chance to participate in Outward Bound groups composed of four nondisabled people and four individuals with disabilities (Goodwin, 1978). Other programs were also emerging, many willing to accept people considered too disabled by some Outward Bound programs. Wilderness Inquiry in Minnesota, C. W. Hog in Idaho, and Turning POINT in Texas are a few examples of such programs. Through activities such as rock climbing, white-water rafting, canoeing, spelunking (caving), backpacking, and so on, these programs and others like them provide personal challenge at the same time that they foster interpersonal interaction and small group cooperation.

Wilderness-Adventure Experience Components

Philosophy, format, and techniques vary from program to program, but there are some components common to most, if not all, wilderness-adventure programs open to people with disabilities. The following components, although listed separately, are interrelated and combine to form an experience that, it is hoped, has lifelong meaning to participants.

Wilderness-adventure activities offer participants personal challenges that demand discipline, concentration, and trust in others. Rappelling, for example, requires both individual skill and dependence upon fellow participants.
(Courtesy of Wilderness Inquiry and Erin Broadbent/Photo by Greg Lais)

1. *The experience takes place in the out-of-doors.* Most people in technological societies experience a variety of artificially constructed constraints in their daily lives. Windowless rooms in modern buildings shut out "distractions"; city lights and signs tell people when to cross the street, where to park their cars, what products to buy, and so on; schools restrict movement by insisting that each student sit at a desk until a bell rings its approval to move (usually to another desk). Examples of these constraints are limitless.

People with disabilities experience all of these constraints as well as many barriers that do not limit people who do not have disabilities. Wilderness settings, however, offer a chance to overcome barriers that have not been imposed by other human beings. Adaptive behavior is required by mother nature, not by architects or school officials. For people who have disabilities that do not limit mobility, such as learning disabilities, the wilderness also offers an important chance for freedom of movement and expression while, at the same time, providing a natural, yet orderly, environment.

2. *Small group cooperation and trust in others is emphasized.* Some individuals with disabilities by necessity devote much of their daily lives to individual challenges. Not only must they overcome obstacles that do not confront their peers without disabilities, but they also may find their contributions to a group or family effort ignored or devalued. It is little wonder, therefore, that some people with disabilities have limited experience in cooperative efforts. Wilderness-adventure programs, however, provide for group experiences that require cooperation and trust. Each participant has the opportunity to contribute to a clearly defined group goal, and because the group is small, that contribution is evident to everyone. The freshly caught fish frying over an open fire will be shared among those who caught the fish *and* those who gathered the firewood. Everyone learns that his or her efforts were of value; there could not have been a meal without *each* person's contribution. In time, a series of such activities results in a cohesive group characterized by members who not only cooperate with each other, but also trust that everyone will do his or her part. As noted by Herbert (1999), wilderness-adventure activities are "designed to address themes of trusting and respecting one another, supporting others, knowing how to ask for help, promoting interdependence, using effective communication skills, and challenging internal fears and overcoming obstacles" (p. 204).

3. *Stressful objectives are systematically presented and successfully achieved.* In Robert Frost's poem *The Death of the Hired Man,* a farm worker who is elderly is referred to as being in a hopeless situation. He has nothing in his past to be proud of, and his future holds no hope for improvement. Unfortunately, some people feel like they are in the same situation. Their lack of success in

the past, whether in school or in other aspects of their lives, has resulted in a feeling of futility toward the future. As one youth expressed emphatically, "Why should I try, man? I'd just [mess] up again!" Wilderness-adventure programs offer the participant much more than a hodge-podge of outdoor experiences. They are composed of activities that are carefully selected and systematically introduced (Herbert, 1996). Whether these challenges are contrived, as with some Outward Bound activities, or occur naturally in the process of an expedition, each requires the accomplishment of a specific objective. Each objective is challenging enough to induce feelings of stress, but not so difficult that it should result in failure. To cross a stream by use of a fallen tree, the young woman with a disability must overcome her fear of falling. As important, however, is that she may also be making progress toward overcoming her fear of *failing.*

4. *The group's leader is critical to program effectiveness.* Leading wilderness-adventure activities requires a great deal of experience and skill, especially when the activities involve stressful situations in unfamiliar surroundings. The leader of a wilderness-adventure group must guide the group so that objectives are achieved *by the group members.* Dattilo and Murphy (1987) emphasize that the leader should systematically reduce the level of assistance provided, thus encouraging participants to assume a greater role in decision making and greater ownership of outcomes. At the same time, the leader needs to remain alert to the optimum level of stress for the group. Too little stress prevents a feeling of accomplishment, but too much stress can result in feelings of failure. As noted by Kimball (1980), "There is only a small difference between tension that is creative and growth oriented and tension that is defeating" (p. 12). The leader must be able to anticipate events and likely reactions of

group members. He or she must not only know the techniques for accomplishing group goals, but *when* to use them. This requires an understanding of the difference between risk and danger. Some amount of risk is an essential element of wilderness-adventure activities, and the right to experience risk belongs to all participants, whether or not they have a disability (Johnson, 1994). However, leaders must understand that safety is paramount and that the creation of a dangerous environment for participants threatens the integrity of any wilderness-adventure program. (McAvoy, 1987)

Project Adventure, one of the leading organizations focusing on adventure-based programming and counseling, includes two important concepts in all of its challenge activities. They are *Full Value Contract* and *Challenge by Choice*. The Full Value Contract is not a written contract; rather, it is "the process in which a group agrees to find positive value in the efforts of its members. This positive value is expressed in encouragement, goal setting, group discussion, a spirit of forgiveness, and confrontation" (Schoel, Prouty, & Radcliffe, 1988, p. 33). The Full Value Contract means that group members agree, in advance, to work together toward group goals, adhere to safety and appropriate group behavioral guidelines, and both give and receive constructive feedback (positive and negative). Challenge by Choice is a separate, but interrelated, concept. Challenge by Choice provides the student with:

- A chance to try a potentially difficult and/or frightening challenge in an atmosphere of support and caring.
- The opportunity to "back off" when performance pressures or self-doubt becomes too strong, knowing that an opportunity for a future attempt will always be available.
- A chance to try difficult tasks, recognizing that the attempt is more significant than performance results.
- Respect for individual ideas and choices. (Schoel et al., p. 131)

Project Adventures activities also include a debriefing, which is essential for complete understanding among participants of the meaning and outcomes of an activity. The debriefing answers three simple questions: *What?* (discussing the facts of what occurred); *So What?* (discussing what is the meaning of what happened, thus giving participants the chance to abstract and generalize what was learned); and *Now What?* (discussion used to introduce the next activity and/or focus on how what was learned may be applied in participants' daily lives).

Leading a wilderness-adventure program provides immense personal reward because behavior changes and personal growth among participants become clearly visible as the experience progresses (Crase, 1988; McAvoy, Schatz, Stutz, Schleien, & Lais, 1989; Witman, 1987). The wilderness-adventure program leader is the catalyst who enables these positive results to occur. Fortunately, many wilderness-adventure programs provide an opportunity for experienced participants who have disabilities to assume leadership of groups. Wilderness Inquiry, for example, has several previous participants with disabilities leading their challenging expeditions. C. W. Hog and Turning POINT, on the other hand, were formed by persons who have disabilities *and* extensive experience in the out-of-doors.

Wilderness-Adventure Activities and Outcomes

Wilderness-adventure programs usually offer a wide variety of challenging activities that take place in outdoor environments. These activities include, but are not limited to, mountain climbing, rappelling, kayaking, SCUBA diving, dogsled treks, cross-country ski trips, caving, canoeing, backpacking, and white-water rafting. Regardless of the type of activity, expeditions and group-oriented challenges are perceived to be the most important to participants (Hollenhorst & Ewert, 1985). The significance of such activities becomes clear when one examines the outcomes from participation in wilderness-adventure activities.

McAvoy and Lais (1999) have reviewed the literature on benefits of wilderness-adventure programs. Their review documents benefits to participants with disabilities that include improved self-concepts, self-esteem, and self-fulfillment; perceptions of personal growth; enhanced leisure skills; improved social adjustment and cooperation; enhanced body image; and positive behavior change. McAvoy and Lais are careful to note, however, that these benefits are not unique to persons with disabilities. Rather, the outcomes of wilderness-adventure programs are consistent for all participants, whether or not they have disabilities.

Although the benefits of participation in outdoor adventure programs are well documented, one of the challenges of providing these types of experiences to persons with disabilities is access. Rugged terrain and undeveloped natural areas, along with weather conditions and other elements of nature, can make access very challenging, and sometimes impossible for some people. Making wilderness experiences accessible often conjures up thoughts of leveling mountains, paving and ramping trails, and providing motorized access. The truth is that people with disabilities do not want these extreme approaches to access any more than many people without disabilities. In a research study by Moore, Dattilo, and Devine (1996), people with disabilities were found to have the same basic preferences for natural settings as people without disabilities. Improving access while preserving nature is a challenge, but providing people with disabilities with as much information as possible about the level of accessibility of an area can promote inclusion. Examples of this include providing information on access to restrooms, trail conditions, slopes, surface types, access to water, and weather conditions. This type of information can help people with disabilities prepare for and make appropriate choices before and during an outdoor adventure experience.

Specific examples of wilderness-adventure achievements of people with disabilities include Wilderness Inquiry's five-day Boundary Waters (Minnesota) ski and dogsled trip (Rawland, 1998), a 16-day raft trip through the Grand Canyon (Szychowski, 1993), mountain expeditions across six countries in an off-road wheelchair (Porret, 1998), and Mark Wellman's dramatic scaling of the face of 3,200-foot El Capitan in Yosemite National Park. The latter took place in 1989 and captured the imagination of the nation as Wellman, who has paraplegia, executed 7,000 pull-ups as he advanced six inches at a time up the vertical rock-face. To date, only one other person with paraplegia (wheelchair athlete Trooper Johnson) has duplicated Wellman's feat. Johnson's assent took him five and one-half days.

In 1998, Tom Whittaker, along with five other world-class climbers, became the first person with a disability (single leg amputee) to successfully reach the summit of Mt. Everest, the world's tallest mountain (29,028 feet). Paciorek and Jones (2001) described the climb as a "terrific athletic accomplishment and provided great evidence that people with disabilities desire to participate in adventure activities" (p. 9).

In May 2001, Erik Weihenmayer repeated the venture by becoming the first man who is blind to reach Everest's summit. An experienced climber, Weihenmayer had already climbed four of the Seven Summits (the tallest peaks on each of the seven continents). When interviewed by ABC News about the Everest climb, Weihenmayer said the goal was "not just to stick a blind person [*sic*] on top like a sack of potatoes but to prove a blind person can be a part of a real team. You're a climber first and a blind person second." In his book, *Touch the Top of the World,* Weihenmayer (2002) states that he thinks many people have low expectations of what people who are blind can do. He says that "some guy told me that I needed to realize my limitations. I think that too many people sit around realizing their limitations, when, maybe they should spend more time realizing their potential" (p. 181). Weihenmayer has spent much of his life learning about his potential. At one time a man who could not get a dishwashing job in college because people did not believe he was capable, Weihenmayer is now a role model in the mountaineering world for people both with and without disabilities.

Inclusive Wilderness-Adventure Activities

Both the Boundary waters trip and Mt. Everest ascent mentioned earlier were inclusive experiences in which individuals without disabilities participated along with people who had disabilities. Such expeditions need to be organized with careful attention to group structure to ensure social interaction and acceptance. Describing Wilderness Inquiry canoe trips into the boundary waters along the U.S.-Canada border, Lais and Schurke (1982) noted that:

> A usual group would include two people who use wheelchairs, two who are sensory impaired, three "able-bodied" persons, one who uses crutches and two group leaders. Consideration is given so that groups are intergenerational, balanced in the number of men and women, and include persons from a wide variety of occupations and lifestyles. (pp. 25–26)

Schleien, McAvoy, Lais, and Rynders (1993) state that the "underlying goal of integrated high adventure programs is to provide positive experiences for everyone in the group in settings that empower them to expand perceived limitations" (p. 10). They also indicate that adventure programs provide participants with opportunities:

• To experience social integration in settings far removed from the everyday environment
• To increase self-esteem and self-confidence
• To promote independent living skills for persons with disabilities
• For persons without disabilities to look beyond disabilities and to discard negative stereotypes
• To recognize similarities between people with and without disabilities (p. 10)

For more than 20 years, Wilderness Inquiry, Inc. of Minneapolis, Minnesota, has organized and implemented inclusive wilderness-adventure trips and expeditions. Wilderness Inquiry's activities have realized the potential attributed to inclusive wilderness-adventure experiences; however, careful planning and professional implementation are essential if inclusive wilderness-adventure activities are to achieve their goals (Sable, 1995).

To prepare for trips and to ensure that participants are appropriately grouped, Wilderness Inquiry has an extensive training curriculum for staff (McAvoy & Lais, 1999). This curriculum features units on disability awareness, social integration, risk management, group processing, specific disability information, technical disability skills, and adapted equipment. Herbert (2000) underscored the importance of a comprehensive training program to facilitate inclusive wilderness-adventure activities. He found that wilderness-adventure program directors usually believed that they provided adequate training to their staff; however, staff members were certain that their training was insufficient to meet the demands of their jobs.

Wilderness Inquiry's staff training curriculum is implemented within the context of the Universal Program Participation Model (UPPM). McAvoy and Lais (1999) describe this training model as follows:

> UPPM is essentially a process of matching people's needs with the service capacity of the provider, the demands of the environment, and the needs of other participants in order to provide high quality, socially integrated activities. It is a process of seeking the right "fit" between participant needs and quality experiences, allowing service providers to analyze the factors that go into successful programming. (pp. 406–407)

The UPPM system emphasizes that inappropriate placement of people may negate the benefits inherent in a well-run wilderness-adventure activity. Thus, the following considerations are taken into account before group placement is finalized: environment, activity, participants, and resources. For a more thorough description of UPPM, the reader is referred to McAvoy and Lais (1999).

Inclusive wilderness-adventure programs enable each group member to use his or her unique skills and abilities. People with disabilities are usually accepted for their abilities (Lais, 1985), and participants without disabilities accept the responsibility for performing tasks that are difficult or impossible for people who have disabilities. It is a learning experience for everyone, and each person is expected to respond to the challenge at hand. As one participant with cerebral palsy explained, "You are encouraged to do things you never thought possible but, with a little effort and ingenuity, you find out that you can do them" (Lais & Schurke, 1982, p. 27). Moreover, such integrated experiences have been demonstrated to have positive outcomes for *all* participants, irrespective of the presence of a disabling condition. Samples of individuals with and without disabilities who participated in Wilderness Inquiry trips were found to have reduced trait anxiety after the trip. Both groups also reported posttrip improvements in a number of important areas, including interpersonal relationships, attitudes toward persons with disabilities, confidence levels, willingness to take risks, feelings about self, and tolerance of stress (McAvoy et al., 1989). McAvoy and Lais (1999) also cite research that demonstrates people without disabilities return from inclusive wilderness-adventure experiences with an increased understanding of the capabilities and limitations of people with disabilities, more favorable attitudes toward persons with disabilities, and increased tolerance of differences among people. Anderson, Schleien, McAvoy, Lais, and Seligmann (1997) also demonstrated that many of these benefits remain stable over time and that wilderness-adventure experiences often lead to lasting friendships between persons with and without disabilities.

Segregated Wilderness-Adventure Activities

Some expeditions are composed exclusively of participants with disabilities. One example of a segregated experience was the ascent of Guadalupe Peak, the highest point in Texas (8,751 feet). In 1982, six members of POINT (now Turning POINT), who used wheelchairs, set out to climb this peak without the direct assistance of people without disabilities. One goal of such trips may be the feeling that participants receive from successfully "going it alone," or not depending on nondisabled companions to assist with difficult tasks. Successfully overcoming wilderness challenges can increase a person's self-confidence (McAvoy et al., 1989; Wright, 1983) and overcoming them without the aid of participants without disabilities can provide unparalleled feelings of personal control and achievement. Despite that only three of the six POINT members who began the ascent of Guadalupe Peak reached the summit, all participants shared in the joy of accomplishment.

Outcomes of Wilderness-Adventure Activities

The outcomes of any successful wilderness-adventure program are similar, whether or not they include people with disabilities. Participants enjoy the beauty and wonder of nature, share experiences with other human beings, and overcome challenges that enable feelings of self-worth and personal control. In addition, such experiences form the foundation for lasting friendships and provide participants with lifelong outdoor leisure skills (McAvoy & Lais, 1999). The presence of people with disabilities in such programs may intensify these outcomes for everyone. As Corty (1979) wrote, on returning from one expedition, "Looking around the table at those faces I have come to know so intimately, I realize that we have been voyageurs not only through the boundary waters, but through the hearts of ourselves and each other. . . . It has been a voyage that will continue long after the paddles are put away" (pp. 10–12). We hope the outcomes of a wilderness-adventure experience will help all participants, including those with disabilities, enjoy smoother and more satisfying voyages through life.

SUMMARY

Organized camping and wilderness-adventure experiences offer everyone, including people with disabilities, unique opportunities for enjoyment and personal growth. Experts have attributed many beneficial outcomes to participation in these experiences, including improved interpersonal skills, increased strength and endurance, greater independence, friendship formation, and enhanced feelings of self-worth. Despite these benefits, however, only a small percentage of people with disabilities in the United States and Canada have had the opportunity to participate in organized camping and wilderness-adventure programs. As these programs expand to accommodate more people with disabilities, it is essential that they (1) have clearly stated objectives, based on a sound philosophy; (2) provide effective staff training that emphasizes empathy for participants; and (3) offer well-organized and safe activities that are consistent with the skills and interests of *all* participants.

SUGGESTED LEARNING ACTIVITIES

1. Identify eight topics that you feel should be included in any orientation program for a camp with persons who have disabilities. Develop a learning activity for one of these topics.

2. Interview the director of a residential camp or wilderness-adventure program. What does he or she feel are the *unique* benefits that can be derived from participating in the program?

3. Vinton and coworkers (1978) list five basic principles for camps to follow to create an appropriate atmosphere for achieving its objectives. Discuss how each principle facilitates the personal growth of campers with disabilities.

4. List 10 qualities important for a camp counselor to exhibit. Discuss the importance of each.

5. Name the four experience components that are common to most wilderness-adventure programs. Discuss the benefits to participants provided by each component.

6. Access the Bradford Woods research site on the Web at http://www.bradwoods.org/research.html. Click on "View Bradford Papers Online." Locate one online article about camping or wilderness-related activities for persons with disabilities. Write a one-page critique of the article, including its strengths and weaknesses.

7. Participate in a professionally organized and directed wilderness-adventure trip (e.g., Wilderness Inquiry). Maintain a log of your experiences and share highlights from your log with fellow students.

8. Volunteer at a day camp or resident camp that includes persons with disabilities. Discuss the camping experience with campers who have disabilities and compare their opinions about the benefits of organized camping with those listed in this chapter.

REFERENCES

American Camping Association. Jobs at Camp: Careers in the Community. [Online]. Available: http://www.acacamps.org/career.htm, 2003.

American Camping Association. What is the role of camping? *Camping Magazine, 57*(4), 22–24, 1985.

Anderson, L., S. J. Schleien, L. McAvoy, G. Lais, & D. Seligmann. Creating positive change through an integrated outdoor adventure program. *Therapeutic Recreation Journal, 31,* 214–229, 1997.

Arick, J. R., S. Brannan, A. Fullerton, & J. Harris. The National Inclusive Camp Practices (NICP) Study: Research on Practices and Effects of Inclusive Programs 1997–2001. In S. Brannan, A. Fullerton, J. Arick, G. Robb, & M. Bender, Eds. *Including Youth with Disabilities in Outdoor Programs,* Champaign, IL: Sagamore, 2003, pp. 185–203.

Bedini, L. A. Campers with disabilities: Encouraging positive interaction. *Camping Magazine,* 21–24, March/April 1995.

Corty, J. Disabled blaze new trails in the wild. *The New York Times,* October 21, 1979, pp. D10–12.

Crase, N. Wilderness on ice. *Sports 'n Spokes, 14*(1), 7–12, 1988.

C. W. Hog. [Online]. Available: http://www.isu.edu/cwhog/general.html, 2003.

Dattilo, J., & W. D. Murphy. Facilitating the challenge in adventure recreation for persons with disabilities. *Therapeutic Recreation Journal, 21*(3), 14–21, 1987.

Feeley, J. E. Should every handicapped person have a camping experience? In J. A. Nesbitt et al., *Training Needs and Strategies in Camping for the Handicapped.* Eugene: University of Oregon Press, 1972, pp. 44–45.

Fullerton, A. Planning and developing an inclusive outdoor program. In S. Brannan, A. Fullerton, J. Arick, G. Robb, & M. Bender, Eds. *Including Youth with Disabilities in Outdoor Programs,* Champaign, IL: Sagamore, 2003, 57–79.

Goodwin, G. Outward Bound. *Sports 'n Spokes, 4*(1), 1978, 5–7.

Hardt, L. J. *Easter Seal Guide to Special Camping Programs.* Chicago: The National Easter Seal Society for Crippled Children and Adults, 1968.

Havens, M. D. *Bridges to Accessibility: A Primer for Including Persons with Disabilities in Adventure Curricula.* Hamilton, MA: Project Adventure, 1992.

Herbert, J. T. Therapeutic effects of participating in an adventure therapy program. *Rehabilitation Counseling Bulletin, 41*(3), 201–215, 1999.

Herbert, J. T. Use of adventure-based counselling programs for persons with disabilities. *Journal of Rehabilitation, 62*(4), 3–9, 1996.

Herbert, J. T. Director and staff views on including persons with severe disabilities in therapeutic adventure. *Therapeutic Recreation Journal, 34,* 16–32, 2000.

Hollenhorst, S., & A. Ewert. Dissecting the adventure camp experience: Determining successful program components. *Camping Magazine, 57*(4), 32–33, 1985.

Hourcade, J. Effect of a summer camp program on self-concept of mentally retarded young adults. *Therapeutic Recreation Journal, 11*(4), 178–183, 1977.

Iso-Ahola, S. E., D. LaVerde, & A. Graefe. Perceived competence as a mediator of the relationship between high risk sports participation and self-esteem. *Journal of Leisure Research, 21,* 32–39, 1988.

Johnson, A. M. The right to risk through outdoor adventure recreation. In R. D. Steadward, R. N. Ewen., & G. D. Wheeler, Eds. *VISTA '93— The Outlook Companion.* Edmonton, Alberta, Canada: Rick Hansen Centre, 1994, pp. 409–411.

Keung, J. L. W., & D. DeGraaf. A world of diversity: Including campers of all abilities in your program. *Camping Magazine,* 20–24, March/April 1999.

Kimball, R. O. *Wilderness/Adventure Programs for Juvenile Offenders.* Chicago: University of Chicago, School of Social Service Administration, 1980.

Lais, G. Paddling the Yukon. *Sports 'n Spokes, 10*(6), 9–12, 1985.

Lais, G., & P. Schurke. Wilderness Inquiry II. *Sports 'n Spokes, 8*(2), 25–27, 1982.

Lundegren, H. Self-concepts of special populations. In B. van der Smissen, Compiler. *Research Camping and Environmental Education.* State College: The Pennsylvania State University, 1976, pp. 253–273.

Lyle, B. *Camping—What Is It?* Martinsville, IN: American Camping Association, 1947.

McAvoy, L. Outdoors for everyone: Opportunities that include people with disabilities. *Parks and Recreation, 36*(8), 24–36, 2001.

McAvoy, L. H. Education for outdoor leadership. In J. F. Meyer, T. W. Morash, & G. E. Welton, Eds. *High Adventure Outdoor Pursuits.* Columbus, OH: Publishing Horizons, 1987, pp. 459–467.

McAvoy, L., & G. Lais. Programs that include persons with disabilities. In J. C. Miles & S. Priest, *Adventure Programming.* State College, PA: Venture, 1999, pp. 403–414.

McAvoy, L. H., E. C. Schatz, M. E. Stutz, S. J. Schleien, & G. Lais. Integrated wilderness adventure: Effects on personal and lifestyle traits of persons with and without disabilities. *Therapeutic Recreation Journal, 23*(3), 50–64, 1989.

McCormick, B., C. White, & F. A. McGuire. Parents' perceptions of benefits of summer camp for campers with mental retardation. *Therapeutic Recreation Journal, 26*(3), 27–37, 1992.

Moore, R., J. Dattilo, & M. Devine. A comparison of rail-trial preferences between adults with and without disabilities. *Adapted Physical Activity Quarterly,* 13, 27–37, 1996.

Paciorek, M. J., & J. A. Jones. *Disability Sport and Recreation Resources* (3rd ed.). Traverse City, MI: Cooper, 2001.

People Spot. Erik Weihenmayer. [Online]. Available: http://www.peoplespot.com/people/ erikweihenmayer.htm, 2003.

Polenz, D., & F. Rubitz. Staff perceptions of the effects of therapeutic camping upon psychiatric patients' affect. *Therapeutic Recreation Journal, 11*(2), 70–73, 1977.

Porret, J. Peak performance. *Sports 'n Spokes, 24*(6), 22–28, 1998.

Rawland, A. Howlin' with the huskies. *Sports 'n Spokes, 24*(1), 48–51, 1998.

Robb, G. M. A correlation between socialization and self-concept in a summer camp program. *Therapeutic Recreation Journal, 5*(1), 25–29, 1971.

Robb, G. M., & S. G. Shepley. Forging partnerships: The real challenge. *Camping Magazine, 61*(2), 18–21, 1988.

Robinson, F. M., & S. S. Skinner. *A Holistic Perspective on the Disabled Child: Applications in Camping, Recreation, and Community Life.* Springfield, IL: Charles C. Thomas, 1985.

Ryan, J. L., & D. T. Johnson. Therapeutic camping: A comparative study. *Therapeutic Recreation Journal, 6*(4), 178–180, 1972.

Rynders, J., S. Schleien, & T. Mustonen. Integrating children with severe disabilities for intensified outdoor education: Focus on feasibility. *Mental Retardation, 28*(1), 7–14, 1990.

Sable, J. Collaborating to create an integrated camping program: Design and evaluation. *Therapeutic Recreation Journal, 26*(3), 38–48, 1992.

Sable, J. R. Efficacy of physical integration, disability awareness, and adventure programming on adolescents' acceptance of individuals with disabilities. *Therapeutic Recreation Journal, 29,* 206–217, 1995.

Schleien, S. J., L. H. McAvoy, G. J. Lais, & J. E. Rynders. *Integrated Outdoor Education and Adventure Programs.* Champaign, IL: Sagamore, 1993.

Schoel, J., D. Prouty, & P. Radcliffe. *Islands of Healing.* Hamilton, MA: Project Adventure, 1988.

Sessoms, H. D. Organized camping and its effects on the self-concept of physically handicapped children. *Therapeutic Recreation Journal, 13*(1), 39–43, 1979.

Shasby, G., C. Heuchert, & B. Gansneder. The effects of a structured camp experience on locus of control and self-concept of special populations. *Therapeutic Recreation Journal, 18*(2), 32–40, 1984.

Stearn, S. Accessible programs. *Camping Magazine, 56*(7), 12–15, 1984.

Szychowski, E. River of dreams. *Sports 'n Spokes, 18*(1), 19–22, 1993.

Turning POINT. [Online]. Available: http://www.turningpointtexas.org, 2003.

Vinton, D. A., D. E. Hawkins, B. D. Pantzer, & E. M. Farley. *Camping and Environmental Education for Handicapped Children and Youth.* Washington, DC: Hawkins & Associates, 1978.

Weihenmayer, E. *Touch the Top of the World.* New York: First Plume Printing, 2002.

Wilkinson, R. E. *Camps: Their Planning and Management.* St. Louis, MO: C. V. Mosby, 1981.

Witman, J. P. The efficacy of adventure programming in the development of cooperation and trust with adolescents in treatment. *Therapeutic Recreation Journal, 21*(3), 22–29, 1987.

Wright, A. N. Therapeutic potential of the Outward Bound process: An evaluation of a treatment program for juvenile delinquents. *Therapeutic Recreation Journal, 17*(2), 33–42, 1983.

10 THE ARTS— FOR EVERYONE

(Courtesy of *New Mobility Magazine*)

T he more a person travels around the world, the more he or she becomes aware of the cultural differences among human beings. Behaviors that are acceptable, or even rewarded, in one country are taboo in another. Ideas that are received with acclaim by members of one culture are rejected as absurd by people with different heritages. Yet, despite many differences, people throughout the world demonstrate similar desires for aesthetic experiences. Appreciation of beauty, in its many forms, appears to be universal. Enjoyment of beauty created by human beings is so fundamental to human existence that the right "to enjoy the arts" is included in the United Nations' Universal Declaration of Human Rights. Through the arts, people are offered an opportunity for interaction on an aesthetic level. Such interaction, based on positive feelings for beauty, is an important part of human society. Much of our knowledge about the customs, values, and beliefs of ancient societies is based on archeological analysis of their artwork. The arts, it seems, help to form and also to reflect the national character (ethos) of a society.

The arts are so essential to a society that they make an important contribution to individual development. Hayman (1969) underscored this importance in the following statement:

> Art can and should be an experience shared by all [people] every day of their lives; this does not mean that all [people] must be painters, architects, authors, composers, nor does it mean that they must spend all of their days in museums, their evenings in theatres and concert halls. Rather, it means that [people's] innate sensitivities to the arts must be allowed to develop and, by early encouragement and education, must be given opportunity for growth so that the whole [individual] can emerge. (p. 11)

The arts are essential to each citizen's life. From the small child drawing with crayons to the senior citizen reflecting on a lifetime of experiences through poetry, the arts provide a basis for discovery, self-expression, and human growth. Access to and participation in the arts is important for *all* persons in our society. Moreover, the Americans with Disabilities Act mandates that U.S. society realize its obligation to ensure that arts-related programs and services are accessible to everyone.

WHAT CONSTITUTES "THE ARTS"?

The term *the arts* is used frequently in everyday conversation, yet defining this term is difficult. As Roehner (1981) pointed out,

> On the one hand, the arts are those human endeavors that are known as art, dance, drama, filmmaking and photography, music and writing. On the other hand, the arts is also a whole battery of working methods of styles and constantly developing skills. . . . The arts embody a way of working and learning. (p. 6)

"The arts," therefore, has more than one definition. The term refers to a set of creative activities, but it also implies a concept that encompasses many methods and processes.

Regardless of art form, the arts is founded upon one essential element—creativity. Participation in the arts, on any level, provides the individual with an opportunity to organize, interpret, and express his or her *own* perceptions of the world. In other words, the arts offer a uniquely personal experience to everyone. Creativity, as noted by Diamondstein (1974), "involves the capacity to be open to experience, to welcome novelty, to be intrigued by discovery, and to exercise new dimensions of imaginative thought" (p. 15).

The National Institute on Disability and Rehabilitation Research (1991) cites research by Teresa Amabile of Brandeis University that examines the basic ingredients of creativity in the arts. These ingredients include

> (1) *expertise*—information, talent, and technical ability in relevant fields; (2) *creativity-specific skills*—a work style characterized by concentration and persistence plus a thinking style conducive to generating new possibilities; and (3) *intrinsic task motivation*—the most important component—delight in doing something for its own sake. (p. 1)

Dr. Amabile's research indicates that creativity, unlike many human behaviors, cannot be operantly conditioned because extrinsic rewards appear to reduce creativity.

Creativity in the arts is not necessarily limited to the act of developing an artistic creation. Someone else's effort, such as a musical score, offers the chance for creativity, too. For example, a pianist may play his or her own interpretation of another's creation. Carrying this idea a little farther, some authorities even insist that merely perceiving a work of art is, in itself, a creative act. Poitevin (1990) refers to this phenomenon as "an exercise in reciprocal acceptance" (p. 53). Participation in the arts, therefore, offers a person the chance to have an aesthetic experience on one (or more) of three levels—as the *creator,* the *performer,* or the *perceiver* of a work of art.

The *creator* of an artwork, no matter what medium is used, is providing an expression of his or her own being. The creator gives form to symbols or objects in such a way that beauty results, and this beauty is shared with, and affects, others. The *performer* takes a creator's efforts and, through his or her own artistic feelings and skill, transmits the work of art to others. As noted, the *perceiver* views the performance or work of art and experiences it in a creative way. The perceiver "feels" the artistic effort, but unlike the creator and performer does not share with others what is felt. It is not necessary (or possible in some cases) for all three levels of participation to be offered by a given work of art. The painter does not need a performer to transmit his or her work of art to an audience. Also, the same person may be involved on different levels, as when a poet recites his or her own poems. Nonetheless, the arts cannot be fully understood without recognizing the presence of these three levels of participation.

It is especially important for people providing recreation services to recognize that three levels of participation are offered through the arts. Rehabilitation professionals, advocacy groups, and people with disabilities complain that people who have disabilities are too often spectators while others perform. This is a valid complaint. Every effort should be made to ensure that individuals with disabilities are provided opportunities through the arts to experience creativity as creators and performers. But it should be recognized, also, that "spectators" of the arts are *active* perceivers of a creative work of art. Moreover, observing a performance or work of art may inspire the perceiver to later become a creator or performer (Tomlinson, 1982).

All three levels of participation are important and offer unique opportunities for everyone, including individuals with disabilities. The woman with mental retardation who paints a sunset provides a lasting testimony to her talent and her view of the world. She is a creator. The youth with a visual impairment who faithfully practices his guitar lessons may use his musical talents to entertain others. In so doing, he brings the composer's work to life and provides enjoyment to the listeners. He is a performer. The man with cerebral palsy who attends a ballet performance can appreciate the agility and grace of another's movement. He has an emotional reaction to the ballet's beauty that is uplifting and deeply moving. He is a perceiver. All three of these participants are engaged in "the arts," and all three are receiving the many benefits that arts participation provides.

BENEFITS OF ARTS PARTICIPATION

The benefits received from participation in the arts are not necessarily different for individuals with and without disabilities. However, barriers may limit opportunities for persons with disabilities to participate in community arts activities. Thus, people who have disabilities may not receive as many personal growth experiences as their nondisabled peers. If arts programs are made available to *everyone,* however, the three levels of arts participation offer limitless opportunities for enjoyment and satisfaction, as well as personal growth. Baer (1985), who uses a motorized wheelchair because of quadriplegia, used her personal experiences to conclude that art experience "represents a valuable coping tool for human beings, particularly those living with debilitating and irreversible physical

Participation in the arts enables a person with a disability to "create" an expression of his or her own being.
(Courtesy of Hospital for Sick Children, Washington, DC/Photo by Rhoda Baer)

conditions" (p. 213). An examination of the following six benefits of participation reveals why the arts are so important to everyone in the community.

Self-Discovery

Creativity, the cornerstone of arts participation, requires that an individual get in touch with his or her feelings and perceptions. Participation in the arts, therefore, may enable a person to become more aware of his or her individuality. Diamondstein (1974) emphasized the importance of self-discovery through involvement in the arts by noting that it can "open new windows on the world and enable [the participant] to perceive his world more richly" (p. 3). Dance, for example, may provide the opportunity for a young man with a psychological disorder to focus on the sensations of muscle relaxation and tension. Once focused on these sensations, the connection between his emotional feelings and muscular responses may become clearer to him. Such discoveries may not only aid in self-awareness, but may also make future happiness a more realistic goal (Williams, 1977). Judy Leasure, organizing committee member of the Miami (Ohio) Valley *VSA arts* Festival, observed that participation in the arts "transcends bigotry, racism, and cultural differences" and allows people with disabilities to maximize their human potential (Patyrala, 1998, p. 64).

Communication with Others

The creator and performer levels of arts participation provide unique opportunities for an individual, particularly one with a disability, to communicate with others. For example, people who cannot speak distinctly may use novels, poems, and so on, to share ideas, thoughts, and feelings with others. The late Christy Brown (1932–1981), an Irish author and poet with severe cerebral palsy, was an excellent example of such communication. Able to type only by using the little toe on his left foot, Christy Brown published a renowned novel entitled *Down All the Days.* This book, a fictionalized version of his autobiography, *My Left Foot,* was a powerful personal statement by a talented and perceptive man. In it he was able to express the challenges and frustrations he faced while living with a severe physical disability. Similarly, Tomlinson (1982)

Creativity forms the foundation for arts participation. The girl with a disability who writes a poem is offering an expression of her own being; the beauty that results from her creativity may be shared with others.
(Courtesy of The League: Serving People with Physical Disabilities, Inc., Baltimore, MD)

noted that the theater "allows for enlightenment and education; it is a tool whereby the reality of disability and the realities of people who have disabilities can be introduced, demonstrated and discussed" (p. 13).

As John Kemp, president and CEO of *VSA arts* stated "Art is an opportunity for people with disabilities to talk about their lives—the oppression and sometimes the pride—to use the arts to express the human condition" (Dobbs, 1997, p. 24).

Jacobs (1999) provides an example that brings Kemp's statement to life. He offers the following quote from the mother of an artist with a disability:

> After years of little more than existing, James has a life. He has a passion [for art] unlike any that he ever had before. His mind has begun to soar because he can communicate on his terms and express his emotions, his feelings and even his opinions through his art. (p. 29)

Improved Self-Concept

The way an individual feels about himself or herself is a critical factor in adjustment to life's many stresses. Therefore, activities that provide for successful participation and offer a chance to exert personal control of a given situation are especially important. Arts activities are ideally suited for success and personal control. Most, for example, do not have a right or wrong way of doing things. Whether painting on canvas or dancing to music, the participant should be developing his or her personal style.

Arts activities encourage individuality and are noncompetitive. There is no winner or loser. Participation can be the measure of "success." Perhaps more important than success, however, is a perception of being in control of the situation. The arts offers a unique opportunity for an individual with a disability to be in control. A participant in an arts activity is constantly presented with decision-making opportunities, and the individual controls the outcome of each decision. Personal control is reflected in the photographer's adjustment of a camera's lens, the musician's decision to hold a particular note, and the painter's selection of colors. Hull (1990) observed that "the Arts are creative and imaginative *actions* by individuals and groups that afford self-fulfillment and esteem to the 'doers,' and, perhaps curiously and incidentally, pleasure and enriching experiences to audiences" (p. 29).

In the following testimony to a U.S. Congressional committee, Laureen Summers (1988), a talented weaver who has cerebral palsy, emphasized the feelings of control and the self-confidence offered by arts participation:

> Weaving afforded me many new opportunities to explore and develop a sense of myself. Although my disability affects my coordination, I was able to figure out how to manage yarns and strings and create pleasing textures and designs. The encouragement I had to experiment with materials and ideas on my own helped me feel confident about exploring and defining other areas of my life. I gained confidence because I had proven that I could succeed in an area that was admired and respected by others. I learned to take risks, make choices, and trust myself to know what was right for me. In time I fulfilled my dreams of having my own family, my own career, my own life.

Skill Development

The many activities included within the arts offer opportunities to develop and improve on daily living skills. To cite a few examples, painting and sculpture emphasize fine motor tasks; dance pro-

motes increased coordination, endurance, and flexibility; and literature and drama teach one to communicate through written words and verbal expression. Cognitive, psychomotor, and affective skills may all be enhanced through arts participation.

Appell (1978) examined research that focused on the arts and concluded that the effects of arts programs include "improved social response, gains in school achievement, self-confidence gained by personal achievement, and a better and more integrated existence" (p. 14). The Office of Disabled Student Services at California State University, Northridge, also documented marked improvements in social growth and artistic skill development among participants in its Artistic, Cultural, and Entertainment Program (National Institute on Disability and Rehabilitation Research, 1991).

More recently, *VSA arts* (1999) noted that "the world is beginning to discover that the arts provide critical tools for learning in all academic disciplines, thus helping young people become better students today, and better employees tomorrow." *VSA arts* added that young people who participated in the arts scored nearly 100 points higher on the SAT examination than students without arts experiences. Moreover, the more years they participated in the arts, the higher their SAT scores. The National Endowment for the Arts (NEA) has also documented that the arts may improve critical skills among at-risk youth. Reporting on a research study, the NEA (1999) stated:

> Quantitative findings by researchers indicate improved life skills by youth arts program participants including an increased ability to express anger appropriately, to communicate effectively with adults and peers, and to work cooperatively to resolve conflicts. Results also show a decrease in frequency of delinquent behavior and fewer new court referrals during the program period compared with nonparticipating youth.

The Arts in Education Project developed a conceptual model that illustrates the use of an arts program for skill development (National Committee, Arts for the Handicapped, 1981). This model, which has been modified to include literary

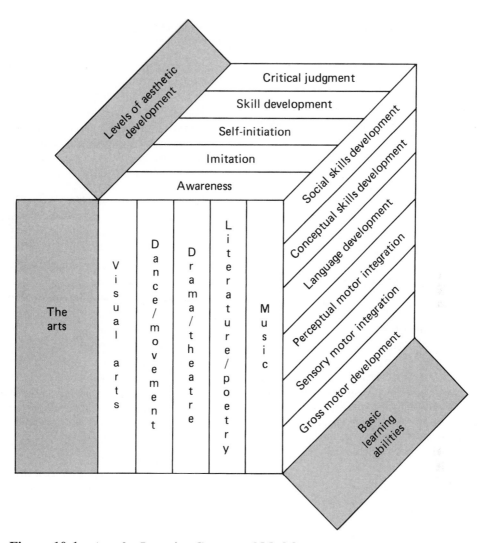

Figure 10-1   Arts for Learning Conceptual Model
(Modified from: *Very Special Arts, Arts Resource and Training Guide.* Washington, DC: NCAH, p. 59.)

activities, appears in Figure 10-1. The primary purpose of the model is to show that basic learning abilities and aesthetic development are interrelated and are enhanced through participation in the arts.

Societal Recognition and Awareness

The arts have proven especially well suited for people with disabilities to share their exceptional talent with others. Christy Brown (literature—cerebral palsy), Stevie Wonder (music—blindness), Joni Eareckson (art—quadriplegia), Sylvia Plath (literature—psychological disorder), Itzhak Perlman (music—polio), and Marlee Matlin (drama—deafness) are just a few of the people with disabilities who have received national and international acclaim through the arts. Their successes have helped make the general public aware that individuals with disabilities have a great deal to offer society. Public awareness is also enhanced by many lesser known participants in the arts. Charlene Curtiss, director of the Light Motion dance company of Seattle, WA, stated, "The visual image of someone moving in dance in a wheelchair is so stimulating it can change people's attitudes about disability" (Lathrop, 1999, p. 27). Yost (1999), describing Chicago's Special Music by Special People All Star Band, wrote that the group uses "the universal language of music to break barriers between people with and without disabilities" (p. 63).

Also, the arts has proven to be an excellent vehicle for public education when the subject (irrespective of the creator and performer) refers to disability. Performing in a Theatre Ashbury production about persons with hearing impairments, high school students from Ontario, Canada, found the need to know more about deafness and individuals with hearing impairments. They "asked for six hours a week of instruction [in sign language]—an immersion in deaf culture" (Mangiacasale, 1993, p. 55). In an earlier production of *One Flew Over the Cuckoo's Nest,* Theatre Ashbury's student actors and actresses also immersed themselves in study about psychological disorders. As Molloy (1978) pointed out, "The arts reflect and inspire the hopes and struggles of society. Struggling for their place in society, [people with disabilities] can infuse the arts with a completely new range of human experiences, and through the arts inspire the public to accept them for their gifts rather than their needs" (p. 39).

Social Interaction

The arts offers tremendous potential as a medium for socially integrating people with disabilities into the mainstream of society. Most arts activities offer cooperative tasks that lend themselves to small group efforts using each participant's unique skills and abilities. These activity characteristics are ideal for successful inclusion (Dattilo, 1994; Hutchison & Lord, 1979; Schleien, Ray, & Green, 1997). For inclusion to occur, however, it is essential that arts-related programs facilitate interaction between people with and without disabilities. Jane

Alexander, pastchair of the NEA, emphasized this when she stated,

> I emphatically reject the notion that special or different arts programs be developed for [people with disabilities]; rather, existing programs of the highest quality should be opened to everyone. It's the only way we know of to avoid creating double standards, to avoid ghettoizing [people who have disabilities]. (Dobbs, 1997, p. 22)

Schleien, Rynders, and Mustonen (1988) have provided support for the use of arts-related activities to promote social integration for individuals with disabilities. They reported on a three-year project (separate investigations) that used a variety of strategies to integrate children with moderate to severe cognitive disabilities into community-based museum activities. These studies found (1) significant improvements in attitude among nondisabled children toward their peers with disabilities; (2) significant increases in positive social interactions by children without disabilities toward peers with disabilities; (3) significant increases in appropriate behavior among younger children with disabilities; and (4) slight increases in cooperative behaviors among participants with and without disabilities. Although more studies of this nature are needed, it is apparent that the arts can help to achieve social integration.

The six benefits of arts participation are not all-encompassing. Nor, should they be interpreted to mean that everyone benefits equally from artistic pursuits. Just as some people display more artistic talent than others, some benefit more than others from arts involvement. It was stated previously that the benefits of arts participation are similar for both people with and without disabilities. The *degree* of benefit may differ, however. For many people with disabilities, the challenges of daily life may increase their need for arts involvement. Regardless of whether their need is greater or the same as everyone else's, however, two important principles should be recognized: (1) Everyone, including people with disabilities, can enjoy and benefit from participation in the arts; and (2) each art form can benefit from the unique perspective offered by participants who have disabilities.

THE ARTS AND DISABILITY CULTURE

The preceding section focused upon the benefits received and contributions offered by *individuals* with disabilities who participate in the arts. Many people, however, maintain that the collective artistic contributions of people with disabilities help to confirm the existence of "disability culture." Oliver (1996), for example, cited the "development of a disability culture and the public affirmation of this through the disability arts movement" (p. 152). In 1999, the Art & Soul Festival in Los Angeles was touted as a celebration of disability culture (Lathrop, 1999).

Does a disability culture really exist? The answer to that question may depend upon how one defines culture; nevertheless, Brown (1998), Gill (1995), Jeffrey (1998), Oliver (1996) and many others have made convincing arguments for the existence of an emerging disability culture. Based on his research, John (1998) thinks that the prerequisites for establishing the existence of a disability culture are in evidence.

> These are tools and technology useful for the person with a disability; a largely shared value system in support of the individual with a disability; and an emphasis on events and information that promote interaction within the disability community and a subsequent empowerment through collective action. (p. 25)

VSA arts (Art Disability Expression: Disability Culture, 2003) defines culture as the "sense of a collective identity, a group of individuals who share related formative experiences and who are influenced by a common history." They go on to say that "a culture finds expression in many ways, such as through the arts or through social organization. People with disabilities demonstrate these common experiences through their personal struggles, writings and histories." Disability culture is revered as a movement that embraces disability as a necessary and valued part of people's lives.

Peters (2000) identifies four essential elements that all people with disabilities must share in order for their experiences to be considered cultural. The first element is common language. There needs to be a common language used by people with disabilities and for use by people external to the culture. This might include using "power" terms that are offensive if used by people without disabilities, but are utilized nonoffensively by people who are within the culture (e.g., gimp, crip). This also means that people without disabilities use terminology that promotes the culture. An example would be using "person first" terminology (e.g., person with mental retardation, rather than mentally retarded person; see chapter 2). The second element would assume that there is a history. There is acknowledgment of the existence of a chronological history among people with disabilities. This history might be evidenced in journal articles, movies and TV shows, social justice movements, sports, and/or political arenas. There is reinforcement and recognition among people with disabilities that other people with disabilities lived before them and an understanding about what others with disabilities historically experienced. The third element is social connection. There is a social connection among people with disabilities in the larger social context. In the 1960s and 1970s, the Independent Living Movement began to emerge, creating opportunities for people with disabilities to live together and share their experiences. In the 1970s, deinstitutionalization and mainstreaming offered the opportunity for people with disabilities to live in group homes in residential communities and participate in the mainstream of society. In the 1990s, the signing of the Americans with Disabilities Act defined disability and promoted inclusion of persons with disabilities in daily life. Each of these events furthers the idea that a disability culture may exist. The final element is a genetic link. The fact that many disabling conditions have genetic links (e.g., muscular dystrophy, autism) supports a generational disability culture. Also, many people who are deaf prefer to raise their children who are deaf in a "segregated" deaf community. According to Peters' perspective, each of these four elements has supporting "qualifications" for the existence of a disability culture.

Barnes and Mercer (2003) contend that the disability arts movement provides support for the emergence of a disability culture. They note that the disability arts movement is "potentially educative, expressive and transformative" (p. 107) and includes several dimensions. First, the movement strives to give artists with disabilities full access to mainstream artistic endeavors. Second, it provides a vehicle for exploring the experience of living with a disability. Finally, and most importantly, the movement gives artists the means to respond to marginalization and exclusion from society. Disability art provides a means for exposing the discrimination and prejudice experienced by persons with disabilities and, at the same time, has the potential to foster a positive group consciousness and identity among all persons with disabilities.

Most people with disabilities who express themselves through the arts, and most arts professionals, avoid the subject of disability culture (Dobbs, 1997). Some even reject the idea that their work somehow reflects disability-related themes. Nevertheless, many people observe themes emerging from the artistic endeavors of persons who have disabilities. Such themes often reflect the many barriers experienced by persons with disabilities, such as "brokenness and the search for wholeness," segregation from society, and oppression (Dobbs, p. 26). As noted by Jacobs (1999), "the chasm separating those persons with severe disabilities from the able-bodied world is a source of great isolation, frustration and pain" (p. 30). David Roche, a comedian who has a disability, agrees that negative disability-related experiences have influenced his work. He commented, "The content of what I do, some of the darker humor, I think comes from the culture of disability" (Lathrop, 1999, p. 26).

Oliver (1996) and others, however, also point to the emergence of more optimistic themes among artists with disabilities. These themes include concepts like empowerment, pride, cohesiveness, and resilience. Oliver contends that these themes challenge the conventional notion of stigma experienced by persons with disabilities. The following poem by Eileen Holland, an individual with multiple sclerosis, supports Oliver's contention.

Outsider's M.S.

—By Eileen Holland

Don't pity me for my problems,
Admire me for how well I cope with them.
If you notice the weakness of my body,
Also notice the strength of my spirit.
Don't feel sad about my struggle,
Respect me because I never stop trying.
If you note how clumsy I am,
Also note my grace under pressure.
If you count the things I can no longer do,
Don't forget to add the things I've learned.
Make me laugh
Instead of crying for me.
See what MS has given me,
Not what it has taken away.
Don't feel sorry about what I have lost,
Help me count my blessings.

Brown (1998) also emphasized that having a disability should be a source of cultural pride. He wrote:

> People with disabilities have forged a group identity. We share a common history of oppression and a common bond of resilience. We generate art, music, literature, and other expressions of our lives, our culture, infused from our experience of disability. Most importantly, we are proud of ourselves as people with disabilities. We claim our disabilities with pride as part of our identity. We are who we are: we are people with disabilities. (p. 9)

Whether the shared experiences, values, and artistic expressions of persons with disabilities constitute a distinct "culture" will probably continue to be debated. Regardless, participation in the arts enables many people with disabilities to express feelings that are based upon disability-related experiences—and these feelings are shared by many, if not most, persons with disabilities.

LEADERSHIP IN THE ARTS

More arts programs that include individuals with disabilities can be achieved only through knowledgeable, energetic, and effective leadership. Personnel working with persons who have disabilities need adequate training in the arts and in how to lead arts activities effectively. It is not possible, within the scope of this chapter, to provide a comprehensive guide for leaders of arts activities that would encompass all art forms and all types of disabling conditions. We may, however, offer a few principles for successful leadership of an arts program that includes participants with disabilities. These principles are essentially the same as leadership principles for any inclusive recreational activity and include the following:

1. *Determine Program Goals.* What you are trying to accomplish through your arts program should be expressed as written goals. These program goals, to a large extent, will guide decision making in such matters as the amount of integration desired, leadership style employed, whether cooperative group projects are more desirable than individual efforts, and so on. One area of special concern in the arts is the relative importance of the final product in comparison with the *process* used to achieve the final product. Although there will be some situations that require a strong emphasis on the finished product, we agree with the following statement by Roehner (1981):

   > a [child with blindness] working with finger paint may express a feeling of being loved by making magnificent circles in finger paint. The product may not be aesthetically pleasing but the kinesthetic treatment of the soft paint with circular motions indicates that the student perceives something of emotion, love, and is responding to it and to the medium. It is the art of expressing that is important, not the product. (p. 6)

   Putting the final sentence of Roehner's commentary into a written goal statement would help ensure that program leaders approach all arts activities in a consistent way.

2. *Encourage Creativity.* The arts should provide activities that encourage, rather than discourage, creative expression. Prefabricated or highly structured arts activities should be minimized or eliminated, and program leaders should emphasize flexibility in each activity. The leader's importance in fostering creativity cannot be overemphasized. The leader can serve as a role model by expressing his or her individuality while, at the same time, communicating to each participant that there is no such thing as failure in the arts (Kunkle-Miller, 1981). Successful integration is much easier to attain when creativity is emphasized. Children with mental retardation, for example, may be able to achieve high status in an integrated arts group because they do not differ significantly from their nonretarded peers on nonverbal measures of creativity (Sherrill & Cox, 1979). Ross (1980) also stressed the importance of creativity and stated that arts leaders should create conditions of creativity by:
   1. establishing the sanctity of mutual truthfulness.
   2. developing trust (trustworthiness and mutual trustfulness).
   3. being free enough to free students to act playfully, to explore and invent an atmosphere that is nonjudgmental, where error is essential to trial.
   4. providing conditions of psychic safety—being compassionate.
   5. being devoted to the child's learning and growth. (p. 110)

   Unless creativity is allowed to flourish, many of the benefits of arts participation will be lost.

3. *Individualize Activities.* Each arts activity should be geared, as much as possible, to the skill level and personal needs of each participant. The demands of a given activity should be compared with the participant's capabilities, and modifications made

when appropriate (Copeland, 1984). The following are a few considerations for offering arts activities to participants with disabilities:

1. Time, space, and materials may need to be limited to meet specific needs.
2. Emphasis should be placed on the senses by using appropriate materials—e.g., sand, finger paints, soft cloth or yarn, aromatic fragrances, audible devices.
3. Small group size is often preferable to larger groups, and forming a circle increases feelings of unity in some activities, such as dance.
4. A logical progression of skill development should occur, starting with tasks that have been mastered and proceeding to more difficult ones.
5. Reinforce accomplishments with appropriate praise. This rewards participation and gives the individual a feeling of success.

Harlan (1992) also notes that open-ended projects should be used because they "allow the participant to determine the outcome of the art experience to as great an extent as possible" (p. 2). Ananda Coomaraswamy, an Indian writer, is credited with stating that "the artist is not a special kind of man, but every man is a special kind of artist" (Shaw, 1980, p. 73). Individualizing arts activities brings out the "specialness" in each participant, irrespective of disability.

4. *Plan for Access.* It often is necessary to make special preparations to ensure that arts programs are accessible to and usable by people with disabilities. Architectural barriers often limit participation by those who have disabilities, but public attitudes are important, also, when planning for access. The use of "tactile" art galleries, which allow artifacts to be handled by individuals who are blind, is criticized by some museum officials because "they fear that artifacts will be at worst destroyed and at best soiled by repeated handling" (Educational Facilities Laboratory and the National Endowment for the Arts, 1975, p. 20). Sadly, such attitudes serve to prevent people with disabilities from becoming patrons of the arts. Access depends on the removal of physical obstacles *and* change of attitudinal barriers.

5. *Attend In-Service Training Programs.* As the arts participant increases in skill, his or her changing needs may require a change in teaching methods and materials. Similarly, the leader of an arts program should continue to grow by seeking relevant and informative in-service training opportunities. Unfortunately, many such programs focus solely on awareness or sensitivity training in one specific arts area. Selecting *quality* in-service programs, however, can result in benefits. The National Committee Arts for the Handicapped (NCAH) (1981), now *VSA arts,* cautioned potential in-service participants, "the frequency and length of individual training sessions has much less to do with effectiveness, than the quality of the instructor, format and resources" (p. 169). Careful selection is required, but in-service training for arts leaders can result in better arts programs for everyone.

ARTS PARTICIPATION—EXAMPLES

This chapter has provided information about the arts and people with disabilities, but to understand the *personal* nature of arts involvement we need to examine examples of arts participation. We have selected two in-depth examples that reveal the meaning of arts participation to persons with disabilities. One of these focuses on an individual participant, Claudia Fowler, and the deep personal fulfillment she received from writing poetry. The other, Theatre Unlimited, presents group participation in the arts (theater), and highlights creative expression, attitude change, and inclusion through the arts. We have also included detailed information on *VSA arts,* an international organization that

For inclusion to occur, arts-related programs must facilitate social interaction between people with and without disabilities.
(Courtesy of *Palaestra,* 1989, Vol. 6, No. 1, Dr. Boni Boswell and Mike Hamer/Photo by Tony Rumple)

promotes inclusion of persons with disabilities in a wide variety of arts programs. These examples are followed by brief descriptions of other noteworthy arts programs that include persons with disabilities.

Claudia Fowler

Claudia Fowler died at the age of 32. In most ways, Claudia's life was not exceptional, but she had cerebral palsy and scoliosis, which resulted in almost complete dependency on others. She could not walk; neither could she dress, bathe, eat, or use the toilet unassisted. Claudia could speak, but only people who spent a great deal of time with her

could understand her. Many whose lives touched Claudia's thought she had severe mental retardation—they did not take the time to find out if she could comprehend what they were saying. "Claudia couldn't understand why people who knew her, even some relatives, would speak to her as if she were a child," commented her mother, Catherine L. Fowler. "That's something I will never understand, either," she added, slowly shaking her head.

Claudia attended "special" elementary and junior high schools in the Baltimore, Maryland, area. It was many years before the Individuals with

Claudia's poems are reprinted courtesy of Catherine L. Fowler.

Disabilities Education Act (IDEA), however, so the regular high schools were not accessible to individuals using wheelchairs. Denied the right to attend high school, Claudia was taught by home tutors until she received her high school diploma in 1968. Home instruction did enable Claudia to develop her cognitive abilities, but it deprived her of one important aspect of the teen years—social interaction with peers.

Community programs developed exclusively for individuals with physical disabilities became Claudia's primary source for social interaction. Many of these programs, however, required that she conform to the leader's plans, rather than allowing her the freedom to pursue her own interests. "Claudia became very frustrated with some of the programs she attended," her mother recalled. "A woman at one program *insisted* that she participate in a cooking class. After the class Claudia said to me, 'Mother, I'll never be able to cook! Why can't I be allowed to do what I want?'" Few of these programs could offer her the freedom she desired—the freedom to express her individuality in her way. This need for self-expression was met when Claudia began to write poetry.

"It is a bit difficult to describe just how I come up with a poem," wrote Claudia. "It builds up inside of me, but not in my mind, until I start to type.

The words just keep coming 'til I type the last word in a poem. It is sort of like giving birth." Most of the thoughts included in Claudia's poems evolved while she lay in bed at night reflecting on her favorite themes of animals, nature, and human emotions. In the morning, her poems were "born" at an electric typewriter. Claudia could not use her arms and hands to type, but she did have some control of her head movements. She painstakingly pecked at the typewriter keys using a metal pointer attached to a head band. As with many people who have cerebral palsy, the amount of muscular control Claudia possessed varied from moment to moment. The more relaxed she was, the better she was able to type. She wrote, "To type a poem takes me anywhere from half an hour to a week depending on the length of the poem and how nervous I feel. Of course, some days are better than others." Claudia could relax best when she was able to spend time outdoors. Whether she was sitting behind her rural home overlooking acres of fields and woods, or on a hike at the resident camp she loved, Camp Greentop, Claudia was fascinated by the wonders of nature. Her poems often contained a "nature" theme.

It was at Camp Greentop, located in western Maryland, that Claudia met Peter Setlow and his wife, Barbara. Pete, the camp's program director,

Feelings

People are not just specimens of the physical anatomy,
*   they consist of mysterious and unpredictable things which*
*   are known as feelings.*
Feelings aren't something that we can control
*   although sometimes we'd give anything if we could;*
*   they're a part of life which is involuntary.*
Occasionally, we become timid about expressing our feelings,
*   and they grow into a whirlpool of frustrations within us.*
To share our feelings with someone,
*   is like releasing a herd of wild mustangs;*
*   it places our innermost soul in a state of tranquility*
*   and freedom.*

(Claudia, 1978)

Remedy for Loneliness

Today, pearl-gray clouds fill the sky,
*   making the solitude seem more intense,*
Loneliness is the most agonizing sickness,
*   with no chemical pain reliever known;*
*   it is the slowest form of suicide*
Being lonely and withdrawn from people,
*   is just as poisonous as any*
*   type of malignancy.*
This senseless illness has the simplest remedy in the world,
*   a friend.*
One other thing is also needed,
*   a willingness to trust your fellow man.*

(Claudia, 1977)

appreciated Claudia's intellect and took a sincere interest in her. The friendship between Claudia and the Setlow family, particularly Pete, continued year-round until Claudia's death. The importance of friendship in anyone's life cannot be overestimated, but to someone with a severe disability the joy of having a genuine friend may transcend all other emotions. Pete, Barbara, and later their children, Barry and Jenny, added much happiness to Claudia's life. But, as the Setlows are quick to point out, knowing Claudia also enriched their lives immensely.

The last few months of Claudia's life were spent in the hospital. She was not physically strong, but her faith and friendships sustained her. Finally, however, respiratory failure claimed Claudia's life.

Final Comment

Claudia Fowler was not included in this chapter because she possessed exceptional literary talent. Until now, none of her poems has been published, although a friend did have some of them bound into a volume entitled *A Bridge to My Thoughts.* Claudia was unique because every individual, whether having a disability or not, is unique. The arts provided Claudia with a meaningful way of expressing her individuality. A British woman, who had a disability that distorted her facial features and prevented speech, once wrote, "It's my body you see, not my mind." Through her poems, we get a glimpse of Claudia Fowler's bright and sensitive mind.

Theatre Unlimited

Theatre Unlimited[1] is a dramatic ensemble that shatters popular myths about mental retardation. Composed half of actors with developmental disabilities and half of actors without disabilities, the company is dedicated to a creative process that provides a vision; the vision is that of a community of spirit, where love sparks the transformation process allowing the performer to risk and the viewer to perceive in new ways. Through visual and corporeal images, a spectrum of pain and exhilaration is revealed. Theatre Unlimited is changing the context and aesthetics of theatre. Performances throughout the nation provide a model for artists, educators, recreators, and therapists, and present new attitudes and approaches to the general public.

[1]Theatre Unlimited is a program of RCH, Inc., in San Francisco, CA. The company's publication, *Theatre Unlimited,* was funded by a grant from the Evelyn J. and Walter Hass, Jr., Foundation and the Sandy Foundation. The booklet was written by David Morgan, Herb Felsenfeld, and Richard Heus and appears in modified form with permission of the authors and RCH, Inc.

Life

Life is a strange thing,
which can't be explained in just a few words.
It is the happiness found in a new healthy baby,
or the sadness of a senseless death.
The gleam in the eyes of a child as he tried to
blow out the candle on his first birthday cake
or the empty look in the eyes of a lonely old
man as he gazes out the window on his ninety-first
birthday.
That hard struggle of a young intelligent girl lifting
herself from the apathy of the slums,
or the wealthy sophisticated debutante;
who has her desires and goals handed to her
without having to strive for them.
It is seeing and appreciating the beautiful wonders of nature,
and not taking them for granted.
Life is made of these things and so much more,
but above all else, it is the most precious thing
that we will ever have and
it should be cherished.

(Claudia, 1976)

Process

Theatre Unlimited's work is based on transformation and revelation. The ensemble addresses many of its members' needs—physical, emotional, and intellectual—while offering society a model for the future. In addressing these needs, the actors approach a nurturing quality of spirit that, when viewed by an audience, has applications in many realms.

The persona of the actor is central to this process. The actor transforms images of sound and movement and quantities of time and space for the sin~~c~~' ~~p~~urpose of exposing a soul in public. As ~~a~~nce member discovered, "There is some-~~thing~~ ~~her~~e, who is beyond labels, beyond pity ~~. . . some~~one who is more like myself than I ~~thought.~~"

~~. . .~~ Theatre Unlimited lie in develop-~~ing a re~~latively new approach, this form ~~trains the~~ actor physically and vocally,

with an extra emphasis on emotional development and group process or ensemble work. Theatre Unlimited defines an ensemble as "a group of supporting players who work together to create a single effect." This ensemble process is reflected in all aspects of the company's work and play. Concentration and focused interactions are nurtured and find expression through sound, movement, and physical contact. Like improvisational theatre (another approach used by Theatre Unlimited), ensemble process demands the development of trust, support, and cooperation. Through this approach emerges a level of honesty and caring that has allowed the company to clearly mature from year to year.

While it is true that an actor without a disability can express a movement or a dramatic gesture with more fluidity than a performer with cerebral palsy, it is equally true that sincerity of ensemble effort achieves artistic excellence. Theatre Unlimited has forged its own identity, and there is much

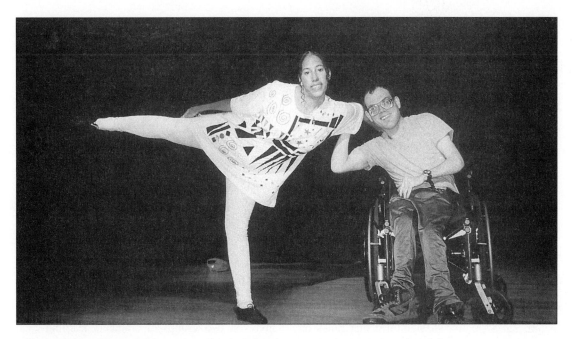

Theatre Unlimited's performances are a direct and logical outgrowth of rehearsals and workshops.
(Courtesy of Theatre Unlimited/RCH, Inc., San Francisco, CA)

that can be done only by the artists in Theatre Unlimited. The work is built on discipline and imagination, the principal ingredients of theatre art.

Rehearsal

Initially, Theatre Unlimited decided that each three-hour rehearsal would consist of a full hour of physical warm-ups, followed by a half hour of partnered exchanges such as mirror exercises and give-and-take games, an hour for the introduction of ensemble activities, and a half hour at the end for group discussion and sharing: It turned out, however, that too much structure too soon inhibited growth and the possibility of new discoveries.

While building and maintaining a ritual of starting with group warm-ups, and closing with a circle for discussion and sharing, the company loosened the time in between to allow for spontaneous occurrences and to accommodate specific rehearsal needs.

The warm-up routine incorporated traditional theatre exercises along with the company's collective knowledge of techniques from yoga, T'ai Chi,

mime, and dance. Particularly important was the time taken to study and learn the essential skill of relaxation. From a calm basis, sessions continually maintained a flow of energy that rarely demanded a break. From the beginning, energy was high and the intensive level of training produced slow yet steady progress. The ratio (actors with and without disabilities) of the company allowed the participants to become close working partners. At first, some members were confused by the abstract nature of the work. To them, drama meant putting on a play. Common questions were: "What's this mirror for?" or "Why am I relaxing?" Then and today, it is necessary to continually struggle for a common vocabulary, one accessible to all company members. The group concentrated on the basic building blocks of actor training, sound and movement, and began to put more imagery to its physical work. By connecting concrete images to movement, understanding began to increase and entire movement combinations were assimilated.

Much early work focused on building the trust necessary to function well as an ensemble. Games and exercises were introduced that demanded this response. Actors leaned on each other with full body weight. They formed a tight circle and took turns falling into waiting arms. One partner led the other, blindfolded, through strange environments. Success was easily noted because these games placed few cognitive demands.

Learning is frequently divided into three categories: cognitive, affective, and physical. While research shows that those with normal intelligence score significantly higher in verbal measures of creativity—or the cognitive domain—there are no significant differences between people with and without retardation on nonverbal measures of creativity. Persons with developmental disabilities often show strengths in imaginative behavior and willingness to trust, take risks, and be spontaneous. From its inception, Theatre Unlimited's process has been built on this research and on the belief that a creative theater form that relies on nonverbal activity can evolve.

The mirror game is the best example of this kind of nonverbal activity. With its many variations, it has been an essential part of ensemble training. A partnered exercise of follow-the-leader, the mirror exercise demands great concentration. Often performed to slow, flowing music, it involves precise imitation and creative initiation. As roles are reversed and partners changed, actors begin to know each other as individual expressive people.

At the end of each three-hour session the ensemble sits in a circle and talks. When pressed for reactions to the evening's rehearsal, members with disabilities often find it difficult to articulate specific feelings. It has been particularly gratifying for the company to become close enough for all to share reactions and feelings. Sharing, especially in nonverbal ways, began to balance in importance with the pace of Theatre Unlimited's skill building. One participant stated:

> Here I've learned about timing—after ten years of working with disabled people. I've finally allowed myself the time to wait. It's different timing than I would use. But when someone else uses it, it's unique. Here, I find

that disabled people "can do." For years we've been told that they can't. The progression is amazing—people are expressing themselves, they are saying things to each other, to the audience. I can take that knowledge of slow steady growth back to my job and use that with my hope that people will change. It may take 2 or 3 weeks, maybe 2 or 3 years.

Performance

Theatre Unlimited views its approach to performance as a direct and logical outgrowth of rehearsals and workshops. Performance is looked at as a way station along a developmental continuum, and the audience is invited to participate in the viewing of this process.

The company's first performed score (an outline of events that occur in sequence around a theme) was called "The Initiation." Its theme involved two groups of strangers learning each other's rituals and eventually coming together. The score was also an accurate reflection of the company's stage of development. Tensions, anxieties, and mistrust existed. Instead of being looked at as problems, these fears were incorporated into the creative process, and solutions, developed through rehearsal, were shared in public. Technical aspects of the piece remained simple—as much out of choice as out of financial necessity. Performing barefoot in leotard tops and drawstring pants against a dark backdrop, the group used masks and live percussion accompaniment.

The outcome of the first year's exploration involved work that was primarily in sound and movement. Work was at a level of physical interaction akin to dance theater. Because of its grounding in improvisation, the company was able to transform mistakes, missed cues, and delayed entrances into appropriate happenings. A style was beginning to evolve. The audience saw that support could be a demanding and exciting physical discipline.

Another level of development happened during the second year. The score grew in complexity. New elements included performing parts of the sequence in American Sign Language; creating a particular place, a playground, through the actors' imaginative skills; refining the company's sound and movement skills to extend into the area of physical and spatial transformation; and integrating song and poetry into the sequence. Audience response—especially during moments when the planned "next move" did not occur—gave the company reassurance. People were once again genuinely intrigued by what they saw. The awkward, the amateurish, were transformed into the deeply human, the deeply affecting. The audience participated in the event. The act of faith *played.*

For Theatre Unlimited, performance is a laboratory where the group can explore and reveal greater understanding of the developmental process. The performance laboratory is a place where ideas, not personalities, dominate.

Workshops

Workshops are the way Theatre Unlimited reaches out and opens its process to the audience. Here the momentum of performance winds down, the fourth wall between viewer and actor opens, and the empty space fills with the activities of revelation.

People—from school-age children on up—are involved in an intensely physical experience. What begins as two groups, actors and viewers, soon coalesces into one group that functions on different levels. The line starts to blur. What of the disability? Does it make any difference?

Here the viewer is put into a unique situation: Working, for example, with a man who has Down syndrome, is almost nonverbal, and is engaged in bending over to touch the top of his head to his toe. Not knee. Toe. Perception shifts, and the mind moves on to the next level of wonder. A woman with mental retardation shows a university professor how to master an isolation exercise. Ground is broken, and the meaning of the word disability changes.

The most uninhibited reactions, and in many ways the most challenging and gratifying, are those involving schoolchildren. Students in the second and third grades have not learned to label and stereotype. They can hardly wait to share energy and games. As they look to all company

members as equals, their learning is accelerated and they are soon involved in a joyful experience. The workshop atmosphere is exciting, with a sense of wonder that is barrier-free, as the following quote attests:

> What I want from the general public is honesty. I see how our process has changed people in our company, because now people are together with those they can trust, we can confide in each other, talk and really feel like we're getting honest feedback. There was not communication, before, between some of these people. You could sit down and listen to people talk, and one person would be talking and the other person would respond on a totally different subject. There was no real communication, there was no feeling. Now I sit and listen to our company talk and it's amazing. it's almost too much. It's "you know, I really like you." All this out front stuff.

Theatre Unlimited functions as a reflection of our particular time and culture, in addition to acting as a model of events about to happen. As long as the model remains healthy, it will point toward a time of unobstructed access to creative tools for all people.

VSA arts

VSA arts is an international nonprofit organization founded in 1974 by Ambassador Jean Kennedy Smith. *VSA arts* is creating a society where people with disabilities can learn through, participate in, and enjoy the arts. Nearly 5 million people with disabilities participate in *VSA arts* programs every year through a network of affiliates in 49 states and 64 countries worldwide.

Dedicated to artistic excellence and providing lifelong opportunities for people with disabilities, *VSA arts* implements a wide variety of programs in music, dance, drama, creative writing, and the visual arts through its extensive affiliate network. These programs help to develop learning skills, encourage independence, and promote access and inclusion.

VSA arts has four guiding principles that demonstrate the organization's mission and dedication to providing people with disabilities opportunities to excel and achieve.

- Every young person with a disability deserves access to appropriate arts learning experiences.
- All artists in schools and art educators should be appropriately prepared to include students with disabilities in their instruction.
- All children, youth, and adults with disabilities should have complete access to community cultural facilities and activities.
- All individuals with disabilities who aspire to careers in the arts should have the opportunity to develop appropriate skills.

VSA arts has a variety of programs that are targeted toward specific priorities—K–12 education, professional development through the *VSA arts* Institute, the International *VSA arts* Festival, and research and evaluation. *VSA arts* has been mandated by the U.S. Congress to be the coordinating organization for arts programming for children and youth with disabilities. Not to stop there, *VSA arts* has also taken the lead in providing arts programming for adults with disabilities as well, believing that people with disabilities are entitled to lifelong learning through the arts.

Professional development of teachers and educators is essential to *VSA arts'* mission. The *VSA arts* Institute provides training to artists and art educators to be able to include effectively students with disabilities in their instruction. As a result, more inclusive programs and classrooms will benefit all students, with or without disabilities.

As one of the most important global educational and artistic events in arts education, the International *VSA arts* Festival celebrates equity and excellence in the arts. Artists with disabilities from around the globe gather in one place to share their talents and abilities with the thousands of international participants that flock to the Festival. Educators are offered numerous opportunities to learn about new developments in the area of increased access to the arts, such as Universal Design, Cultural Access, and inclusive classrooms.

Participants gain a general understanding of the arts, education, and disability and how all three fit together in creating a society where people with disabilities have the opportunity to learn through, participate in, and enjoy the arts.

Achieving great strides in research and evaluation, *VSA arts* continues to spearhead initiatives that analyze and examine arts programs and their impact on learning for all students, those with and without disabilities. *VSA arts* also takes a look at the accessibility of the arts for people with disabilities. Often, facilities assume that physical access is enough. It's not. What society needs is accessible programming as well.

In line with its research efforts, *VSA arts* positions itself as a leading resource for art, education, and disability information, forging the path to explore the impact of the arts in the lives of people with disabilities.

For more information on *VSA arts,* please visit www.vsarts.org, e-mail info@vsarts.org, or call 1-800-933-8721.

Other Arts—Related Programs

Form in Art (Philadelphia, PA)

The award-winning program Form in Art by the Philadelphia Museum of Art celebrated its 30th anniversary in 2001. The focus of this 3-year program that offers arts-based courses for persons who are blind or partially sighted is sculpture and art history, and the museum's collection is used to provide hands-on learning experiences for participants. Art history lessons, lectures by museum staff members, and "touch tours" of original art objects are used to expose participants to a wide range of periods and styles of art. Program participants also create sculptures in a variety of artistic media. In addition to Form in Art, the Philadelphia Museum of Art offers a wide variety of programs for persons with disabilities. These programs include workshops for persons with psychological disorders, arts instruction for people with developmental disabilities, a telephone course ("ART TALK") for older adults, and workshops for persons living with HIV and AIDS. For more information call (215) 684-7601 (voice) or (215) 684-7600 (TTY), or visit their website at http://www.philamuseum.org.

AXIS Dance Company (Oakland, CA)

Developed by dancers with and without disabilities, AXIS has been in the forefront in creating powerful and inclusive dance form, called physically integrated dance. Ten performers with and without disabilities have graced the stages throughout the United States and abroad. Although based in the Bay Area and on tour throughout the United States, AXIS has also performed in Germany and Siberia and has quickly gained international recognition. In collaboration with Dance Umbrella, AXIS planned and implemented the International Festival of Wheelchair Dance in June 1997. This was the first recognized event of this size in the history of the relatively new and inclusive dance form of physically integrated dance. It was also the beginning of an international dialogue about the philosophy, aesthetics, and quality of physically integrated dance. Sonya Delwaide, choreographer of AXIS, offered this statement in response to her work with a recent dance performance: "Every dance commission brings new discoveries. When I start a project I do not know how the dancers will react to my vocabulary; the creative process is based on an exchange. I like to see what each individual has to offer and what they do with the movement. It is the same in the case of AXIS; the only difference was that I had to get to know and understand how the different types of wheelchairs function. For me the wheelchair is just an extension of their body and even the choice of chair (power or manual) can help define their way of moving and/or character."

AXIS Dance Company also has an extensive outreach and community education program called Dance Access. Dance Access and its youth component, Dance Access/KIDS!, offer an ongoing program of classes for adults and youth of all abilities. The company participates in a wide variety of lecture demonstrations, residency activities, and school assemblies. AXIS recently took part in the Kennedy Center's Imagination Celebration at the 2002 Olympic Arts Festival and is on the roster of Young Audiences Bay Area and San Jose. For more information on Access, call 510-625-0110, email info@axisdance.org, or visit http://www.axisdance.org.

Homeland Neighborhood Cultural Center (Long Beach, CA)

This community-based center, operated by the City of Long Beach Department of Parks, Recreation and Marine, supports the work of local artists, including at-risk youth, and provides a wide variety of arts-based educational experiences. The center provides an environment of acceptance in which gang members, prison inmates, and previously incarcerated youth and adults can share experiences and learn to express themselves through the arts. Program offerings include artist-in-residence projects, dance workshops, multicultural art exhibits and instruction, writers' workshops, and a neighborhood mural program. Dixie Swift, the center's founder, observed, "This is the most diverse, poorest and highest crime area in the city. And it's the richest in traditions" (Ransom, 1996, p. 46). The Homeland Neighborhood Cultural Center provides a means for expressing and perpetuating these cultural traditions. For more information call (562) 570-3100 (voice) or visit http://www.lbparks.org.

Famous People Players (Toronto, Canada)

This touring theatre company features performers with and without mental retardation. "Making wonderful use of blacklight technology, black-garbed, and thus invisible actors and actresses manipulate all sorts of fluorescent puppets and props under ultra-violet lights. . . . The effects they create are amusing and without exception visually arresting, and one leaves the superbly designed theatre feeling happy and uplifted" (Speck, 1986). Famous People Players use puppets of such well-known people as Elvis Presley, Michael Jackson, Barbra Streisand, and Kenny Rogers, as well as a number of fictional characters such as Darth Vader. "It's amazing how [people with disabilities] develop and mature as they gain confidence in the fact that others have confidence in them," stated Diane Dupuy, the founder of Famous People Players. For more information call (416) 532-1137 or visit http://www.fpp.org.

Theatre Access Project (TAP) (New York, NY)

For over 20 years, this organization has responded to the needs of persons with hearing impairments by providing sign language interpreters for theatre productions. One significant challenge for interpreters is to allow theatergoers to understand not only what is being said but who is doing the talking. Schaefer (1992) quoted one staff member who said, "You're not acting, but you need to match a character, to give the audience an idea of who's talking now. . . . You're dealing with a ping-pong effect—the audience still needs to be able to watch the play" (p. 12C). Because of the group's success and implementation of the Americans with Disabilities Act, demand for TAP's services has been increasing dramatically. In 1997, TAP offered the first open captioned performance on Broadway and has since provided open captions for more than 150 performances of more than 100 different Broadway and off-Broadway productions. In addition to services for persons who are deaf or hard of hearing, TAP promotes theatre access for persons with a variety of physical disabilities. TAP is spon-

sored by New York's Theatre Development Fund in partnership with the New York State Council on the Arts (NYSCA). For more information call (212) 221-1103 (voice) or (212) 719-4537 (TTY) or visit http://www.tdf.org.

Association of Mouth and Foot Painting Artists (AMFPA) (London, England)

This worldwide organization provides support to more than 650 painters who, due to a variety of disabling conditions, are not able to use their hands to create works of art. The official slogan of the AMFPA is "No pity please," and the requirements for high artisitc standards among their members supports this slogan. As noted by Art Historian Dr. Richard Hiepe (1999), "Amongst the mouth and foot painters one can find talented artists whose works are excellent examples of the most differentiating and modern styles such as abstract, realistic, surrealistic and expressionistic." The association has offered services to artists with disabilities for over 40 years, and artists from over 60 countries currently belong to AMFPA. AMFPA emphasizes self-determination and independence through artistic involvement. For more information access AMFPA's website at http://www.amfpa.com.

SUMMARY

The arts help to form and also to reflect the national character of society. As a result, it is essential that *all* members of society be provided the opportunity to participate in the arts. Such participation may be through the creation of an original work of art, but it also may be through performing the work of another artist or even perceiving the artistic efforts of another in a creative way. These three levels of art participation offer limitless opportunities for enjoyment and satisfaction and personal growth. This is especially true for people who have disabilities because their opportunities for personal growth experiences may be more limited than those of individuals without disabilities.

SUGGESTED LEARNING ACTIVITIES

1. Name the three levels of participation in the arts, and give (from your own experiences) specific examples of each.
2. Interview a community recreation arts specialist, and determine the ways in which individuals are

encouraged to participate in all three levels of arts participation.
3. Write a poem that expresses your feelings concerning the arts for everyone.

4. Examine the activities offered by a local recreation center. Specify five arts activities that could be incorporated into the program, and discuss the benefits of each activity.

5. Discuss why it is important for individuals without disabilities to experience the artistic efforts of people with disabilities.

6. Discuss ways that community recreators can use the arts as a tool to allow individuals with disabilities to express their feelings or needs.

7. Write a paper entitled "Does Disability Culture Exist?" Take a position (pro or con) regarding its existence and justify your position.

8. Access the website for *VSA arts* (www.vsarts.org); then open the Online Exhibit. Select your favorite piece in the exhibit and write a one-page reaction paper describing the piece and the emotions that it elicits.

REFERENCES

About AXIS: AXIS Dance Company. [Online]. Available: http://www.AXIS.org, 2003.

Appell, M. J. An overview: Arts in education for the handicapped. In *The Arts and Handicapped People: Defining the National Direction.* Washington, DC: National Committee, Arts for the Handicapped, 1978, pp. 13–17.

Art Disability Expression: Disability Culture, *VSA arts.* [Online]. Available: http://www.vsarts.org, 2003.

Association of Mouth and Foot Painting Artists. [Online]. Available: http://www.amfpa.com, 2003.

Baer, B. The rehabilitative influences of creative experience. *The Journal of Creative Behavior, 19*(3), 202–214, 1985.

Barnes, C., & G. Mercer. *Disability.* London: Polity, 2003.

Brown, S. E. "Poster kids no more": Perspectives about the no-longer emerging (in fact, vibrant) disability culture. *Disability Studies Quarterly, 18*(1), 5–19, 1998.

City of Long Beach Cultural Program. [Online]. Available: http://www.lbparks.org/dept_info/index.htm, 2003.

Copeland, B. Mainstreaming art for the handicapped child: Resources for teacher preparation. *Art Education, 37*(6), 22–29, 1984.

Dattilo, J. *Inclusive Leisure Services.* State College, PA: Venture, 1994.

Diamondstein, G. *Exploring the Arts with Children.* New York: Macmillan, 1974.

Dobbs, J. State of the arts. *New Mobility, 8*(47), 22–33, 1997.

Educational Facilities Laboratory and the National Endowment for the Arts. *Arts and the Handicapped: An Issue of Access.* New York: Educational Facilities Laboratory, 1975.

Gill, C. A psychological view of disability culture. *Disability Studies Quarterly, 15*(4), 16–19, 1995.

Harlan, J. E. *A Guide to Setting Up a Creative Art Experiences Program for Older Adults with Developmental Disabilities.* Bloomington, IN: Institute for the Study of Developmental Disabilities, 1992.

Hayman, d'A. Introduction. In United Nations Educational, Scientific and Cultural Organization, *The Arts and Man: A World View of the Role and Functions of the Arts in Society.* Englewood Cliffs, NJ: Prentice-Hall, 1969, pp. 11–26.

Hiepe, R. [Online]. Available: http://www.amfpa.com/~vdmfk/files/info/eng/hiepe.html, 1999.

Hull, J. E. Laying the foundations: The centrality of arts in the curriculum. In S. S. Segal, Ed. *Creative Arts and Mental Disability.* Bicester, Oxon, England: A B Academic Publishers, 1990, pp. 29–34.

Hutchinson, P., & J. Lord. *Recreation Integration.* Ontario, Canada: Leisurability Publications, 1979.

Jacobs, C. The work of art. *Active Living, 7*(6), 28–30, 1999.

Jeffrey, A. J. Indications of disability culture in magazines marketed to the disability community. *Disability Studies Quarterly, 18*(1), 20–26, 1998.

John, J. A. Indications of disability culture in magazines marketed to the disability community. *Disability Studies Quarterly, 18*(1), 20–26, 1998.

Kunkle-Miller, C. Handicapping conditions and their effect on the child's ability to create. In L. H. Kearns, M. T. Ditson, and B. G. Roehner, Eds. *Readings: Developing Art Programs for*

Handicapped Students. Harrisburg, PA: Arts in Special Education Project of Pennsylvania, 1981, pp. 8–20.

Lathrop, D. Art & soul of disability. *New Mobility, 10*(68), 24–27, 1999.

Mangiacasale, A. The sounds of silence. *Disability Today,* 2(2), 54–55, 1993.

Molloy, L. Public facilities and handicapped patrons. In *The Arts and Handicapped People: Defining the National Direction.* Washington, DC: National Committee, Arts for the Handicapped, 1978, pp. 37–39.

National Committee, Arts for the Handicapped. *Art Resource and Training Guide.* Washington, DC: Author, 1981.

National Endowment for the Arts. [Online]. Available: http://arts.endow.gov/endownews/news99/YouthARTS.html, 1999.

National Institute on Disability and Rehabilitation Research. Disability and the arts. *Rehab Brief: Bringing Research into Effective Focus, 8*(6), 1991.

Oliver, M. *Understanding Disability.* New York: St. Martin's Press, 1996.

Outsider's M.S., We Love to Write Poetry. [Online]. Available: http://www.geocites.com/Heartland/Shores/5237/Poetry.html, 2003.

Patyrala, L. Accessible expressions Ohio: Making a world of difference. *Parks & Recreation, 33*(3), 60–67, 1998.

Peters, S. Is there a disability culture? A synchronization of three possible world views. *Disability and Society, 15,* 1–14, 2000.

Poitevin, J. Changing images through the performing arts. In S. S. Segal, Ed. *Creative Arts and Mental Disability.* Bicester, Oxon, England: A B Academic Publishers, 1990, pp. 45–54.

Ransom, J. M. Arts for at-risk youth. *Parks & Recreation, 31*(3), 40–46, 1996.

Roehner, B. G. What is an arts program? In L. H. Kearns, M. T. Ditson, & B. G. Roehner, Eds.

Readings: Developing Arts Programs for Handicapped Students. Harrisburg, PA: Arts in Special Education Project of Pennsylvania, 1981, pp. 5–7.

Ross, M., Ed. *The Arts and Personal Growth.* New York: Pergamon Press, 1980.

Schaefer, S. Theatre interpreters give signs of progress for the deaf. *USA Today,* December 10, 1992, p. 12C.

Schleien, S., M. T. Ray, & F. P. Green. *Community Recreation and People with Disabilities: Strategies for Inclusion* (2nd ed.). Baltimore: Paul H. Brookes, 1997.

Schleien, S. J., J. E. Rynders, & T. Mustonen. Arts and integration: What can we create? *Therapeutic Recreation Journal, 22*(4), 18–29, 1988.

Shaw, R. Education and the arts. In M. Ross, Ed. *The Arts and Personal Growth.* New York: Pergamon Press, 1980, pp. 69–78.

Sherrill, C., & R. Cox. Personnel preparation in creative arts for the handicapped: Implications for improving the quality of life. In C. Sherrill, Ed. *Creative Arts for the Severely Handicapped,* Springfield, IL: Charles C. Thomas, 1979, pp. 3–11.

Speck, G. Handicapped make delightful "Magic" at Lyceum. *New York City Tribune,* October 29, 1986, p. B-6.

Summers, L. Testimony before Congressional subcommittee on Americans with Disabilities Act, September 23, 1988.

Theatre Access Project. [Online]. Available: http://www.tdf.org, 2003.

Tomlinson, R. *Disability, Theatre, and Education.* Bloomington, IN: Indiana University Press, 1982.

VSA arts. Frequently Asked Questions. [Online]. Available: http://www.vsarts.org/info/faq.html, 1999.

Williams, R. M. Why children should draw. *Saturday Review,* September 3, 1977, pp. 101–106.

Yost, E. J. It's not only rock 'n' roll: A model of inclusive programming. *Parks & Recreation, 34*(3), 60–69, 1999.

CHAPTER

11 COMPETITIVE SPORTS

(Photo by Nancy Crase. Copyright *Sports 'n Spokes*/Paralyzed Veterans of America)

Y ou only have to pick up a newspaper or turn on a television to be reminded of the importance of competitive athletics in North America. Game results for local sports teams are often noted on the front page of major metropolitan newspapers, and it is not unusual for local television news programs to devote 20% or more of their air time to sports topics. But the influence of organized sports on our culture goes much deeper than merely the reporting of athletic events by the mass media. Indeed, there are few areas of modern society that are not influenced in some way by the presence of sport.

SPORTS FOR PERSONS WITH DISABILITIES

Despite the widespread influence of sport in our society and the recognition of its contribution to individual growth and development, the role of sport in the lives of persons with disabilities has received relatively little attention. Occasional articles on sports for athletes who are disabled may appear in newspapers or other publications, but they rarely appear in the sports sections and are usually treated as "human interest" stories rather than genuine examples of competitive sporting events. Even the major network television sports shows, which seem anxious to televise almost anything remotely resembling sport, have failed to provide coverage of organized and highly competitive sports competition among athletes who have disabilities. Hardin and Hardin (2003), for example, wrote that the biggest difference between the 2002 Winter Olympics and the corresponding Winter Paralympic Games was not the intensity and level of competition or nationalistic pride; rather, it was the awareness and publicity for the event.

Appropriate sport-related coverage in the media is vital if athletes with disabilities are to receive the recognition they have earned. Sports

On June 27, 1989, Natalie Bacon, the first female wheelchair athlete to compete in the New York Marathon, lost her battle with cancer. This chapter is dedicated to Natalie's memory and to her incredible competitive spirit.

participation should enable athletes with disabilities to reject externally imposed roles of inferiority and invisibility within society (Hardin & Hardin, 2003; Thomas & Katz, 2001). The media's coverage of disability sport, however, is not only infrequent but sometimes degrading. It reinforces images of the person with a disability as dependent or, even worse, irrelevant. Kelly (2003), commenting on television coverage of the 2002 Boston Marathon, noted that the commentators consistently used words of condescension and dismissal. When the winner of the women's wheelchair division, Christina Ripp, expressed her overwhelming joy in a post-race interview, the commentator not only failed to validate her feelings but dismissed her accomplishment, as well. Kelly wrote:

> [The host] turned to the camera. "That's good news for Christina," he said, "but the real story has to be the continuing dominance in the men's division by the Kenyan men." Ripp's victory, his comment seemed to say, wasn't "real"; it spoke of nothing of any shared exaltation of the moment, but simply revealed a not-very-important moment in one woman's (pathetic) life.

Why, with sport's influence so important in our culture, has society's acceptance of competitive sports programs for athletes with disabilities been so slow to develop? Perhaps one reason is the comparative newness of organized sports for people with disabilities. Although sports historian Earle Zeigler (1979) dated the first recorded sports competitions as occurring during the Early Dynastic period of the Sumerian civilization (3000–1500 B.C.), organized sports for people with disabilities is largely a 20th-century phenomenon. Most sports programs for individuals who are disabled are less than 60 years old.

Newness alone does not account for the lack of public attention, however. Probably a more fundamental reason for the absence of public awareness and interest in sports for people with disabilities is the widespread belief that such programs are solely "therapeutic." The needs and motivations of athletes who have disabilities are often viewed as different from their nondisabled counterparts, and the primary emphasis of such competition is seen as rehabilitation. While the rehabilitative potential of sports involvement is undeniable, emphasizing this aspect to the exclusion of the other benefits to the individual participant is unfortunate. Such emphasis merely strengthens the public's view of individuals with disabilities as "different" or "abnormal." Rather than stressing differences, the desire for sports participation among many people who have disabilities is a classic example of the *similarity* of *all* people.

Fortunately, there is evidence that athletes with disabilities are beginning to receive the recognition they deserve. A sold-out crowd of over 64,000 people attended the opening ceremonies of the 10th Paralympics in Atlanta, Georgia. More importantly, the competitions were nationally broadcast in the United States for the first time, and competitors were also interviewed on CNN and on NBC's *Today* show. The 10th Special Olympics World Summer Games, in Durham, North Carolina, drew over 400,000 spectators and received worldwide coverage by more than 1,500 members of television, radio, and print media. Additionally, prize money supplied by corporate sponsors now attracts wheelchair athletes from around the world to compete in some major sports events. The appearance of published compendiums on sports for people with disabilities, such as *Sports and Recreation for the Disabled: A Resource Handbook* (Paciorek & Jones, 2001) and *Disability and Sport* (DePauw & Gavron, 1995) also demonstrates increased public acceptance of and interest in sports for persons with disabilities. It appears that DePauw and Gavron may be correct: "Sport for and including individuals with disabilities is a movement whose time has come" (p. 225).

Common Goals of Sports Participation

As noted by Paciorek and Jones (2001), many sports opportunities throughout the United States and Canada are available to people with disabilities. Football, racquetball, softball, track and field, basketball, rugby, and tennis are a few of the many wheelchair sports providing outlets for athletes with mobility limitations. People with visual impairments, sometimes using sighted guides, can participate in such sports as beep baseball, golf, archery, bowling, and many winter sports (Montelione & Mastro, 1985; Rarick, 1984; Spraggs, 1984). The Special Olympics offers opportunities for winter and summer competition among people with mental retardation. In addition, senior citizens with and without disabilities compete in the Senior Olympics. Each of these programs, as well as others providing sports competition for people with specific needs, makes unique contributions to participants. Each differs from the others in many ways, including administrative procedures, type of athletic contests offered, basic rules of competition, fund-raising techniques, and so on. Yet, there are a number of things that competitive programs for people with disabilities have in common. Most, if not all, of these programs, do the following:

- Provide a method of informing the public about the unique *abilities* that participants possess.
- Promote independence, sports skill development, and increased physical fitness among their participants.
- Promote maximum participation by offering local or regional events but also provide for recognition of outstanding performances through national and international competition.
- Have some system of classification, such as degree of disability, to make the competition in events as fair as possible.
- Use the classification system as a method of increasing participation opportunities among individuals with severe disabilities.

Segregation vs. Inclusion

One of the most controversial issues regarding sports for persons with disabilities relates to segregated competition. Most of the sports programs mentioned previously have regulations that prohibit participants without disabilities from competing against athletes who have disabilities. Such segregation may help to equalize competition, but some authorities believe that participation in these sports denies significant social and psychological benefits that result from meeting, sharing, and becoming friends with athletes without disabilities (Brasile, 1990; McClellan & Frogley, 1994; Page & O'Connor, 2001; Pensgaard & Sorensen, 2002). Although many segregated programs do include volunteers who socially interact with competitors who have disabilities, the role of a volunteer often places the person without a disability "above" the competitor. To be effective, social interaction between peers with and without disabilities should be on an equal level.

Advocates of programs that exclude participants without disabilities, however, counter that criticism with several logical points. First, they note that sports programs are but one aspect of a person's life. Fundamental changes are needed in other societal institutions, such as education, and transportation, to promote integration of individuals with disabilities into society. In effect, sports programs for individuals with disabilities are a reaction to a segregated society, not a cause of it. Second, supporters of these programs contend that providing the athlete who has a disability with a fair chance for success in sporting events may require excluding individuals without disabilities from competition. Having peers who do not have disabilities serve as volunteers may also offer the chance for social interaction in a cooperative, rather than a competitive, situation. Third, advocates maintain segregated sports participation enhances the development of social and physical skills in an environment of acceptance and understanding. This social and physical development, enhanced by successful competitive experiences, promotes confidence, self-esteem, and empowerment among participants (Pensgaard & Sorensen, 2002).

Brasile (1990), opposed to segregated sports competition among athletes with disabilities, has suggested that sports for persons with disabilities adopt a "reverse integration" approach whereby people without disabilities are integrated into sports activities that have traditionally been restricted to athletes with disabilities. Using wheelchair sports as an example, Brasile urged adding

persons without disabilities to wheelchair basketball teams, thus fostering "an atmosphere for social integration in which all participants will be competing on an equal basis" (p. 4). Thiboutot, Smith, and Labanowich (1992) agreed that for recreational sports activities, Brasile's ideas are logical and might facilitate inclusion of persons with disabilities into society. They disagreed strongly with Brasile, however, about using reverse integration in organized competitive sports for persons with disabilities. Thiboutot et al., noted that the primary emphasis of Brasile's reverse integration concept "appears to be rehabilitation, rather than competitive sports. As such, it represents a step backward for the wheelchair sports movement in the U.S." (p. 291). Lindstrom (1992) also took issue with inclusion of athletes without disabilities into competitive sports for athletes with disabilities. He stated, "If the meaning of integration is to equalize conditions of a minority group to those of a majority, then participation of able-bodied athletes in elite sports adapted for the disabled is an anomaly . . . participation of the able-bodied in elite sports in wheelchairs, with blindfolds, or with hands tied in the back is out of the question" (p. 58).

Vertical Integration

Rather than promoting reverse integration in elite competitive sports, many authorities advocate the use of *vertical integration*. This concept involves assimilation of elite athletes with disabilities into mainstream competitions, without necessarily having direct competition between persons with and without disabilities. Vertical integration, for example, might involve athletes with disabilities routinely competing against each other at the same time and location, and with the same awards and recognition, as athletes without disabilities. Vertical integration could also result in some competitions among athletes with disabilities receiving full medal status at the Olympic Games. Although wheelchair track competitions have been featured in the Olympics since the 1980s, these events have been considered exhibitions and "official" Olympic medals have not been awarded to the winners. Vertical integration could correct this inequity.

Although the vertical integration concept has not yet been adopted within the Olympic movement, there have been many changes that have improved the competitive situation of elite athletes with disabilities in the United States. USA Cycling provides support to the U.S. Disabled Cycling Team in the form of staffing, collaboration on events, and joint revenue opportunities (Huebner, 2003). Olympic committee training centers are now open for use free-of-charge by athletes with disabilities. In addition to facilities, these centers offer physiological testing and biomechanical analyses to athletes with disabilities (Steadward, Ewen, & Wheeler, 1994). Funding for training and travel to many international competitions has also been provided to sports programs for elite athletes who have disabilities.

Paciorek and Jones (2001) contend that one potential outcome of vertical integration is that disability-related sports organizations could increase their efforts at the local level. An excellent example is provided by the Integration Project in Ontario, Canada (Active Living, 2002). This effort, organized by Sport for Disabled—Ontario (SDO), has a goal of having disability sport competition included as another division within each local sporting organization. Disability would be a category of competition, just as age and gender currently are. Laura Miller, SDO's integration project coordinator, stated, "Don't put the wheelchair first, or put 'disabled' in front of 'athlete.' They are athletes. [Vertical integration] is also an opportunity for athletes to train and compete together, which will assist in increasing the level of ability for that athlete. . . . It's a win/win situation for everyone. Athletes with a disability will have greater opportunities to train and compete, and events will now be run for all athletes—with or without a disability" (p. 9).

Classification of Athletes with Disabilities

One of the most perplexing aspects of sports for persons with disabilities is classification of athletes.

In an attempt to provide fair and equitable competition, most organizations that govern specific sports for athletes with physical disabilities use some form of a classification system (wheelchair basketball classification is described later in this chapter). As noted by Dummer (1999), an athlete's classification can have a huge impact on his or her success in an individual sporting event because it determines the caliber of competition the athlete faces. Classification is also important in team sports. Whether the player gets into a game may hinge upon his or her classification because the number of players in a given classification category is often restricted.

Traditionally, *medical classification* has been used. In this system, competition is based upon type and degree of disability as determined by medical diagnosis (e.g., amount of vision loss, level of spinal cord injury). In many sports, the result has been a plethora of competitive categories that confused spectators and diluted competition. More recently, *functional classification* was proposed and implemented by some sports' governing bodies. Using a functional system, an athlete is classified based upon his or her functional abilities (e.g., range of motion, balance, coordination), irrespective of disability or diagnosis. Ideally, this system allows reducing the number of competitive categories in individual sports and provides for more equitable competition. Currently, *functional classification by sport* is being advocated by many. This system applies the concept of functional classification to a specific sport. Thus, the athlete is classified based upon his or her ability to perform specific sport-related skills.

Unfortunately, no classification system is perfect. Steadward and Peterson (1997), for example, have noted that some athletes have been penalized for using successful training techniques. Because of high-level training, their performances exceed disability-related expectations; thus, their "reward" for becoming highly trained is to be pitted against athletes with less severe disabilities. Another, more common problem with classification relates to unethical behavior by some athletes. To gain a competitively advantageous classification, some athletes cheat by faking their performances (i.e., disguising their capabilities by deliberately underperforming). An athlete, for example, might fake losing his or her balance to appear more disabled. Sadly, Dr. Caibre McCann, a veteran classifier, noted that cheating is by far the biggest problem associated with classification of athletes with disabilities (Steadward et al., 1994).

Attempts to reduce the number of competitive categories at the Paralympic Games have also caused classification problems and competitive inequities, particularly when people with vastly different disabilities are required to compete against each other. Steadward and Peterson (1997) discussed the competitive disadvantage for most athletes with cerebral palsy when they are placed into the same track event with athletes who have spinal cord injuries. Conversely, at the 10th Paralympics, swimmers with spinal cord injuries, who had to start in the water, were required to compete against swimmers with disabilities who could stand and dive in from the starting blocks (Crase, 1996). As Crase wrote, the swimmers with spinal cord injuries did not have "a snowball's chance in the waters of hell" (p. 6).

Nevertheless, calls for a unified classification system to reduce competitive categories persist. Advocating for a unified system, Tweedy (2003) noted that the primary purpose of a unified classification system should be to enhance the sport by increasing participation, improving competition, and enhancing public interest. Tweedy added:

> The guiding principles should balance two competing concerns. First, within a single class, the range of activity limitation experienced by athletes must be sufficiently small to ensure that the athlete with the greatest extent of activity limitation is not unduly disadvantaged when competing against the athlete with the least extent. Second, classes must span a sufficiently large range of activity limitation to ensure that there are enough people eligible for each class to hold viable competitions. The minimum number of classes needs to be created to balance these criteria. (p. 10)

Classification, despite significant problems, will continue to be an important aspect of sport for persons with disabilities. It is hoped that ongoing efforts to improve the various classification systems will result in competitive balance and fairness for all athletes who have disabilities.

Role of Community Recreation

Although the number of community-based sports programs for persons with disabilities has grown, these programs are inadequate to meet current needs, much less those of potential participants (DePauw & Gavron, 1995). There are a number of reasons why this could be true, including ignorance, prejudice, and fear (Steadward et al., 1994); however, the most logical explanation is the belief that sports programs for persons with disabilities should be the purview of rehabilitation professionals. Ann Cody, a Paralympic gold medalist and therapeutic recreation professional, counters this argument (Steadward & Peterson, 1997). Changes in health care have shortened the length of stay in rehabilitation hospitals and centers, and Cody notes that many people leave rehabilitation centers before they are ready to take part in sports. Therefore, recreation professionals need to ensure that citizens with disabilities in their communities have opportunities for sports competition.

Some of the information in this chapter emphasizes highly competitive sports opportunities (i.e., elite sports) for people with disabilities. It is essential that these elite opportunities are provided for athletes with disabilities, but such programs should not be offered to the exclusion of less competitive programs. Most community recreation programs provide a wide variety of sports opportunities for their citizens without disabilities. Community-based recreation professionals, therefore, should also ensure that a continuum of competitive opportunities is available for persons with disabilities.

Ensuring that sports programs are available for persons with disabilities may not require community recreation agencies to offer these programs directly (Devine, McGovern, & Hermann, 1998). Public recreation agencies, for example, may provide facilities, equipment, and technical assistance to local organizations offering competitive sports to persons with disabilities. The American Youth Soccer Organization's Very Important Player

(VIP) program is an example of a community-based sports organization accepting the challenge of providing opportunities for youth with disabilities (Lavay & Semark, 2001). Appropriate modifications, such as smaller fields with relaxed rules, and trained volunteer coaches help communities ensure that soccer competition is available to every local child who wants to play. Moreover, some school districts have accepted their responsibility to provide competitive sports opportunities for secondary school students. Frogley and Beaver (2002) point to exemplary programs offering interscholastic competition for students with disabilities in Minnesota, Georgia, and Illinois. The Oregon School Activities Association has also initiated wheelchair events in its Oregon State Track and Field Championships (Hansen & Fuller, 2003).

Partnerships between public recreation agencies and community organizations or schools to offer competitive sports for persons with disabilities are also possible, as is sponsoring citizens' groups who wish to form teams or events. Regardless of how it is accomplished, the most important thing is that community recreation professionals realize their obligation to ensure that sports activities, if offered to the general population, are also available to citizens with disabilities.

Local community recreation agencies usually offer a variety of sports programs, including a range of competitive levels, therefore, they are also in an excellent position to facilitate inclusion in competitive sports activities. Moreover, the local level has been cited as the ideal venue for initiating inclusion in sport (Steadward et al., 1994). Unfortunately, coaches and parents of children without disabilities are sometimes reluctant to accept inclusion into community sports programs (Block & Malloy, 1998). To help overcome resistance to inclusion, Devine et al. (1998) have provided guidelines for coaches to include persons with disabilities in community sports teams. These include:

- Conducting a self-assessment by coaches of their own attitudes toward persons with disabilities, as well as their own coaching behaviors and styles (e.g., patience, body language, speech pattern).
- Ensuring that people with disabilities are invited to attend programs (e.g., include statement of adherence to the ADA in promotional literature, market program to groups that provide services to persons with disabilities).
- Conducting a participant assessment by asking on registration materials if a person needs a disability-related accommodation.
- Discussing necessary accommodation with the participant prior to the start of the sports program.
- Using common coaching techniques to facilitate inclusion (e.g., extra practice to master skills, using prompts to promote proper sequencing of skills, rewarding successful actions).
- Providing inclusion-related training for staff, assistant coaches, and volunteers (e.g., disability awareness, accommodation strategies, case studies, ADA requirements).
- Remaining flexible and seeking assistance from experts, if needed.

Inclusion in sport has been cited as instrumental in the successful integration of people with disabilities into Canadian society (McClellan & Frogley, 1994), as well as some U.S. communities (Casteneda & Sherrill, 1997). In addition, it is anticipated that the trend toward inclusion and acceptance of persons with disabilities in sport will continue (DePauw & Gavron, 1995; Devine et al., 1998). Thus, community recreation agencies should be at the forefront of providing inclusive sports opportunities for their citizens.

Competitive Programs

There are hundreds of sports organizations offering a variety of competitive opportunities to people with disabilities. Among these are Disabled Sports USA; Dwarf Athletic Association of America; Special Olympics International; United States Association of Blind Athletes; United States Deaf Sports Federation; United States Cerebral Palsy Athletic

Association; and Wheelchair Sports, USA. Until recently, these organizations were members of the United States Olympic Committee (USOC); however, they now work with a supposedly "separate, but equal" organization, U.S. Paralympics (www.usparalympics.org). The Paralympic Games, which provides world-class competition for elite athletes with disabilities, includes competition in more than 15 different sports.

It would be impossible to describe in this chapter all of the sports programs for athletes with disabilities throughout the United States and Canada; however, two widely known, mostly segregated programs have been selected to serve as examples: (1) wheelchair sports for people with mobility limitations; and (2) the Special Olympics for children and adults with mental retardation. In addition, the Barrie Integrated Baseball Association and the sport of bocce have been included to provide examples of inclusion. It is important for the reader to keep in mind that these programs are merely examples. Readers interested in further information on other sports organizations and programs should consult Kelly and Frieden (1989) and Paciorek and Jones (2001), listed in the references at the end of this chapter. Surfing the Web is also an excellent way to gather information on sports for athletes with disabilities. Selected sports organizations for persons with disabilities, with web addresses, are included in appendix B.

WHEELCHAIR SPORTS

Historical Development

The wheelchair sports movement owes its beginning and continued growth to three primary factors: (1) advances in medical technology, which have resulted in an increasing vitality and life expectancy for individuals with physical disabilities; (2) the competitive spirit and determination of athletes with disabilities who always manage to find ways to overcome personal and organizational difficulties to be able to participate in competitive sports; and (3) foresight among many determined professionals who have provided the leadership

"spark" needed for establishment and continued expansion of wheelchair athletics.

In the United States, the development of organized wheelchair sports has also been stimulated by two simultaneous but separate organizational movements: The National Wheelchair Basketball Association and Wheelchair Sports, USA. A brief examination of each organization's sports program will help explain the state of wheelchair sports in the United States.

National Wheelchair Basketball Association (www.nwba.org)

A complete picture of wheelchair basketball can only come from watching one of the fast and exciting games played between two highly skilled teams. Wheelchair basketball is played according to National Collegiate Athletic Association rules, although a few modifications to these rules are made to accommodate the use of wheelchairs. Each game is played on a full-sized high school or college court, and the baskets remain at the 10-foot level.

Following are some important aspects of wheelchair basketball and the National Wheelchair Basketball Association (NWBA).

Divisions

The NWBA men's teams are currently aligned with one of three divisions. These divisions have distinctively different purposes, although the basic structure of each division is similar. Division I is composed of elite teams that strive to offer players the highest possible level of competition. Division I teams often travel extensively around the country, generally playing other Division I teams. Division II teams usually lack the financial resources of Division I teams and generally do not have the elite players that gravitate toward Division I. Nonetheless, play within Division II is highly competitive and, like Division I, the season ends in a nationwide tournament to crown the Division's National Champion. Division III teams are often in developmental stages and are not yet seeking the competitive emphasis of Divisions I and II.

Women with disabilities compete at a high level in all aspects of wheelchair sports programs.
(Courtesy of *Sports 'n Spokes*/Paralyzed Veterans of America)

Rules

As noted earlier, NCAA rules serve as the standard for wheelchair basketball, but modifications are made when special situations dictate. For example, contact between chairs was not originally considered to be a personal foul. Bob Miller, the first president of the NWBA, described the result:

> Wheelchair Bulldozers we called ourselves, the reason being that in those days before the rules were refined, you could ram a guy all you wanted—when you caught him sitting dead with the ball. You could ram into him and take the ball away from him. And so we picked the name Bulldozers—Wheelchair Bulldozers. (Labanowich, 1975, p. 34)

As a result of such tactics, the wheelchair is now considered to be a part of the player. Other major rule differences between wheelchair basketball rules and NCAA rules include:

- Two pushes on the wheels of the wheelchair are allowed; then, the player must pass, shoot, or dribble at least once. Three consecutive pushes result in a traveling violation.
- There is no double dribble in wheelchair basketball.
- Players on Division II and III teams are allowed 4 seconds in the free throw lane when on offense (vs. 3 seconds in NCAA play).
- Players with the ball may not touch the floor with their feet (violation).
- The "physical advantage foul" prevents players with less severe disabilities from using a functional advantage over opponents. Physical advantage fouls include rising off of the wheelchair's seat (or cushion), pressing a leg or

foot against the wheel to guide the wheelchair while holding the ball, and deliberately kicking the ball. The penalty for a physical advantage foul is similar to a technical foul.

Throughout the years, the sophistication of wheelchair basketball rules has increased to the point that the *Official NWBA Rules and Case Book* is more than 45 pages long. The case book portion of this document gives rule interpretations for more than 60 game situations. See Figure 11-1 for a humorous look at wheelchair basketball rules.

Classification System and Team Balance

Wheelchair basketball requires a great deal of balance, upper body strength, and overall coordination. Players with lower spinal cord injuries (usually, the lower the injury, the more

"Here it is, Nugent . . . rule 27, section 7: No player shall . . ."

Figure 11-1

(Copyright © 1982 Malcolm Hancock. Reprinted by permission)

muscle function a player has) or disabilities only affecting the lower extremities (legs) usually have a competitive advantage over players with more severe disabilities. Despite prohibitions against minimal disabilities, including *temporary* disorders caused by injury, some wheelchair basketball players are able to walk unaided; however, on their feet they could not keep pace with players without disabilities.

To provide opportunities for individuals with severe disabilities to compete in basketball, a classification system was devised based on the athlete's level of spinal cord (or comparable) injury (see Fig. 11-2). Wheelchair basketball players are placed into one of three classes according to the following system:

> *Class I.* Complete motor loss at T-7 or above or comparable disability where there is total loss of muscle function originating at or above T-7.
>
> *Class II.* Complete motor loss originating at T-8 and descending through and including L-2 where there may be motor power of hips and thighs. Also included in this class are amputees with bilateral hip disarticulation.
>
> *Class III.* All other physical disabilities as related to lower extremity paralysis or paresis originating at or below L-3. All lower extremity amputees are included in this class, except those with bilateral hip disarticulation (see Class II).

Although these are based on a medical classification system, classification of NWBA players is supported, whenever possible, by observation of a player's functional skills.

Basketball is a team sport, so merely classifying individuals according to the system described is not enough. Each classification (I, II, and III) is given a numerical or point value as follows:

> *Class I.* 1 point
>
> *Class II.* 2 points
>
> *Class III.* 3 points

NWBA rules prevent a team from placing five players on the floor at the same time whose point

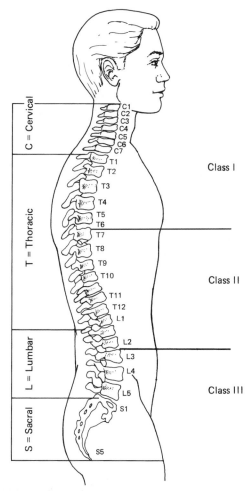

Figure 11-2   Player Classifications in the National Wheelchair Basketball Association Based upon Each Athlete's Level of Spinal Cord Injury or Comparable Level of Disability.

This diagram illustrates the three-level classification system used by the NWBA.

(Originally appeared in *Palaestra*, Vol. 1, No. 2, 1985. Modified and reproduced with permission of Challenge Publications, Inc.)

totals exceed 12 points (11 points for Division III). No more than three Class IIIs are allowed at one time (two in Division III). Thus, the more severely disabled Class I player is provided an opportunity to play because of the NWBA's team balance concept.

Scope

Although originally limited exclusively to males, NWBA teams have been open to participation by both sexes since 1974. Women may join any one of the teams in the association, which includes a number of all-women teams. In addition to the annual National Wheelchair Basketball Tournament for the final four top teams in each Division, the Association also helps to support the National Women's Wheelchair Basketball Tournament and the Intercollegiate Wheelchair Basketball Tournament. A youth division provides support for youngsters learning the sport. Although most of the teams in the NWBA are located in the continental United States, there are also several Canadian teams that have chosen to affiliate with the association.

One of the more favorable aspects of the NWBA is its policy that the players establish all rules, including rules of play and the association's constitution and bylaws. This is accomplished at an annual meeting of team delegates at which all of the association's business is conducted. The idea of recreation consumer input from persons with disabilities is relatively new in the United States, but the NWBA has been practicing this policy since its formation in 1949.

Wheelchair Sports, USA (www.wsusa.org)

Wheelchair Sports, USA (WSUSA) (formerly the National Wheelchair Athletic Association), was formed almost 10 years after the NWBA, but it quickly took on an important role in wheelchair sports development. Wheelchair Sports, USA became the representative body for a varied group of competitors with disabilities because it was not limited to a single sport. The following list of sporting events, governed by WSUSA, gives some idea of this variety: archery, athletics (track and field), shooting, swimming, table tennis, and weightlifting.

Under the leadership of Ben Lipton, WSUSA became the wheelchair sports organization that organized and supervised U.S. participation in most major international competitions. These international events, including the Paralympic Games, became a prized goal for every competitor. Jon Brown, holder of the world heavyweight weight-lifting record, underscored the personal importance of international competition by stating, "I don't remember walking. I've never climbed a stair. I've never run. So for me these games are a dream come true" (Weisman & Godfrey, 1976, p. 121).

As with wheelchair basketball, Wheelchair Sports, USA has several aspects that should be highlighted.

Classification System

WSUSA events usually feature individual, rather than team, competition, therefore some form of classifying the severity of a person's disability is essential. As noted previously, individuals with lower extremity injuries may have a competitive edge over those with injuries that also affect stomach, chest, back, or arm muscles. WSUSA uses a functional classification system modeled after the one used for international competition. As noted by Curtis (1991), there are three distinct advantages of the WSUSA system. First, the functional system allows for sport-specific classification. Thus, the interaction between the requirements of a particular sport and the functional ability of the athlete is taken into consideration during classification. Second, the functional system makes it easier to classify persons with various disabilities. The previous system was based on complete spinal cord injury and required comparing the athlete's physical limitations with spinal levels of muscle innervation. Third, the functional system facilitates efficient organization of events by reducing the number of competitive categories, thus reducing the number of heats, trials, and so on.

Scope

WSUSA's regional, national, and international competitive activities provide a wide range of events for many males and females with mobility limitations. Youth competitions, including the Junior National Wheelchair Games, have been part of the WSUSA since the mid-1980s. Youth

comprise more than 30% of WSUSA's membership. In the late eighties, WSUSA's sports competitions were "decentralized"; that is, the major U.S. championships in each sport (e.g., track and field, weight lifting) were held at separate dates and locations. Previously, most WSUSA sports held their championships at the National Wheelchair Games, located at a single site or area. It is unfortunate that decentralization of competitions has reduced some of WSUSA's camaraderie, but it was an inevitable outcome of the association's continued growth.

Unlike wheelchair basketball, WSUSA's format of individual competition offers almost unlimited competitive opportunities for persons with high spinal cord injuries (quadriplegics). Individual competition also provides athletes with disabilities who live in rural areas an opportunity to compete, because team membership is not necessary.

Benefits of Wheelchair Sports

There is no doubt that participation in organized wheelchair sports, whether through the NWBA or WSUSA, requires a large personal commitment—one involving time, effort, and *money*. The cost of most sports-adaptable wheelchairs, lighter and more durable than conventional chairs, ranges from $1,500 to $4,000 or more.

The investment needed to establish a wheelchair basketball team may exceed $35,000 including wheelchairs, uniforms, equipment, and one season's travel and game expenses. Why, because it is so expensive, do individuals and some organizations provide their financial support to wheelchair sports? The answer to that question can be found in an explanation of three of the benefits that wheelchair sports offer. They are as follows:

1. *Participant Growth and Development.* Sports for individuals without disabilities are claimed to offer great physical and mental benefits. This claim is also made about wheelchair sports because athletes with and without disabilities share similar goals, objectives, motivations, and personal characteristics (Brasile & Hedrick, 1991;

Wheelchair basketball offers an athlete with a lower extremity disability
the chance to demonstrate skill and athletic ability to the public.
(Courtesy of *Sports 'n Spokes*/Paralyzed Veterans of America)

Coutts, 1986; Henschen, Horvat, & French, 1984; Ogilvie, 1990; Smith, 1993). Many studies and journal articles have stressed the importance of wheelchair sports for individuals with physical disabilities. Wells and Hooker (1990), for example, found that athletes with disabilities responded favorably to training and exceeded nonathletes with disabilities on most measures of physical fitness. Others have also demonstrated that regular, vigorous exercise has produced positive cardiovascular outcomes for people with spinal cord injuries (Hoffman, 1986; Hutzler, Ochana, Bolotin, & Kalina, 1998).

With respect to psychosocial aspects, two studies (Greenwood, Dzewaltowski, & French, 1990; Jacobs, 1989) found that psychological profiles of athletes with disabilities demonstrated more vigor and less psychological depression than profiles of nonathletes with disabilities. Research studies by Blinde and McClung (1997), Coutts (1986, 1988), Dallmeijer, Hopman, van As, and van der Woude (1996), Patrick (1986), Steadward and Walsh (1986), Wilson (2002), and many others have provided evidence in support of participant benefits. Increased physical fitness and strength, a better self-concept and social adjustment, and greater awareness of the world through travel are positive aspects of wheelchair sports participation.

2. *Public Awareness.* Wheelchair sports offer the individual who has a disability an excellent chance to display great skill and physical ability to the nondisabled public. As Page and O'Connor (2001) stated, "Sport [for athletes with disabilities] affirmed competence and negated the perceptions of incompetence that others hold" (p. 44). The myth of "dependency" is quickly dispelled by watching displays of athletic skill, and the wheelchair sports spectator may walk away with a newly formed attitude of appreciation and respect toward people with disabilities. Hedrick's (1986) investigation of the effects of participation in an integrated tennis class provided support for this notion. He found that an improvement in perceptions among nondisabled subjects regarding sport-specific efficacy of peers with disabilities may generalize to improved perceptions of *general* physical competence among people who have disabilities.

3. *Motivation for Others.* The skill displayed by wheelchair athletes often provides much needed motivation for youth or individuals with recent disabilities. During the 28th National Wheelchair Basketball Tournament (NWBT) in Baltimore, for example, a large number of young people with physical disabilities attended the games. Later, the director of the tournament was informed by local school personnel that the 28th NWBT resulted in renewed enthusiasm for physical activity and adapted physical education programs. The publicity and excitement of the tournament was "just what the doctor ordered" for the youth of Baltimore. As a result, several of the young spectators at the 28th NWBT are regulars on Baltimore's wheelchair basketball team.

Expanding Opportunities

The wheelchair sports movement has not only experienced phenomenal growth; it has provided the model for others to promote sports for individuals with disabilities who are ineligible for competition against, or not on a competitive level with, the "traditional" wheelchair athlete. Multiple disabilities or those affecting the upper extremities often limit or prevent participation in NWBA or WSUSA events. The National Cerebral Palsy Games, and their preliminary competition on local, state, and regional levels, have helped to fill the void in competitive sports opportunities for people with such disabilities. These games, held by the U.S. Cerebral Palsy Athletic Association, have classification categories for competitors who use wheelchairs, but also have classes for ambulatory and semiambulatory (users of crutches and other walking aids) competitors. Events held at these games include but are not limited to archery, horseback riding, weight lifting, table tennis, soccer, bowling, rifle shooting, and track and field.

The acceptance of competitive sports for all athletes, including those with severe and/or multiple disabilities, was evidenced by the success of the 11th Paralympic Games in Sydney, Australia. Over 4,000 athletes from 122 countries competed in 18 different sports. More importantly, the public in Australia responded with unbridled enthusiasm for the competition. Four years earlier, the 10th Paralympic Games in the United States had set records for ticket sales and attendance. The 11th

Paralympic Games shattered those records. More than 1,100,000 spectators packed the various venues during the Games. As noted by Craft (2001), "Finally, the highly trained Paralympic athletes had opportunities to compete in front of capacity crowds" (p. 22). Throughout these games, the athletes with disabilities were afforded the same respect and admiration the Olympic athletes had received 17 days earlier. Moreover, the worldwide media coverage offered by WeMedia, Inc., provided everyone instant access to the Games via the Internet. Despite some problems (e.g., failed drug tests, heightened security concerns, court-contested results for one event) the 11th Paralympics were, in the words of the president of the International Paralympic Committee, Dr. Robert Steadward, "the best ever."

An Era of Change

Like the rest of society, wheelchair sports has experienced dramatic changes across the past 30 years. One of the most dramatic changes is the evolution of the sports-model wheelchair. Prior to 1978, wheelchair athletes competed in "standard" wheelchairs with, at most, minor modifications such as smaller handrims and lowered seats. At the 22nd National Wheelchair Games in 1978, however, George Murray introduced two innovations that would forever alter the design and use of sports-model wheelchairs. LaMere and Labanowich (1984) noted that Murray modified the wheelchair to elevate

> his knees excessively high to compensate for his lack of sitting balance owing to the [high] level of his [spinal cord] lesion. . . . Through compensating for his lack of sitting balance, Murray was able to generate a complete stroke and follow through. (p. 12)

This alteration, plus Murray's use of steering handles on the front casters of his wheelchair, directly resulted in a liberalization of rules regulating competitive wheelchairs.

There are about 25 manufacturers who produce quality sports wheelchairs that incorporate

Murray's modifications, plus many additional innovative features. One of the most striking differences between present wheelchairs and those of the late 70s, however, is their weight. The wheelchair George Murray used in 1978 weighed about 50 lbs; today, his sports wheelchair probably weighs less than 11 lbs! Besides being lighter, modern sports wheelchairs incorporate a number of design features that increase their efficiency, including a three-wheel design. Even when differences in weight are taken into account, contemporary sports wheelchairs require close to 20% *less* energy to push than conventional wheelchairs (Hilbers & White, 1987).

Technological advances in the sports-model wheelchair, in weight and design, have also helped to make life easier for nonathletes who use wheelchairs. Today's lighter and more maneuverable "standard" wheelchairs were made possible by advancements in wheelchair sports technology.

SPECIAL OLYMPICS (WWW.SPECIALOLYMPICS.ORG)

Historical Development

In 1967, the Chicago Park District sought the assistance of the Joseph P. Kennedy, Jr., Foundation to fund a program for youngsters with mental retardation. At the suggestion of Eunice Kennedy Shriver, the funds were used to finance a nationwide track meet for children with mental retardation. Rather than expending a lot of money and effort on a program that might not succeed, the Kennedy Foundation and the Chicago Park District agreed to test their new idea by holding and then evaluating the success of a single national meet. That meet, held in 1968, included participants from only 24 states, but the enthusiasm and enjoyment displayed by the 1,000 competitors overshadowed the failure of many states to organize teams. Mrs. Shriver represented the Kennedy Foundation at that premier meet, and the joy she saw among competitors convinced her that the concept of a national sports program for people with mental retardation was a solid one. Following that first event, Special Olympics, Inc., was formed, with Mrs. Shriver serving as president. During the years that followed, the Special Olympics grew in participation, competitive events, and public recognition. Today, it is estimated that more than 1.2 million children and adults with mental retardation or related developmental disability participate in Special Olympics programs throughout the world.

Organization and Events

Special Olympics competition is organized to ensure that as many people with mental retardation as possible get an opportunity to participate. Spring

athletic competition, for example, is offered in a large number of "local" meets that do not require a lot of travel by participants. Holding local events close to the communities where the participants live means that event organizers are usually familiar with local agency or school personnel. Such agency or school professionals can be helpful in recruiting and training Special Olympics competitors. Thus, local rivalries may be promoted, local customs observed, and local resources used at this initial level of athletic competition. All of this helps to produce maximum participation among eligible citizens within the community.

Across the past 15 years, the number of competitive events in the Special Olympics grew

The number of Special Olympics sports and events continues to grow. Floor hockey, for example, is included in the Unified Sports program, which features teams comprised of competitors with and without disabilities.
(Courtesy of Pennsylvania Special Olympics; photo by Dane Hildebrand)

dramatically. The traditional events are athletic (track and field) activities, but Special Olympics offers much more to athletes. Fall events and winter sports are commonplace, and the number of official Special Olympics sports and events continues to grow. Currently, there are 26 official sports, offering a wide variety of individual and team events.

In addition to local events, Special Olympics offers a chance to participate in games that draw competitors from larger areas. These may lead to international competitions which are held every two years, alternating between summer and winter games. For example, the 2001 Special Olympics World Winter Games, held in Anchorage, Alaska, attracted over 1,800 athletes and coaches from 69 nations. Over 7,000 volunteers were on hand to support the seven-day event. Competitions were held in seven official sports, and the size of the event was comparable to the Winter Olympics in Nagano, Japan. The 10th Special Olympics World Summer Games, held in North Carolina, included over 7,000 competitors. These competitors were drawn from more than 15,000 Special Olympic events in more than 150 countries. In addition to the athletes, the Games attracted more than 2,000 coaches, 15,000 family members, 35,000 volunteers, and 400,000 spectators. This event was the biggest international sporting event in North Carolina history.

Classification and Eligibility

Individuals are eligible to participate in Special Olympics competition if an agency or professional classified them as having mental retardation, a cognitive delay, or significant learning or vocational difficulties. If a person requires specially designed instruction due to a cognitive delay, he or she is also eligible for participation. Training for Special Olympics events can begin as early as age 5; however, a child is not eligible for competition until he or she is 8 years of age. Special Olympics originally offered athletic opportunities exclusively for children with mental retardation, but today there is no upper age limit for participation.

In the Special Olympics, competitive classification is called "divisioning," which is the cornerstone of the competitive program (Privett, 1999). Divisions are structured so that participants usually compete against others who are (1) the same sex, (2) similar in chronological age, and (3) at approximately the same level of performance. The last criterion is determined by examining performances during prior events. Thus, a 12-year-old girl with moderate retardation might compete in the same 50-meter dash as another girl of similar age, but with mild retardation. Despite the difference in cognitive functioning, the race should be a close one because previous 50-meter dash times were used to place these girls in their competitive division. Exceptions to the three division criteria may be made occasionally, but only to ensure that there are enough athletes to enable a sport or event to be held.

Important Aspects

There are many aspects of Special Olympics that deserve special recognition. A couple of these are as follows.

The 10% Rule

Equality of competition is an important part of Special Olympics sports and events. A closely matched contest provides a more exciting and enjoyable time for spectators and athletes. But the reason for ensuring basic competitive equality goes much farther than just enjoyment: The self-esteem of a participant may be harmed if he or she is entered against athletes at vastly greater skill levels. Even physical injury could result from such situations, particularly if the less skilled competitor tries to duplicate a difficult maneuver without prior experience and training. To avoid physically and psychologically harmful situations caused by competitive imbalance, Special Olympics has the 10% rule. This rule requires that participants should be matched within competitive divisions that include athletes who perform within approximately 10% of each other. A 15-year-old boy who usually throws the softball about 30 meters should be grouped for competition with boys of similar ability who usually throw approximately 27 to 33 meters. Although this rule is a flexible guideline and cannot always be enforced, it serves as an excellent standard to alert event organizers to the importance of equality of competition.

Inclusion

Since 1989, the Unified Sports program of Special Olympics has promoted competition and inclusion by offering team-oriented sports for persons with and without mental retardation. As noted by Shriver (1990), Unified Sports "is designed to provide a new alternative for athletes with mental retardation, promote equality and teamwork, and certainly serve as a transition to community sports programs" (p. 10). Unified Sports teams are comprised of approximately equal numbers of persons with and without disabilities. Participant selection is based on skill level and ability to contribute to the team's success, and teammates are grouped according to age and performance (i.e., skill). Moreover, Unified Sports teammates are *required* to practice together on a regular basis. The Special Olympics Unified Sports Handbook identifies 24 sports that are part of the Unified Sports program. Because the Unified Sports program is implemented in cooperation with existing community programs such as recreation departments and school districts, it responds to criticism that Special Olympics does not promote inclusion. In addition, Unified Sports's community orientation helps to foster friendships between community residents with disabilities and those without disabilities. Siperstein and Hardman (2001) noted that one goal of Unified Sports is for athletes with and without mental retardation to "engage in sports training and competition as a means to improve their specific sports skills, knowledge of sports' rules, sportsmanship, and team play" (p. 1). Also important, however, is improvement in self-esteem and self-confidence for athletes with mental retardation, and promotion of social acceptance among athletes who do not have mental retardation.

Special Olympics' Sports Partnerships program also offers some inclusive activities for athletes with mental retardation and related developmental disabilities. Through *school partnerships,* athletes enrolled in special education can train alongside the school's varsity, junior varsity, or club teams. The program provides opportunities for integrated training, scrimmages, and sometimes competition. In addition, such partnerships may provide schoolwide recognition for athletes with mental retardation, through inclusive sports' award ceremonies and earning of athletic letters. *Community partnerships* enable persons with mental retardation to train and compete alongside recreational league teams, club teams, employee recreation leagues, and so on. Participants often wear the same team uniforms, travel with team members to competitions, and may represent their league or club in Special Olympics events. Sports Partnerships are not completely inclusive programs (see chapter 7); however, they do provide inclusive experiences that may foster friendships and community understanding between persons with and without mental retardation.

Outcomes of Special Olympics

Special Olympics provides a unique training ground for children and adults with mental retardation. Through physical training and competition, particularly if these are conducted according to normalization principles, the participant learns behaviors that aid his or her adjustment in society.

Special Olympics has great potential for increasing physical fitness levels among participants. A meta-analysis by Chanias, Reid, and Hoover (1998) demonstrated that this potential can be realized. Using data from 21 studies, they found that exercise programs for persons with intellectual disabilities improved muscular and cardiovascular endurance, muscular strength, and flexibility. Draheim, Williams, and McCubbin (2003) also found that active Special Olympians had better cardiovascular fitness levels than non–Special Olympians. Specifically, active Special Olympians had lower diastolic blood pressure, abdominal fat, percentage of body fat, triglycerides, and insulin than non–Special Olympians. The increasing

Skill development is an important aspect of Special Olympics programs. Equestrian events provide skills that can be used in community horseback riding programs.
(Courtesy of Pennsylvania Special Olympics; photo by Dane Hildebrand)

number of physical education programs inspired by Special Olympics should result in future gains in these important areas. But Special Olympics offers more than physical fitness. The chance to experience success is essential to everyone, and Special Olympics offers successful experiences to many athletes with mental retardation, particularly those who work hard to get the most from their efforts.

Shapiro (2003) emphasized the importance of understanding the motivations of Special Olympians in order to maximize their outcomes from participation. She observed:

> Special Olympics coaches can foster athletes' attainment of task oriented achievement goals by structuring training sessions in which coaches (a) provide time for fun and excitement in practices by using new and challenging activities; (b) facilitate opportunities for

athletes to assess their fitness and monitor their weight; (c) provide time for athletes to be with friends; and (d) emphasize effort, goal setting, and improvement as explanations for winning ribbons and medals. (p. 163)

Increased levels of fitness, plus recognition that effort and self-discipline lead to success, are valuable outcomes of Special Olympics participation. In addition, research has demonstrated that many Special Olympics participants show (1) more recreation participation after involvement in the Special Olympics (Rarick, 1978); (2) improvement in a variety of recreational skills, including throwing, running, and jumping (Bell, Kozar, & Martin, 1977); (3) a more favorable attitude toward school and physical education; (4) enhanced physical and social self-esteem (Castagno, 2001; Gibbons & Bushakra, 1989); and (5) greater involvement with family members (Klein, Gilman, & Zigler, 1993). Professionals and parents view Special Olympics as beneficial, particularly in terms of social adjustment and quality of life. Dykens and Cohen (1996) found support for these concepts. Reporting on three studies, they found that the length of time in Special Olympics was a powerful predictor of social competence; furthermore, Special Olympians had higher social competence and expressed more positive self-statements than comparison group members who did not participate in Special Olympics. Special Olympics also has been identified as important for promoting public understanding and acceptance of individuals with mental retardation (Klein et al., 1993).

The National Evaluation of the Special Olympics Unified Sports Program (Siperstein & Hardman, 2001) also found significant benefits for participants with and without disabilities. This study gathered data from state directors, family members of athletes, athletes with mental retardation, partners (without disabilities), and coaches. Some areas of concern were identified (e.g., lack of consistency among states, shortage of resources, competitive dominance by partners without disabilities); however, there was overwhelming satisfaction expressed by respondents toward most aspects of the Unified Sports program. Summarizing their findings, the authors stated:

> First and foremost, it can be unequivocally stated that Unified Sports has a positive impact on all participants. In particular, both athletes and partners enjoy participating in Unified Sports, feel that it has helped them improve their sports skills and self-confidence, and, most importantly, given them the overall opportunity to socialize. Further, partners indicate that they have gained a better understanding of mental retardation and have enjoyed participating with their teammates, particularly the athletes with mental retardation. (p. 23)

Special Olympics is not without problems, but it is a rapidly growing, well-run organization that offers many valuable experiences to more than 1.2 million people with mental retardation or related developmental disability.

BARRIE INTEGRATED BASEBALL ASSOCIATION (BARRIE, ONTARIO, CANADA)

It is unusual to find a community-based program that offers *both* social integration and genuine sports competition. The Barrie Integrated Baseball Association, however, is such a program. Originally developed by the staff of Barrie and District Association for People with Special Needs, the Barrie Integrated Baseball Association is an independent voluntary association that provides baseball competition to adults with and without disabilities in the Barrie area.

Historical Development

Started in 1988, the association has grown from its original four teams to the present format that includes more than 10 integrated teams sponsored by local businesses and organizations. The growth in teams has been paralleled by an increase in the percentage of players without disabilities who compete in the league. Originally, 70% of the players had developmental disabilities (i.e., persons

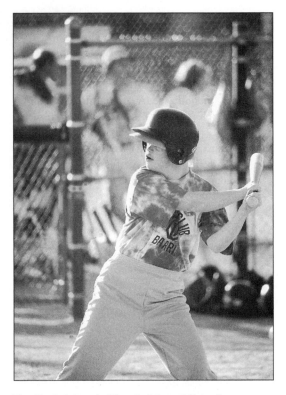

The Barrie Integrated Baseball Association offers opportunities for persons with disabilities to compete on an equal level with persons who do not have disabilities. (Courtesy of Barrie Integrated Baseball Association)

with mental retardation), and most of the players without disabilities were staff members of the Barrie and District Association for People with Special Needs. Now, however, more than 50% of players do not have disabilities, and the number of players from the community continues to grow. Of the 80 players without disabilities who participated in the 1999 season, only 13 were staff members of the Barrie and District Association for People with Special Needs.

Competitive Structure

The association's competitive season runs from mid-May through mid-September, including playoffs, and each team plays approximately 15 games.

The season also includes an All-Star game, and concludes with an awards banquet attended by more than 275 people. Players must be at least 16 years of age to be eligible for participation. Presently, more than 200 players, evenly divided between men and women, participate in the association's competitive schedule.

Organizing and implementing an integrated sports activity that emphasizes competition is not an easy task. The Barrie Integrated Baseball Association's leadership is provided by four volunteer directors, plus a board of directors comprised of community members, players with disabilities, and professional staff from the Barrie and District Association for People with Special Needs. Primary concerns include financial support for the association and public relations to ensure public acceptance of the association's activities. In addition, the Association's leadership strives to ensure that competition takes place in an atmosphere of acceptance and respect for all players. Too much emphasis on winning can interfere with social integration (see chapter 7). Not enough emphasis on winning, however, undermines the intent of competition and can lead to patronizing behaviors and attitudes among players without disabilities. "It is a hard balance to reach," stated Brett Millar, one of the founders of the Barrie Integrated Baseball Association. According to Millar, two factors are important in maintaining this balanced perspective on competition. These factors are: (1) strictly adhering to the association's rules of play (see next section), and (2) maintaining a professional image. To ensure that a professional image is projected during games, all players wear complete baseball uniforms, umpires wear appropriate attire and are paid for their services, and public-address systems are used at each game to introduce players and make announcements.

Selected Rules and Regulations

The rules and regulations of the Barrie Integrated Baseball Association were developed to facilitate competition and ensure that all players participate to their maximum capabilities. More than 40 written rules govern play in the association. The following are some examples of rules developed to facilitate integration:

Rule 1. Team ratio will be 50% special needs players[1] and 50% non-special needs players.

Rule 2. The *rover* is the fourth outfielder and can roam the entire outfield at will. All outfield players must remain on the grassy surface and cannot enter the infield to make a play.

Rule 3. A *buddy* may be added to the outfield only if the special needs player in that position is at risk under the following conditions:

a) has very little or no knowledge of the game

b) is physically unable to play the position alone

c) is in danger of injury if left alone in the field

d) would act out (become very upset) if left alone in the field

The relationship of the buddy and the special needs player is that of a *partnership*. . . . The buddy must ensure that the partner is involved in any play that he or she makes. Any play made by the buddy that does not involve the partner will be cancelled.

Rule 14. There must be a minimum of 3 special needs players on the field each inning (2 infield; 1 outfield).

Rule 15. If a team cannot field 3 special needs players, then that team will forfeit the rover position until enough special needs players arrive.

Rule 25. Batting assistance at the plate will be permitted for those players who require it. The player *must* be given the choice of batting for him- or herself or having assistance.

[1]The term *special needs player* is used by the association to refer to players with disabilities.

Rule 32. All infield players must stay behind the baseline until the ball is hit by the bat. If an infielder is encroaching on the batter when the ball is hit into play, the batter will be awarded first base and all other runners will be awarded a free base.

Communities must respond to the need for competitive sports programs that *include* persons with disabilities. The Barrie Integrated Baseball Association provides a model for communities to emulate. Its program, which maintains a balance in leadership between professional staff and community members (including persons with disabilities), demonstrates that social integration can take place within the context of competitive sports.

BOCCE

Historical Development

The precise origin of bocce is unknown, but games similar to bocce were played as early as 5000 B.C. in Egypt. The modern game most likely evolved from a version brought to Italy by Greek colonists. Few Americans and Canadians understand the intensity of competition this fascinating sport evokes because bocce is not widely played in North America. The history of bocce, however, provides some insight (International Bocce Association, 1999). In the 14th century, King Richard II forbid English citizens from playing the game because it seduced them from the more important sport of archery. Legend also has it that Sir Francis Drake was so fanatical about bocce that he once refused to sail against the advancing Spanish Armada until completing the bocce game he was playing.

Across the centuries, bocce's popularity has ebbed and flowed. During a resurgence in popularity in 1896, however, the first Bocce Olympiad was held in Athens, Greece (Special Olympics, 1999). Since then, bocce has remained part of international Olympic competition, and it is included as a Paralympic event. In the United

States, organized competition in bocce was initiated by European immigrants and began some time after 1900. Today, bocce, along with soccer and golf, is one of the three most-participated sports in the world (The History of Bocce, 1999), and it is growing in popularity in the United States (Daspin, 1998).

Competition

Bocce is played on a level court (usually grass). The dimensions of the court often vary according to the space available. The number of competitors on a team may vary according to the rules being used, but most competitions include 2 to 4 players per team. The game begins by one of the players of the starting team tossing the "pallino" (smaller ball) toward the end of the court and over the opposite foul line. Next, the same player rolls or tosses a larger ball as close to the pallino as possible. The competing team then bowls (larger balls called "boccia") until one of its competitors gets a ball closer to the pallino than the starting team's ball. Play continues alternating until one of the teams has bowled all of its balls. At that point, the competing team bowls the remaining balls. One point is awarded to the team with the ball closest to the pallino, and an additional point is awarded for every ball closer than the closest ball of the opposing team. Usually, 12 points conclude the game.

Unlike the popular sport of bowling in the United States and Canada, tossing the ball may include either underhand or overhand throws, with the ball either being rolled on the ground or lobbed into the air. Which technique is used depends on the experience and personal preference of the bowler and the strategy being used. Strategy is particularly important in bocce because an opponent's balls can be knocked away from the pallino; conversely, knocking it away from its location may also change the position of the pallino. Strategy also includes bank shots off of the wooden court walls. The strategy used by bocce devotees has been likened to the strategy of a chess match, with each move requiring concentration and forethought.

Important Aspects

Bocce is included in this chapter for two reasons. First, bocce is an internationally popular sport that offers challenging, competitive opportunities for people with *severe* physical disabilities. Many competitive sports require movements, coordination, and balance that limit participation among people with severe disabilities. Bocce, however, emphasizes skills that can be mastered by competitors who have severe limitations (e.g., precision, strategy). Trowbridge (1997), for example, described how one young bocce player with cerebral palsy was able to compete through painstakingly training his muscles to execute the requisite throwing motion. Emphasizing skill and strategy, Trowbridge wrote:

> Poised with a red leather ball in his hand, he studies the placement of his opponent's ball and the white target ball already on the court. After a few moments, Hawker, 17, gently tosses the red boccia ball onto the court. It coasts to within inches of the target ball, knocking his opponent's out of the way, and he assumes the lead. (p. 17D)

Elizabeth Dendy (cited by Steadward & Peterson, 1997) also stressed that bocce demands skills that can, with training, be achieved by people with severe disabilities. Referring to Paralympic

Bocce tournaments, such as the city of Baltimore's annual event, offer an ideal opportunity for inclusive sports competition.
(Courtesy of the City of Baltimore's Department of Recreation and Parks)

competitors, she said, "Nobody who has seen [bocce] played at a high level doubts the amount of skill that those athletes show despite their severe disabilities, or doubts the amount of training they put in" (pp. 162–163).

The second, and most important, reason for including bocce in this chapter is that it is an ideal sport to promote inclusion, without having to change or modify the rules of play. Mike Naugle, director of Baltimore City's Wheelchair Bocce Tournament, credited inclusion as his motivation for promoting the sport among Baltimore's citizens who have disabilities.

Naugle said, "Bocce is very popular in Baltimore's Little Italy, and I saw it as a way to include people with disabilities in an activity that is very important to our community" (Naugle, 1999).

Baltimore's wheelchair bocce program includes persons with and without disabilities competing on an equal level and boasts more than 12 competitive teams. Bocce is also one of the sports included in the Special Olympics' Unified Sports program, as athletes with and without developmental disabilities compete together in doubles and team events.

Additional benefits of playing bocce were identified by the National Center on Physical Activity and Disability (n.d.). These included the game helping to develop strategy-related skills, increasing hand-eye coordination, enabling the use of chutes and ramps as aids in placing the game balls, and offering a variety of competitive options for people of all ages and all abilities.

SUMMARY

Despite widespread emphasis on sports in North America, relatively little attention has been given to sports for people who have disabilities. One reason for this may be overemphasis on the rehabilitative benefits of sports participation, rather than recognition that the needs and motivations of all athletes are basically the same. Providing opportunities for parallel competition is one way to emphasize these similarities without creating inequities that might result from direct competition between athletes with and without disabilities. The phenomenal growth of programs such as wheelchair sports and the Special Olympics emphasizes the need for and benefits of sports competition among people who have disabilities. Opportunities for inclusion of persons with disabilities into a community's sports program, such as the Barrie Integrated Baseball Association or the sport of bocce, should also be provided.

SUGGESTED LEARNING ACTIVITIES

1. Observe (or participate in) a competitive wheelchair sports event, and write a two-page report on the experience. Try to include positive and negative reactions.

2. Interview an athlete who has a disability and determine what personal benefits he or she attributes to sports participation.

3. Make a list of 10 topics that you would consider when preparing and training volunteers for a Special Olympics event.

4. Discuss the benefits of participation in competitive sports for individuals with disabilities.

5. Access the Special Olympics website (www.specialolympics.org). Identify and describe one "initiative" that is not included in this chapter.

6. Using the cartoon pictured in Figure 11-1 as an example, create a cartoon illustrating sports for people with disabilities.

7. Organize a bocce tournament that includes persons with and without disabilities.

REFERENCES

Active Living. Moving to inclusion: Everybody plays, everybody wins! *Active Living, 11*(3), 9, 2002.

Bell, N. J., W. Kozar, & A. W. Martin. *The Impact of Special Olympics on Participants, Parents, and Community.* (Research study funded by Special Olympics, Inc.) Lubbock, TX: Texas Tech University, 1977.

Blinde, E. M., & L. R. McClung. Enhancing the physical and social self through recreational activity: Accounts of individuals with physical disabilities. *Adapted Physical Activity Quarterly, 14,* 327–344, 1997.

Block, M. E., & M. Malloy. Attitudes on inclusion of a player with disabilities in a regular softball league. *Mental Retardation, 36,* 137–144, 1998.

Brasile, F. M. Wheelchair sports: A new perspective on integration. *Adapted Physical Activity Quarterly, 7*(1), 3–11, 1990.

Brasile, F. M., & B. N. Hedrick. A comparison of participation incentives between adult and youth wheelchair basketball players. *Palaestra, 7*(4), 40–46, 1991.

Castagno, K. S. Special Olympics Unified Sports: Changes in male athletes during a basketball season. *Adapted Physical Activity Quarterly, 18,* 193–206, 2001.

Casteneda, L., & C. Sherrill. Challenger Baseball and TOPS Soccer: Sports success story. *Teaching Exceptional Children, 30*(2), 26–29, 1997.

Challenging the champions. *Sports 'n Spokes, 22*(6), 28–39, 1996.

Chanias, A. K., G. Reid, & M. L. Hoover. Exercise effects on health-related physical fitness of individuals with an intellectual disability: A meta-analysis. *Adapted Physical Activity Quarterly, 15,* 119–140, 1998.

Coutts, K. D. Physical and physiological characteristics of elite wheelchair marathoners. In C. Sherrill, Ed. *Sport and Disabled Athletes.* Champaign, IL: Human Kinetics, 1986, pp. 157–161.

Coutts, K. D. Heart rates of participants in wheelchair sports. *Paraplegia, 26,* 43–49, 1988.

Craft, D. H. Impressions from Australia. *Palaestra, 17*(1), 20–35, 2001.

Crase, C. It's over. *Sports 'n Spokes, 22*(6), 6, 1996.

Curtis, K. A. Sport-specific functional classification for wheelchair athletes. *Sports 'n Spokes, 17*(2), 45–48, 1991.

Dallmeijer, A. J., M. T. E. Hopman, H. H. J. van As, & L. H. V. van der Woude. Physical capacity and physical strain in persons with tetraplegia: The role of sport activity. *Spinal Cord, 34,* 729–735, 1996.

Daspin, E. Bocce strikes a chord with the country-home set. *Wall Street Journal,* January 23, 1998, p. B12.

DePauw, K. P., & S. J. Gavron. *Disability and Sport.* Champaign, IL: Human Kinetics, 1995.

Devine, M. A., J. N. McGovern, & P. Hermann. Inclusion in youth sports. *Parks & Recreation, 33*(7), 68–76, 1998.

Draheim, C. C., D. P. Williams, & J. A. McCubbin. Cardiovascular disease risk factor differences between Special Olympians and non–Special Olympians. *Adapted Physical Activity Quarterly, 20,* 118–133, 2003.

Frogley, M., & D. Beaver. Is the time right— Interscholastic athletics for student-athletes with disabilities? *Palaestra, 18*(2), 4–6, 2002.

Dummer, G. M. Classification in disability sport: Assessment issues. *Palaestra, 15*(1), 58–59, 1999.

Dykens, E. M., & D. J. Cohen. Effects of Special Olympics International on social competence in persons with mental retardation. *Journal of the American Academy of Child and Adolescent Psychiatry, 35,* 223–229, 1996.

Gibbons, S. L., & F. B. Bushakra. Effects of Special Olympics participation on the perceived competence and social acceptance of mentally retarded children. *Adapted Physical Activity Quarterly, 6,* 40–51, 1989.

Greenwood, C. M., D. A. Dzewaltowski, & R. French. Self-efficacy and psychological well-being of wheelchair tennis and wheelchair nontennis participants. *Adapted Physical Activity Quarterly, 7,* 12–21, 1990.

Hansen, K., & L. Fuller. Varsity wheelers. *Sports 'n Spokes, 29*(1), 34–38, 2003.

Hardin, B., & M. Hardin. Conformity and conflict: Wheelchair athletes discuss sports media. *Adapted Physical Activity Quarterly, 20,* 246–259, 2003.

Hedrick, B. N. Wheelchair sport as a mechanism for altering the perceptions of the nondisabled regarding their disabled peers' competence. *Therapeutic Recreation Journal, 20*(4), 72–84, 1986.

Henschen, K., M. Horvat, & R. French. A visual comparison of psychological profiles between able-bodied and wheelchair athletes. *Adapted Physical Activity Quarterly, 1,* 118–124, 1984.

Hilbers, P. A., & T. P. White. Effects of wheelchair design on metabolic and heart rate responses during propulsion by persons with paraplegia. *Physical Therapy, 67,* 1355–1358, 1987.

Hoffman, M. D. Cardiorespiratory fitness and training in quadriplegics and paraplegics. *Sports Medicine, 3,* 312–330, 1986.

Huebner, C. U. S. Paralympics forum. *Palaestra, 19*(2), 9, 2003.

Hutzler, Y., S. Ochana, R. Bolotin, & E. Kalina. Aerobic and anaerobic arm-cranking power outputs of males with lower limb impairments: Relationship with sport participation intensity, age, impairment and functional classification. *Spinal Cord, 36,* 205–212, 1998.

International Bocce Association. [Online]. Available: http://www.borg.com/~iba/history.html, 1999.

Jacobs, D. A comparison between the psychological profiles of wheelchair athletes, wheelchair nonathletes, and able-bodied athletes. *Palaestra, 5*(3), 12, 1989.

Kelly, J. B. Condescension. Ragged Edge Online. [Online]. Available: http://www. raggededgemagazine.com/extra/marathon03.html, April 23, 2003.

Kelly, J. D., & L. Freiden, Eds. *Go for It.* Orlando, FL: Harcourt Brace Jovanovich, 1989.

Klein, T., E. Gilman, & E. Zigler. Special Olympics: An evaluation by professionals and parents. *Mental Retardation, 51*(1), 15–23, 1993.

Labanowich, S. *Wheelchair Basketball: A History of the National Association and an Analysis of the Structure and Organization of Teams.* Unpublished doctoral dissertation, University of Illinois, 1975.

LaMere, T., & S. Labanowich. The history of sport wheelchairs: Part III. *Sports 'n Spokes, 10*(2), 12–16, 1984.

Lavay, B., & C. Semark. Everyone plays—including special needs children in youth sport programs. *Palaestra, 17*(4), 40–43, 2001.

Lindstrom, H. Integration of sports for athletes with disabilities into sport programmes for able-bodied athletes. *Palaestra, 8*(6), 28–32, 58–59, 1992.

McClellan, R. R., & M. Frogley. The classification debate. In R. D. Steadward, R. N. Ewen, & G. D. Wheeler, Eds. *VISTA '93—The Outlook.* Edmonton, Alberta, Canada: Rick Hansen Centre, 1994, pp. 260–268.

Montelione, T., & J. V. Mastro. Beep baseball. *Journal of Physical Education, Recreation and Dance, 56*(6), 60–61, 1985.

National Center on Physical Activity and Disability. *Boccia.* Chicago: University of Chicago, n.d.

Naugle, M. Personal communication. August 19, 1999.

Ogilvie, B. C. Applications of sport psychology for the athlete with cerebral palsy. *Palaestra, 6*(5), 42–48, 1990.

Paciorek, M. J., & J. A. Jones. *Disability sport and recreation resources* (3rd ed.). Traverse City, MI: Cooper, 2001.

Page, S. J., & E. O. O'Connor. Leaving the disability ghetto: A qualitative study of factors underlying achievement motivation among athletes with disabilities. *Journal of Sport and Social Issues, 25,* 40–55, 2001.

Patrick, G. D. The effects of wheelchair competition on self-concept and acceptance of disability in novice athletes. *Therapeutic Recreation Journal, 20*(4), 61–71, 1986.

Pensgaard, A. M., & M. Sorensen. Empowerment through the sport context: A model to guide research for individuals with disabilities. *Adapted Physical Activity Quarterly, 19,* 48–67, 2002.

Privett, C. The Special Olympics: A tradition of excellence. *The Exceptional Parent, 29*(5), 28–36, 1999.

Rarick, G. L. Adult reactions to the Special Olympics. In F. L. Smoll & R. E. Smith, Eds. *Psychological Perspectives in Youth Sports.* New York: John Wiley & Sons, 1978, pp. 229–247.

Rarick, G. L. Recent advances related to special physical education and sport. *Adapted Physical Activity Quarterly, 1,* 197–206, 1984.

Shapiro, D. R. Participation motives of Special Olympics athletes. *Adapted Physical Activity Quarterly, 20,* 150–165, 2003.

Shriver, E. K. Special Olympics . . . the Unified Sports program. *OSERS News in Print, 3*(1), 10–11, 1990.

Siperstein, G. N., & M. L. Hardman. National Evaluation of the Special Olympics Unified Sports Program. Washington, DC: Special Olympics, Inc., 2001.

Smith, R. W. Sport and physical activity for people with physical disabilities. *Parks & Recreation, 18*(2), 21–25, 27, 96, 1993.

Special Olympics. [Online]. Available: http://www.specialolympics.org/sports/ w_bocce.html, 1999.

Spraggs, S. Archery with the sightless sight system. *Palaestra, 1*(1), 38–39, 1984.

Steadward, R. D., R. N. Ewen., & G. D. Wheeler. *VISTA '93—The Outlook Companion.* Edmonton, Alberta, Canada: Rick Hansen Centre, 1994.

Steadward, R. D., & C. Peterson. *Paralympics.* Edmonton, Alberta, Canada: One Shot Holdings, 1997.

Steadward, R., & C. Walsh. Training and fitness programs for disabled athletes: Past, present, and future. In C. Sherrill, Ed. *Sport and Disabled Athletes.* Champaign, IL: Human Kinetics, 1986, pp. 3–19.

The History of Bocce. [Online]. Available: http://www.sites2c.com, 1999.

Thiboutot, A., R. W. Smith, & S. Labanowich. Examining the concept of reverse integration: A response to Brasile's "new perspective" on integration. *Adapted Physical Activity Quarterly, 9,* 183–292, 1992.

Thomas, D., & R. Katz. Technology increases avenues for disabled athletes. *The Tampa Tribune,* July 7, 2001, p. 16.

Trowbridge, J. On a roll! Cerebral palsy victim finds success in boccia ball. *Chicago Tribune,* April 20, 1997, p. 170.

Tweedy, S. M. Biomechanical consequences of impairment: A taxonomically valid basis for classification in a unified disability athletics system. *Research Quarterly for Exercise and Sport, 74*(1), 9–16, 2003.

Weisman, M., & J. Godfrey. *So Get On with It.* Garden City, NY: Doubleday, 1976.

Wells, C. L., & S. P. Hooker. The spinal injured athlete. *Adapted Physical Activity Quarterly, 7,* 265–285, 1990.

Wilson, P. E. Exercise and sports for children who have disabilities. *Physical Medicine and Rehabilitation Clinics of North America, 13,* 907–923, 2002.

Zeigler, E. F. *History of Physical Education and Sport.* Englewood Cliffs, NJ: Prentice-Hall, 1979.

PART

IV

Resources and Trends

(Courtesy of *New Mobility Magazine*)

The thought that communities are made up of individuals who function together in applying their resources toward the common good is basic to chapter 12, Community Resources. A process by which citizens collaborate to bring about change in the well-being of the community, referred to as community development, is discussed in the chapter. Particular emphasis is placed on (1) community resources as they relate to recreation for persons with disabilities and (2) understanding the community from a sociocultural perspective.

In chapter 13, Trends in Inclusive Recreation, an attempt is made to look into the future to understand how the area of leisure services for persons with disabilities will evolve. Drawing on the views of experts, trends for the future are discussed in terms of programming, new approaches, community relations, financial matters, and professional concerns. The chapter concludes on a positive note about increased acceptance of inclusive recreation services by those directing leisure service delivery systems.

CHAPTER

12 COMMUNITY RESOURCES

(Courtesy of Maryland-National Capital Park and Planning Commission, Special Populations Division; Photo by Steve Abramowitz)

W hat are community resources? How do community resources help provide for inclusive and special recreation services? What basic knowledge of and skills in community development are helpful in establishing community services for persons with disabilities? This chapter addresses these questions. Perhaps the best way to begin is by defining the term *community resources*.

The term community is used in at least three ways. First, a community may be conceived as being made up of people who live in a particular geographic area. Second, a community may be thought of as a group of like-minded individuals linked by a common interest (e.g., religious community). Third, a community reflects a sense of togetherness and mutual concern in which the members possess a sense of social unity or a sense of belonging (Schuler, 1996). Sessoms' (1980) sociologically based definition encompasses the three elements identified by Schuler and provides the most complete definition of community found in recreation literature. Sessoms has written:

> Sociologists define a community as a collection of individuals who live within a specific geographical area, share a common bond of interdependency and commitment, and function as a group in achieving and fulfilling human needs and wishes. More simply stated, a community is people, geographically living and working together, sharing the benefits of their labor and other endeavors. (pp. 120–121)

Resources, according to the dictionary, are "a source of supply or support: an available means." Resources are persons or things that can be drawn upon as they are needed to meet an end. They may include:

- human resources
- informational resources
- financial resources
- facility and equipment resources
- transportation resources

All these types of resources will be discussed in this chapter as they relate to a community providing inclusive and special recreation services.

Community resources, as used here, are those available means by which communities meet the recreational needs of persons with disabilities.

THE IMPORTANCE OF COMMUNITY RESOURCES

Why is an understanding of the community resources necessary for leisure service professionals? The answer to this question is simple. Resources are required to accomplish any goal the leisure service professional may have. Without a knowledge of potential resources and how to use them, it is unlikely that goals will be realized. Leisure professionals need to develop a working knowledge of existing resources and to know how to draw upon these to achieve any goal, including providing inclusive recreation services. The goal of fulfilling the recreational needs of *all* community members requires developing particular types of community resources.

HUMAN RESOURCES

Human resources that may be employed in conducting programs for persons with disabilities include volunteers, existing agency staff, students completing professional field experiences, personnel from related agencies, and consultants who have skills that may add to the program. Some may assist on a sustained basis; others may become involved only as they are needed. For example, some individuals may volunteer regularly to work with a particular activity or participate as a member of an advisory council. Others may become involved only with special events or those events that call for their particular skills.

Developing and cultivating human resources is a primary task of the professional coordinating community inclusive recreation services. There are many ways to go about locating people who may serve as resources. Once an advisory council is formed, its members can be a ready source of information in identifying individuals to fulfill needed roles. Similarly, members of interagency councils can supply names of individuals who may be resources. In some communities, directories of social services are available. Contacts at colleges and universities are another source of human resources. Many colleges and universities have student volunteer bureaus. Faculty members may have students wishing to complete field experiences and may also serve as consultants, identifying human service personnel in the community. Labor unions, churches, and civic clubs offer additional sources of human resources.

No matter what approaches are used to identify human resources, the information collected should be organized in a way that is systematic and easily retrievable. Each time a person is identified, the individual's name, address, e-mail address, telephone number, and how he or she could be a potential resource should be recorded on a card or placed in a computer system for future reference.

Volunteers

Budget-conscious administrators may use volunteers to meet the needs of persons with disabilities while providing services under limited budgets. Volunteers offer a way to stretch an agency's resources. But volunteers supply far more than inexpensive labor in the absence of paid staff. They offer a wealth of diversity in backgrounds and skills that would rarely be available within a regular staff. Volunteers also share a dedication to service. They can accomplish tasks that would be difficult or impossible without their efforts because of their diversity and dedication.

Janet Pomeroy, founder and director of RCH, Inc. in San Francisco, has spoken of the wide base of community support found on the original center's board of directors (Pomeroy, 1974). Among those on the board were

- several medical doctors
- a social worker
- several attorneys
- a real estate and insurance broker
- a superior court justice
- a recreation educator
- a physical educator
- a member of the Social Services Commission

- a food broker
- a product executive
- an architect
- other businessmen and businesswomen
- parents representing the center's auxiliary

The center's board members were able to take on a number of assignments including fundraising, transportation, insurance, recruitment of staff and volunteers, reviewing legislation for funding sources, obtaining supplies and equipment, assisting with preparation of grant applications, and contacting city officials regarding contractual services for the center because of their diverse talents.

Every community has a number of persons who desire to volunteer their services to meaningful projects. These persons may wish to serve on a board or advisory council; to do face-to-face leadership; or to work in a supportive capacity in administration, promotion, transportation, or some other aspect of the program.

Recruiting Volunteers

Pomeroy (1974) employed a number of means to recruit volunteers at RCH, Inc. She stated that a primary means is to get potential volunteers to visit the center. Pomeroy explained, "We can show the need for the program; we can demonstrate the benefits of recreation; and we can stimulate interest—all of which makes them want to help" (p. 11). Promotion is a second means Pomeroy has used to secure volunteers. The center provides presentations to service clubs, fraternal organizations, and other groups and conducts planned campaigns in newspapers and on radio and television. Finally, program volunteers are recruited through contacts with junior high schools, hospitals, youth service agencies, volunteer bureaus, and participants in the center's program.

The concept of using volunteers from among the center's participants merits further discussion. Volunteer service can be an especially meaningful leisure pursuit for persons with disabilities, enabling them to give rather than receive. In addition to persons with disabilities, Tedrick (1990) has suggested other groups as sources of volunteers.

These include preteens, older adults, and individuals who have been court-assigned to complete community service. Another source for volunteers is through corporate volunteer programs (Stensrud, 1993).

Inclusive Volunteering

The notion of using volunteers with disabilities has been termed *inclusive volunteering*. There exists an inclusive volunteering movement reflected by literature in both the United States and Canada. For example, in the United States an article has appeared in *Parks & Recreation* on inclusive volunteering titled "Better to Give Than Receive" (Phoenix, Miller, & Schleien, 2002). The organization Volunteer Canada, in 2001, published a manual titled *Volunteer Connections: Creating an Accessible and Inclusive Environment,* to encourage the use of volunteers with disabilities within Canada.

This concept of persons with disabilities being involved as volunteers transcends inclusive and special recreation services to include all organizations that rely on volunteers. Because persons with disabilities are often perceived by agencies to only be recipients of services, they may be overlooked as potential resources to provide services to others. As Phoenix, Miller, and Schleien (2002) have stated: "People with disabilities are typically viewed as the recipients of volunteer services rather than potential contributors of services" (p. 26). Yet, they have indicated that "people with disabilities have a wealth of abilities, talents and knowledge to contribute" (p. 29), and in contributing as volunteers these individuals can focus on their abilities, rather than their disabilities. Using their abilities in volunteering can have positive outcomes for persons with disabilities. Benefits identified in a pilot project included skill development, increases in social interaction, and gains in pride and empowerment (Miller, Schleien, Rider, Hall, Roche, & Worsley, 2002).

Keys to Successful Volunteer Programs

Three key elements must exist in any successful volunteer program. These are (1) involving volunteers in the program; (2) recognizing the volunteers'

contributions; and (3) providing proper training for volunteers. Volunteers must be made to feel a part of the program by being included in decisions. Volunteers, who give freely of themselves, do not wish to be "told what to do." They want to have a voice in the program. Volunteers also need to receive positive feedback when it is deserved. This praise should be given on a daily basis, with special recognition shown through an established awards program. Finally, volunteers must be provided with orientation and training to enable them to succeed.

An outline for the in-service training of volunteers is contained in the Project LIFE (Life Is For Everyone) resource and training manual produced at the University of North Carolina at Chapel Hill (Bullock, Wohl, Webreck, & Crawford, 1982, pp. 106–107). Topics include

1. understanding characteristics of various disabilities, noting possible limitations and special considerations (emergency and health care procedures should be outlined here also)
2. gaining knowledge of general activity and equipment modification techniques
3. overviewing the least restrictive environment concept and how it is being implemented in the department
4. assessing existing attitudes of recreation professionals (and volunteers) toward individuals with disabilities
5. creating peer acceptance
6. using instructional aides and volunteers
7. finding additional resource information for a specific disability

Henderson and Bedini (1991) have suggested 10 strategies for conducting successful volunteer programs.

1. *Carefully consider the tasks* to be completed by volunteers to ensure that each task is appropriate for a volunteer and that a good match is made between the individual and the assignment.
2. *Keep all staff informed* of how volunteers are to be used with the agency so that staff do

not feel their jobs are threatened and understand the importance of volunteers.

3. *Match tasks with qualifications and interests of volunteers* by assessing skills and interests of volunteers and then placing each volunteer in a position whereby he or she may use existing skills or develop new ones.

4. *Acknowledge that everyone is a potential volunteer* in order to seek out not only individuals but civic groups who may volunteer as units for particular events.

5. *Give volunteers verbal feedback* on a regular basis to praise them for positive performances and to offer constructive criticism.

6. *Periodically evaluate* individual volunteers and the overall volunteer program.

7. *Provide recognition in many ways* including daily social reinforcements (e.g., thank-yous, pats on the back) and formal recognition (e.g., awards, recognition nights).

8. *Stay up-to-date* on issues surrounding volunteering, such as liability insurance, tax deductions, and legislation.

9. *Recognize the connection between volunteering and leisure activity* because volunteering can be a positive leisure experience and an atmosphere provided by staff to foster leisure can enhance volunteer experiences.

10. *Provide appropriate training* so volunteers may feel comfortable in their roles and clients may enjoy maximum profit from the volunteers.

A final key to successful volunteer programs is to make sure that staff know how to work with volunteers. Staff do not necessarily automatically recognize the value of volunteers. It is wise to train staff so that they may understand the contributions volunteers may add to the agency's program and how to build positive relationships with volunteers.

A good beginning point is to let staff consider how they may effectively use volunteers in the agency's program. This will help to establish the value of volunteers. An idea to be shared with staff is that volunteers should be thought of as consultants, rather than employees (Henderson & Silverberg, 2002). Once a commitment to a volunteer program is established by staff, then simple concepts for building staff/volunteer relationships may be implemented. These include knowing each volunteer by name; treating volunteers as colleagues by being welcoming and friendly with them; displaying interest in volunteers and what they are doing; and, in general, supporting the work of volunteers.

Volunteering as a Means to Developing Social Capital

The term *social capital* has been employed to represent the idea that a sense of community can be built by those volunteering, thus adding a valuable resource to make the community a better place (Henderson & Silverberg, 2002). While social capital has been defined in a number of different ways, it is perhaps best construed as the social cohesion developed by "the norms and networks that enable collective action," according to the World Bank (2003). The World Bank has explained that social capital involves "the institutions, relationships, and norms that shape the quality and quantity of a society's social interactions. Increasing evidence shows that social cohesion is critical for societies to prosper economically and for development to be sustainable. Social capital is not just the sum of the institutions which underpin a society—it is the glue that holds them together." By providing mutual aid a sense of "we" is developed that bonds people together. Or a norm of reciprocity is established where those in social networks do things for each other, thus building "social capital."

Henderson and Silverberg (2002) have written: "Volunteering in a community can create social capital, and the more social capital produced, the more volunteering can be facilitated. Volunteering may create bonding social capital, which strengthens the ties that already exist, and bridging social capital, which creates ties among people unknown to one another" (p. 30). Thus, volunteers may be perceived to not only provide direct assistance to those being served but add to the overall sense of community and the quality of life in the community.

Existing Agency Staff

Leisure service personnel typically do not possess the attitudes, knowledge, and abilities to be able to include persons with disabilities, therefore, special staff members are often hired to provide this service. Schleien, Ray, and Green (1997) have warned against this practice. Instead, they have stipulated that leisure service agencies must help their regular staff members understand that it is *their responsibility* to provide persons with disabilities access to facilities and inclusion in programs. Further, Schleien and his colleagues have indicated that agencies must train general staff "on ways to apply typical services in order to

eliminate unnecessary reliance on specialized staff" (p. 54).

Schleien et al. (1997) go on to point out that staff training must be continuing, well-designed, and conducted by a CTRS or other professional with expertise in the area of inclusion. They comment that agencies may wish to employ a full-time inclusion specialist, whose role would be a proactive one to ensure that individuals with disabilities are appropriately included in their agency's programs and settings. Suggested titles for the inclusion specialist are community leisure planner (CLP) or community leisure facilitator (CLF).

Students Completing Professional Field Experiences

University departments providing professional preparation for recreation and parks services have students who are required to complete professional field experiences. These experiential learning

A student intern can be a valuable resource in any special recreation program.
(Courtesy of Courage Center, Golden Valley, MN)

opportunities may be part-time, usually accomplished during a few hours each week, or they may take the form of full-time internships. Such internships or field work experiences are often done over a quarter (10 weeks) or semester (15 weeks). University students can make valuable contributions, provided the agency is willing to offer professional supervision for them. While most students should have some educational preparation in inclusive and special recreation, it is important that agencies complete an early assessment of each student's competencies so that appropriate responsibilities may be assigned and gaps in knowledge or skills may be filled through additional training.

Contracting for Services

Another means of obtaining necessary human resources is to contract for the services of individuals who perform specific tasks. During the initial stage of program development, the most feasible approach may be contractual arrangements that include consulting with regular staff and conducting programs for people with disabilities.

Consultation services can be arranged with administrators of existing recreation programs for persons with disabilities, with university faculty who have experience in working with inclusive recreation programs, or with private consultants with expertise in community inclusive recreation programs. Personnel from other community agencies often have the competencies necessary to provide direct service functions. These persons may be employed part-time to lead programs. For example, therapeutic recreation specialists for local hospitals or rehabilitation centers may be contracted to offer programs within community recreation and parks facilities.

Studies (Austin, Peterson, & Peccarelli, 1978; Edginton, Compton, Ritchie, & Vederman, 1975; Vaughan & Winslow, 1979) have identified the lack of trained program personnel as a major hurdle to clear to establish community special and inclusive recreation services. The creative use of human resources may offer a vehicle by which to launch needed community recreation programs for people who have disabilities.

INFORMATIONAL RESOURCES

Many resources exist that can offer information valuable to establishing and developing community recreation services for people with disabilities. These range from local resource persons to national computer retrieval systems.

Local Resource Persons

First, in many communities, or in close proximity, will be colleges and universities that have faculty members with backgrounds in recreation for persons with disabilities. Second, therapeutic recreation specialists in local hospitals, rehabilitation centers, associations for retarded citizens, behavioral health centers, and other facilities are often anxious to assist in the development of inclusive and special recreation programs. Finally, recreation and parks staff in neighboring communities or park districts may be able to share information concerning leisure services for persons with disabilities.

Literature

Books on inclusive recreation have begun to appear. Among these are *Inclusion: Including People with Disabilities in Parks and Recreation Opportunities* by Anderson and Kress (2003), *Introduction to Recreation Services for People with Disabilities* by Bullock and Mahon (2000), and *Community Recreation and People with Disabilities* by Schleien et al. (1997). Two journals—*Journal of Leisurability* and *Therapeutic Recreation Journal*—have frequent articles on inclusive recreation, and *Parks & Recreation* magazine has regularly published articles on the topic. For those interested in sports and other active types of recreation for persons with disabilities, *Sports 'n Spokes* and *Palaestra* provide current and comprehensive coverage. Computer information retrieval systems offer a means to identify a full spectrum of publications that apprise the reader of recent developments on the topic of recreation and leisure services for persons with disabilities.

Organizations

Another source of information on inclusive and special recreation services is through various organizations. State and local professional recreation and parks societies often have committees or individuals who may provide information to practitioners. National professional organizations may also offer assistance. Two of the major organizations in the United States are the American Alliance for Health, Physical Education, Recreation and Dance (AAHPERD) and the National Recreation and Park Association (NRPA). AAHPERD has offered consultation and literature on programs for persons with disabilities. NRPA offers useful publications and an institute on recreation inclusion.

Athletic and recreational organizations for persons with disabilities, such as the National Wheelchair Basketball Association, National Wheelchair Athletic Association, Special Olympics, American Blind Bowling Association, and other similar organizations, offer information regarding their particular area of recreational interest. These organizations are listed in appendix B. Appendix A lists selected organizations concerned with specific disabilities. Among these, several have been particularly active in promoting special recreation programs, including the American Foundation for the Blind, the Epilepsy Foundation, and the National Easter Seal Society. An example of the efforts of such groups has been the publication of *Recreation Programming for Visually Impaired Children and Youth* (Kelley, 1981), an extensive book produced by the American Foundation for the Blind. Finally, youth-serving agencies have attempted to serve the needs of persons with disabilities. Two examples are the Girl Scouts of the USA and the YMCA of the USA. Of particular note has been the Mainstreaming Activities for Youth (MAY) project, conducted by the YMCA Office of Special Populations, which brought together 10 youth-serving agencies in a collaborative effort to enhance their mainstreaming activities.

Continuing Education

Continuing education opportunities abound. The largest providers of conferences, teleconferences, institutes, and workshops are professional societies and universities. The AAHPERD and the NRPA annual conferences regularly offer educational programs on recreation for persons with disabilities. Universities also provide workshops and institutes for the development of community-based services for people with disabilities. Recreation and leisure studies curricula are the usual sponsors of these programs.

While information on inclusive and special recreation services has been relatively limited in the past, its growth has been inspired by the desire of many professionals and citizens to establish community-based programs. It is likely that the amount of information available will grow as interest in the area builds.

An excellent example of the growing interest in inclusive recreation is a national inclusion institute now being conducted annually by the National Recreation and Park Association (NRPA). The first NRPA National Institute on Recreation Inclusion was held September 8–11, 2000, in suburban Chicago. This institute attracted more than 200 participants from across the United States, including Hawaii (McGovern, 2000).

FINANCIAL RESOURCES

Perhaps no single resource area attracts as much attention as that of financial resources. Without adequate financial support, no program can continue to exist. Those concerned with developing programs for persons with disabilities must be knowledgeable about financial resources.

Vaughan and Winslow (1979) found that the major funding source for special recreation programs is the general tax fund. Slightly more than 87% of all recreation and parks agencies surveyed used the general tax as a source of funding. Fees and charges were the second greatest source, used by 44.2% of the agencies. Sources beyond these depended largely on the size of the community.

Communities of less than 100,000 tended to fund 30% to 40% of their program from donations. Government grants were a major source of funding for those cities with more than 250,000 people. Other sources of funds were special taxes, private grants, and contractual agreements.

Vaughan and Winslow (1979) state that the major funding source for inclusive and special recreation programs should be the general tax fund. We concur that such recreation programs should be supported to the largest degree possible through existing tax structures. However, in a time of budget limitations, professionals must be aware of alternative sources as well. This is particularly true when beginning new programs. Once established, inclusive and special recreation programs usually are supported by the citizenry. Special appropriations may be needed, however, to initiate services.

Special Taxes

Park districts and municipalities in the state of Illinois have been highly successful in establishing special recreation programs. One reason for the success in Illinois has been legislation that allows park districts and other governmental bodies to cooperate by forming special recreation associations and to levy a special tax up to $.04 for $100 of assessed valuation for special recreation programs. Thus, at least one state has used legislation to establish financial means to support special recreation programs. Refer to chapter 3 for more detailed information.

Fees and Charges

Fees and charges can provide another financial resource for inclusive and special recreation programming. Just as other public recreation and parks programs are supported by fees and charges, programs for people with disabilities can likewise receive support. Fees should be in line with other fees charged by the agency.

Contractual Agreements

Recreation and parks agencies can enter into contractual agreements with schools, nursing homes, and other agencies to provide recreation services for people with disabilities. Although contractual agreements are likely to be a minor financial resource, they do offer additional means of support.

Fund-Raising

Fund-raising projects are another means to obtaining revenue for special and inclusive recreation programs. Many techniques may be used in fund-raising. These include governmental and foundation grants, memorial giving, house-to-house and direct mail solicitations, capital fund campaigns, and special events.

Following are some useful tips for successful fund-raising:

1. *Set your goal.* Setting a clear goal can motivate those involved in fund-raising. If your agency did a fund-raising campaign last year, go the extra mile and try to beat last year's total.
2. *Develop a list.* Using all available sources, make a list of individuals, groups, social clubs, and agencies or organizations for target contacts.
3. *Make your fund-raising campaign known.* Call, write letters, fax, and send e-mails to those names on the list and ask for their financial support. Clearly state that their donation directly benefits inclusive recreation programs. Make sure that your appeal asks for a donation and includes a return address.
4. *Chart your course.* Make a money thermometer to show others how "hot" your fund-raising status really is!
5. *Have fun.* Plan and implement mini-events to facilitate the fund-raising campaign.
6. *Appreciate your donors.* Let your sponsors know how much your agency appreciates their support of your program. Thank them on behalf of participants with disabilities!

Grants

Grants may be made by a governmental agency or through a private foundation. In the past, federal grant monies have been available through a number of sources including Title IV of the Social Security Act for Aid to Families with Dependent Children, Title XIV of the Social Rehabilitation Act, the Developmental Disabilities Services and Facilities Construction Act of 1970 (PL 88-164) and Amending Law (PL 91-517), the Architectual Barriers Act of 1968 (PL 90-480), and the Rehabilitation Act of 1973 (PL 93-112). The governmental grant picture is constantly changing, therefore it is wise to refer to recent information sources when seeking grant funding. Community and university libraries (reference sections) can provide assistance with locating current resources on grants and guides or books to assist with proposal writing.

Grant writing takes a great deal of time and persistence. Many times applicants succeed only following their second or third try. If a proposal is not funded, it does little good to become angry. Instead, the wise grant writer will attempt to learn the reasons for the rejection so that a revised and improved application can be prepared and resubmitted.

The first thing that a grant writer needs to do is to define the project for which grant support is being sought. The purpose of the project must be clear so that a mission statement can be prepared and project goals specified. Of course, the need for the project must be well documented so that a compelling case for the project may be presented. Accurate facts or statistics provide the documentation for a winning argument.

Once a well-defined project has been outlined, appropriate funding sources must be identified. Sources may be private foundations or governmental granting agencies. By contacting possible foundations or agencies information can be gained to learn if the project fits with the interest and scope of the funder's program. Once a grant source has been identified, then proposal guidelines can be requested. The guidelines will stipulate submission deadlines, the parts of the application, the format to be followed (e.g., number of pages, margins, spacing), and the number of copies to submit. If the published guidelines are not followed as directed, there is a real danger that the proposal will not even be considered by the funding source.

In preparing the narrative of the proposal it is critical that the project description be presented in a way that aligns it with the purpose and goals of the funding source. This is of upmost importance because the reviewers will scrutinize the proposal to make sure that it fits with the philosophical position of the foundation or agency. Program information typically includes (1) a description of the project and how it will be conducted (including a timetable for the project); (2) anticipated outcomes from the project and how they will be evaluated; and (3) anticipated staffing needs (including deployment of existing staff and the hiring of any new staff) (Corporation for Public Broadcasting, 2003; The Foundation Center, 2003). Typical components of proposals are outlined in Table 12.1.

Summary to Financial Resources Section

As we have seen, there are many different potential financial resources available for inclusive and special recreation programs. Funding can come from general taxes, special taxes, fees and charges, contractual agreements, fund-raising projects, governmental grants, or foundation grants. The point should be reiterated, however, that the primary funding for inclusive and special recreation programs should come from the normal funding source of recreation and parks and not from grants or other special sources.

FACILITY AND EQUIPMENT RESOURCES

Potential facilities for inclusive and special recreation programs include parks, forests, pools, community centers, gymnasiums, bowling lanes, athletic fields, and other places where organized recreation commonly takes place. Equipment includes lasting articles or apparatus needed to conduct programs. While adapted equipment is necessary for a few activities, standard recreational equipment is frequently employed in programs for people with disabilities.

TABLE 12.1	Components of Grant Proposals
Executive Summary	The executive summary briefly presents all of the key information of the proposal. It contains (1) a problem statement that presents the problem or need being met; (2) a short description of the project; (3) funding requirements with plans for funding following the period of the grant; (4) information on the history, purpose, and activities of the agency that displays the agency's capacity to conduct the project.
Statement of Need	The statement of need offers a brief, persuasive statement establishing why the project is necessary. It builds on the executive summary by helping the reader to understand the problem that the project will remedy.
Project Description	The project description explains exactly how the project will be implemented and evaluated.
Budget	The budget is the financial description that details how much the project will cost.
Organizational Information	Organizational information provides information about the agency seeking the grant including its history, governing structure, primary activities, services, and who it serves.
Conclusion	The conclusion provides a summary of the proposal's main points.

Source: The Foundation Center. *Proposal Writing Short Course*. [Online]. Available: http://www.fdcenter.org/learn/shortcourse/prob1.html, September 5, 2003.

Facilities

The major facilities for inclusive and special recreation programs should be those controlled and programmed by the agency. Existing facilities have to be evaluated to make certain they are accessible and usable by persons with disabilities before they are scheduled for programs.

Most communities have a wide array of potential facilities that may be used for inclusive and special recreation programs. In addition to those of the recreation and parks department, facilities may be made available through schools, voluntary and youth-serving agencies (e.g., YMCA, YWCA), bowling lanes, churches, hospitals, rehabilitation centers, and other public and private organizations. As a general rule, programs should be conducted in facilities usually used for programming by the recreation and parks department or park district.

A facility resource file should be maintained so that a current list of facilities is available. Included should be the name and address of the facility, the agency controlling it, accessibility information, special equipment available at the facility, any cost for use, the contact person, and a phone number. Many communities have published accessibility guides that would be useful in establishing such a resource file. Advisory councils and interagency councils are also potentially rich sources of information in identifying suitable facilities for inclusive and special recreation programming.

Equipment: Including Assistive Devices

An assistive device is equipment used to maintain or improve the functional abilities of persons with disabilities. Assistive devices may be purchased or constructed. Because assistive devices can take on a gimmicky quality if not well conceived, it is best to consult with an expert before purchasing or building equipment when unsure about the type of equipment or the necessity to have it. Therapeutic recreation specialists often can provide expert advice regarding assistive devices. Program

Modification of equipment may allow *everyone* in the family to participate in leisure activities.
(Courtesy of *New Mobility Magazine*)

participants may also have expertise regarding assistive devices.

Examples of assistive devices include handle-grip bowling balls (handles automatically retract to be flush into the ball when released), bowling rails to guide visually impaired bowlers, bicycle buddy bars (permit two regular bicycles to ride side-by-side), tricycle body supports (enable children with poor balance to use tricycles), and floor sitters (resemble chairs without legs that allow children to sit up during floor play) (Austin & Powell, 1980). There are scores of assistive devices that may be purchased or constructed. A number of commercial suppliers list assistive devices in their catalogues.

Another idea is to use recreational equipment in nontraditional ways or to employ equipment that is not typically associated with recreational use. Such uses have been termed "alternative equipment" by Williams (2003). In his book on assistive devices Williams has written:

> Alternative equipment is either traditional equipment used in a non-traditional way, or equipment that is not usually associated with athletic or recreational uses. The shuffleboard cue is a traditional piece of equipment for shuffleboard. During floor hockey, however, the shuffleboard cue may be used in an alternative way to guide a puck across the floor. Likewise, an electric leaf blower, which is not usually associated with volleyball, may be used to blow balloons or beach balls up into the air and over the net. (p. 29)

TRANSPORTATION RESOURCES

Schleien et al. (1997) have stated, "Some of the most prevalent concerns that people with disabilities have are the availability and quality of transportation services to community recreation settings . . ." (p. 55). Bullock and Mahon (2000) have exclaimed that "Lack of transportation will be a major factor limiting the access of people with disabilities to community recreation participation" (p. 253). To solve the problem of providing adequate transportation resources, Vaughan and Winslow (1979) have suggested the following:

- *Car Pooling.* Participants, families, and friends may serve as resources for developing car pools organized by the recreation and parks system.
- *Service Clubs and Social Service Agencies.* Groups such as the Red Cross, Kiwanis, and Lions Clubs may provide transportation for participants. Service clubs may also possibly purchase vans for the recreation and parks department.
- *Federal Funding to Purchase Vans.* In the past, federal legislation has provided funding sources for transportation. The Federal-Aid Highway Act of 1973 (PL 93-87) and the Developmental Disabilities Services and Facilities Construction Act of 1971 (PL 91-517) are examples of federal laws for the allocation of funds for transportation.
- *Contractual Agreements.* Contractual agreements may be drawn with schools, health agencies, or other organizations. Such agreements have the added advantage of possibly bringing more participants into the inclusive and special recreation programs from the contracting agency.
- *Public Transportation.* Current federal legislation calls for public transit systems to obtain accessible vehicles: therefore, mass transit offers a viable resource to assist in solving transportation problems for inclusive and special recreation programs.

The effective use of existing community resources can enable the leisure service professional to meet the recreational needs of persons with disabilities. Creative use of community resources presumes a knowledge of available resources. The first, and largest, segment of this chapter has provided information for locating potential resources. The final portion of the chapter deals with the basic skills in and understanding of community development[1] needed to establish services for persons with disabilities.

KNOWING THE COMMUNITY

Communities are diverse, each being unique from the next. The term *sociocultural* has been employed to encompass the essential features of social organizations and social norms that help make communities distinctive, according to Edwards and Jones' (1976) now classic work titled *Community and Community Development.* Edwards and Jones' book served as the primary resource for the following segment on sociocultural variables.

Sociocultural Variables

The material that follows deals with the sociocultural variables of concern to the leisure service professional wishing to initiate inclusive and special recreation services. Analysis of the social organization and culture of the community is critical to success in working with structures that bring individuals, agencies, and organizations together to achieve common goals cooperatively.

Features of the social structure in the sociocultural facet of community life are social groups; social stratification; community subsystems such as the family, the economy, education, religion, government, and social welfare; and normative structures dealing with social norms and values.

Social Groups

Groups can be formal or informal. Formal groups are those that have structural rules and regulations

---

[1]The term *community development,* as used in this chapter, refers to the process by which citizens collaborate to take action to improve the well-being of the community.

to govern relationships. They can use formal communications systems that reach relatively large numbers, because of their structure. Examples of formal groups are labor unions, service organizations, and golf and tennis clubs.

Informal groups revolve around interpersonal relationships between group members. Informal groups are relatively small and allow members to meet emotional needs through intimate interactions. Examples of informal groups are family groups and peer groups.

Social Stratification

Social stratification deals with social prestige and power. Social prestige is concerned with social class structure. Power deals with the ability to control others and to effect change. Often those in the higher social classes have the most power, although there is not always a direct correspondence, because some of the "better" families (high social class) may not hold power because of diminished wealth and political influence. In most communities, however, those with the most influence are those in the upper social classes or those who hold high status in one of the subsystems such as government or religion.

Three approaches may be applied to determine power holders in the community. These are the reputational, positional, and decisional approaches. To determine power by the reputational approach, one must ask the questions, With whom do you check before acting? What individual(s), formal groups, or informal groups do you consult on communitywide decisions? The positional approach assumes that those in positions of authority hold the power. Examples are the mayor and the superintendent of recreation and parks. The final approach, the decisional approach, takes for granted that those involved in making decisions for the community hold the power (Sessoms, 1980).

Sessoms (1980) has discussed two situations of power in the community. The first is the *power elite.* The power elite exists in communities where the power is in the hands of a few individuals. In contrast to this monolithic approach is the *multiple*

pyramid system in which no single group holds power. Instead it is a pluralistic system in which the power is held by many.

Jewell (1983), in an article on power structures as they relate to inclusive and special recreation services for persons with disabilities, has discussed four types of communities. These have been termed the (1) dominated or restricted power community, (2) factional or conflict-dissipated power community, (3) pluralistic or accordant power community, and (4) inert or power-avoidance community. Jewell has stated that the ability to analyze the community for these power structures is more important than any other aspect of community analysis.

The first of the community power structures presented by Jewell is similar to the power elite community discussed by Sessoms (1980). In the *dominated or restricted power community,* power is maintained by a single individual or a small group of people. Many times, the person or persons in control run an industry that dominates the community. Citizen boards "rubber stamp" the decisions made by the power elite, so the recreation and parks department is likewise apt to be under their control. In the case of the community with dominated or restricted power structure, it is necessary to gain the support of the power elite in a way that they will not perceive as threatening.

The second of the community power structures is the *factional or conflict-dissipated power community.* Under this structure, longstanding factions of the community constantly fight for power. Governing boards are split by factionalism and therefore have great difficulty agreeing on issues. This is a difficult power structure with which to work. The professional must attempt to make progress with both factions yet must not appear to be siding with one group. The creative professional can enable both groups to see how they would benefit from the new program so their support is guaranteed.

The *pluralistic or accordant power community* is similar to Sessoms' (1980) multiple pyramid system. Here Jewell (1983) states, "sanity and reason do reign and . . . issues and community welfare

are important" (p. 27). Petty thinking does not override the decision-making process. Groups debate in a democratic manner to arrive at a consensus on what is best for the community. The leisure service administrator is likely to be viewed as a knowledgeable resource when making decisions. Therefore, the administrator should have thoroughly researched information on the establishment of community services for persons with disabilities so he or she can properly brief those in authority of the rationale and procedures for establishing the service.

The least common power structure is the *inert or power-avoidance community*. Both those in positions of authority and the citizenry are apathetic. Here the leisure service administrator ends up making decisions that are, in turn, "rubber stamped" by the board. The problem here is getting the community out of its dormant state and into something new. Even in the most inert of communities, there are a few individuals capable of responding, given the right motivation.

Knowing the likely community power structure allows the professional to choose the best strategy when approaching those who hold power. The professional who is not cognizant of the local power structure will likely have problems in establishing inclusive and special recreation services, particularly when the inclusion of persons with disabilities into ongoing programs is a goal, because inclusion brings other participants into direct contact with individuals with disabilities.

Community Subsystems

The third aspect of the sociocultural facet involves community subsystems such as the family, the economy, the government, religion, education, and social welfare. Those who hold high status in the various subsystems are likely to have influence within the community. Knowing these persons and their possible interest in community recreation for persons with disabilities can be helpful in establishing new services. This is particularly true with the social welfare subsystem.

The social welfare subsystem, as defined by Edwards and Jones (1976), deals with three major types of community services. These are social work, health care, and recreation. Often social welfare agencies organize themselves for joint action. Community organization structures can take the form of wide-based cooperation such as a council of human service agencies. In other instances, agencies with particular thrusts may form councils. For example, a local recreation council may form. Recreation councils are usually made up of nongovernmental agencies such as Boy Scouts, Girl Scouts, YMCA, YWCA, Hebrew Association, and governmental agencies such as park districts, or city or county recreation and parks departments. In beginning inclusive and special recreation services, it becomes necessary to know what councils exist in the community so that their support can be gained.

Smaller communities will be less likely to have coordinating councils. Nevertheless, individual social welfare agencies, churches, service clubs, educational systems, and advocacy groups (e.g., parents' groups) are potential allies to initiating inclusive and special recreation programs. It is, therefore, just as important to understand these independent agencies as it is to be knowledgeable of coordinating councils in larger communities.

Normative Structures

The final aspect of the sociocultural facet is the normative structure of the community. Social norms are extremely important to the community because they regulate behaviors through a system of rewards or punishments. Behaviors falling within acceptable norms are rewarded. Those outside of acceptable norms are punished. Therefore, social norms define what are acceptable behaviors and help maintain conformity in the way people act in a community. Further, norms reflect the values of the community so they bring the citizens' behaviors in line with the dominant values held by those who comprise the community (Johnson, 1995). As Edwards and Jones (1976) have stated:

> The social structure of the community—as described above through social groups, social stratification patterns, and subsystems—gets

its stability and order from the fact that it exists within a normative structure. The normative structure is made up of norms, i.e., rules and standards that define what people should and should not do in various facets of their community living; sanctions, in the form of penalties applied for violation of, and rewards offered for conformity to, the norms; and values that represent the priorities people attach to material and nonmaterial features of their culture. (p. 89)

Of particular importance to community development are the social norms and values of the community toward change. Some communities will be slower than others to accept any innovation. Resistance to innovation may be lessened if the change fits the existing community value system. For example, a community that prizes athletic competition may be led to understand how persons with disabilities also need opportunities for sports participation and how the provision of such opportunities can strengthen the athletic image of the community.

Summary: Sociocultural Facet

The sociocultural facet of community life deals with informal and formal groups, social stratification and power, the varied community subsystems, and norms and values. The normative structure gives the community stability and order. It gives the community its "character." Actions leading to community development transpire through the social groups, social stratification patterns, and subsystems of the community. Familiarity with the sociocultural facet of the community can be of great assistance when initiating any new program, including inclusive and special recreation services.

SUMMARY

This chapter has discussed community resources as they pertain to the provision of inclusive and special recreation services. Community resources, including human, informational, financial, and transportation, are necessary to accomplish any goal the leisure service provider may have. Thus, it is important that recreation and parks professionals be knowledgeable of such resources and know how to use them in achieving their goals. The use of volunteers and the seeking of additional funding are two aspects highlighted in this chapter. Also important to the establishment of inclusive and special recreation services is understanding the community from a sociocultural perspective. Knowing the community power structures as they relate to the inclusion of persons with disabilities enhances the capacity of the leisure service professional to provide services for all people, including those individuals who may have disabilities.

SUGGESTED LEARNING ACTIVITIES

1. Volunteer in a special recreation program. If this is for a single event (e.g., wheelchair basketball game), report your observations in class from your perspective as a volunteer. If you volunteer over time, keep a log of your experiences and reactions. Prepare a brief report based on your log.

2. Interview a person with a disability who is volunteering. Ask how he or she became involved as a volunteer and the benefits derived. Bring your notes to class for discussion.

3. Invite several athletes who have disabilities to class to discuss sports organizations with which they are affiliated.

4. Compile a resource file on organizations in your home town that might have an interest in community recreation programs for persons with disabilities.

5. In a group, discuss why it is important for recreation professionals to be familiar with organizations related to people with disabilities.

6. Interview a recreation administrator about funding for inclusive and special recreation services. Take notes on your discussion and report to the class.

7. Work on the following problem in a small group. You are in charge of a camp that includes campers

with and without disabilities. What alternatives can you identify for funding your camp, in addition to having parents pay a fee for their child? Use library resources in preparing your response. Report your conclusions to the class.

8. Locate links to community disability resources on the Web. Evaluate these to identify which site you believe most pertains to inclusive recreation in the community. Send your instructor the address

of the website with a brief message telling him or her the features of the website that most impressed you.

9. Working with a small group of students, analyze the community power structure in your home town, college community, or some other community chosen with your instructor. Write a report of no more than 10 pages on your findings. Then make a presentation in class to highlight your findings.

REFERENCES

Anderson, L., & C. B. Kress. *Inclusion: Including People with Disabilities in Parks and Recreation Opportunities.* State College, PA: Venture Publishing, Inc., 2003.

Austin, D. R., J. A. Peterson, & L. M. Peccarelli. The status of services for special populations in the state of Indiana. *Therapeutic Recreation Journal, 12*(1), 50–56, 1978.

Austin, D. R., & L. G. Powell, Eds. *Resource Guide: College Instruction in Recreation for Individuals with Handicapping Conditions.* Bloomington: Indiana University, 1980.

Bullock, C. C., & M. J. Mahon. *Introduction to Recreation Services for People with Disabilities* (2nd ed.). Champaign, IL: Sagamore Publishing, 2000.

Bullock, C. C., R. E. Wohl, T. E. Webreck, & A. M. Crawford. *Life Is for Everyone Resource and Training Manual.* Curriculum in Recreation Administration, University of North Carolina at Chapel Hill, 1982.

Corporation for Public Broadcasting. *Basic Elements of Grant Writing.* [Online]. Available: http://www.cpb.org/grants/grantwriting.html, September 5, 2003.

Edginton, C. R., D. M. Compton, A. J. Ritchie, & R. K. Vederman. The status of services for special populations in park and recreation in the state of Iowa. *Therapeutic Recreation Journal, 9,* 109–116, 1975.

Edwards, A. D., & D. G. Jones. *Community and Community Development.* The Hague, Netherlands: Mouton & Co., 1976.

The Foundation Center. *Proposal Writing Short Course.* [Online]. Available:

http://fdncenter.org/learn/shortcourse/prop1.html, September 5, 2003.

Henderson, K., & K. Silverberg. Good work, if you can get it: How to attract and retain dedicated volunteers. *Parks & Recreation, 37*(11), 26–34, 2002.

Henderson, K. A., & L. A. Bedini. Using volunteers in therapeutic recreation. *Leisure Today: Therapeutic Recreation—Meeting the Challenges of New Demands.* In *Journal of Physical Education, Recreation & Dance, 62*(4), 49–51, 1991.

Jewell, D. L. Comprehending concepts of community power structure. Prerequisite for recreation integration. *Journal of Leisurability, 10*(1), 24–30, 1983.

Johnson, A. G. *The Blackwell Dictionary of Sociology: A Users Guide to Sociological Language.* Cambridge, MA: Basil Blackwell Inc., 1995.

Kelley, J. D., Ed. *Recreation Programming for Visually Impaired Children and Youth.* New York: American Foundation for the Blind, 1981.

McGovern, J. N. Inclusion institute succeeds: Plans for 2001 under way. *NTRS Report, 25*(4), 7–8, 2000.

Miller, K. D., S. J. Schleien, C. Rider, C. Hall, M. Roche, & J. Worsley. Inclusive volunteering: Benefits to participants and community. *Therapeutic Recreation Journal, 36*(3), 247–259, 2002.

Phoenix, T., K. Miller, & S. Schleien. Better to give than receive. *Parks & Recreation, 37*(10), 26–33, 2002.

Pomeroy, J. One community's effort. *Institute on Community Recreation for Special Populations.* North Texas State University and the Texas Recreation and Park Society, 1974.

Schleien, S. J., M. T. Ray, & F. P. Green. *Community Recreation and People with Disabilities* (2nd ed.).

Baltimore: Paul H. Brookes Publishing Co., 1997.

Schuler, D. *New Community Networks: Wired for Change.* New York: Addison-Wesley Publishing Company, 1996.

Sessoms, H. D. Community development and social planning. In S. G. Lutzin, Ed. *Managing Municipal Leisure Services.* Washington, DC: International City Management Association, 1980, pp. 120–139.

Stensrud, C. *A Training Manual for Americans with Disabilities Act Compliance in Parks and Recreation Settings.* State College, PA: Venture Publishing, 1993.

Tedrick, T. How to have the help you need. *Parks & Recreation, 25*(6), 64–68, 86, 1990.

Vaughan, J. L., & R. Winslow. *Guidelines for Community Based Recreation Programs for Special Populations.* National Therapeutic Recreation Society, a branch of the National Recreation and Park Association, 1979.

Volunteer Canada. *Volunteer Connections: Creating an Accessible and Inclusive Environment*, 2001. [Online]. Available: http://www2.communityleadership.net/newview/Resources%20for%20Staff%2F Volunteers/Human%20Resources/Vol%20MgmtTools%20&%20Templates/%231004534.0/AccessEnglish.pdf, September 8, 2003.

Williams, B. *Assistive Devices, Adaptive Strategies, and Recreational Activities for Students with Disabilities.* Champaign, IL: Sagamore Publishing Inc., 2003.

The World Bank. Social capital for development. [Online]. Available: http://www.worldbank.org/poverty/scapital/index.htm, September 8, 2003.

13 TRENDS IN INCLUSIVE RECREATION

(Courtesy *Sports 'n Spokes*/Paralyzed Veterans of America)

I n this chapter, we attempt to peer into the future to catch a glimpse of what may unfold in inclusive and special recreation services. Knowing today's trends points the way to the world of tomorrow and provides us with visions of future realities.

We know for certain that the world is rapidly changing. Signs of change are all around us. Computers, lasers, virtual reality, satellites, robots, space shuttles, rapid communication systems, and other forms of high technology are already a part of our culture. But unless we are fatalists, we understand that the future will not just "happen." Human beings can and will help shape the future (Schuler, 1996). Godbey (1989) has challenged park, recreation, and leisure professionals "to be actors rather than reactors in the change process" (p. 57).

In the United States, one real part of the future will be the Americans with Disabilities Act (ADA). This far-reaching law gives persons with disabilities the legal right to full inclusion into the mainstream of American society. This right extends to recreational and leisure opportunities for persons with disabilities. As Galambos and Williams (1997) have suggested, the impact of ADA is just beginning to be felt by many agencies and organizations. The wide scope of ADA is coming to be recognized as the issue of program accessibility has emerged to join the already existing concern for physical accessibility. It is likely that as more people with disabilities and their families become aware of ADA and the rights of persons with disabilities, they will greatly increase their demands for access to recreation programs and facilities.

With this in mind, a Delphi survey (Austin, Lee, & Getz, 2003) was conducted to gain the insights of experts regarding trends in inclusive recreation programs. The experts who took part in the study were professionals and educators from the United States and Canada, all of whom had extensive backgrounds in inclusive recreation. The resulting compilation of trends from that research forms the basis for this chapter. The trends are presented with the admission that, as a wag once said, those who live by the crystal ball must learn to eat ground glass. The experts who participated in the Delphi study will probably digest their share.

Trends identified by the experts are discussed under the headings of program trends, approaches to programs and services, trends in community relations, financial trends, and professional trends. Table 13.1 lists the top trends as rated by the experts in the Delphi study.

PROGRAM TRENDS

Outdoor Recreation Programs

Few activities cannot be entered into by persons with disabilities. Therefore, programs for people with disabilities are likely to follow societal trends. The rising interest in outdoor recreation pursuits among persons with disabilities reflects a societal trend. Perhaps amplifying this societal trend for persons with disabilities are improvements in outdoor recreation equipment and expansions in the accessibility of outdoor areas and programs.

Various terms such as *outdoor adventure, high risk,* and *stress challenge* are used to describe programs that offer participants new and challenging experiences in the outdoors. Caving, rappelling, traversing ropes courses, flying, parachuting, jet skiing, speed boating, water skiing, scuba diving, and backpacking are examples of adventure activities enjoyed by many persons. Cold climate pursuits such as ice skating and winter camping are gaining popularity, as is snow skiing. In Canada and the United States, sledge hockey and ice picking, a form of speed skating, have developed. In Scotland, curling is a popular sport for persons with disabilities, including wheelchair users. Other outdoor recreation activities increasing in participation are archery, biking, fishing, gardening, riding, road racing, sailing, and nature study.

Indiana University's Bradford Woods outdoor education, recreation, and leadership-training center (5040 State Road 67 North, Martinsville, IN 46151) is a trendsetter in the provision of programming and training opportunities in outdoor

TABLE 13.1 Top Inclusive Recreation Trends as Rated by Experts in the Delphi Study		
Trend	**Mean**	**Standard Deviation**
Increasing numbers of assistive devices being manufactured for golfers with disabilities (e.g., single-rider golf carts).	4.0	0.7
Increased construction of children's playgrounds to meet the needs of all children.	4.0	0.8
Increased recognition that people with disabilities should have choice of services and opportunities.	3.9	0.7
Increasing numbers of inclusive camps that serve children both with and without disabilities.	3.9	0.9
Increased support from golf organizations, such as the United States Golf Association (USGA), to encourage accessibility to golf for persons with disabilities.	3.9	0.5
Increased understanding of the American with Disabilities Act (ADA) related to compliance and appropriate accommodation.	3.9	0.8
Increased availability of adapted recreational equipment (e.g., pool lifts, fishing aids, bowling equipment).	3.9	0.7
Increased opportunities for continuing education on inclusive and special recreation services.	3.9	1
More widespread fund-raising efforts for special recreation programs.	3.9	0.8
Greater opportunities for travel by persons with disabilities provided by travel organizations specializing in services for travelers with disabilities.	3.8	0.8
Greater accessibility to outdoor recreation programs for persons with disabilities.	3.8	0.5
Increased development of assistive technology to meet the recreational needs of persons with disabilities.	3.7	0.5
Increased use of persons with disabilities as volunteers in community programs for persons with disabilities.	3.7	0.6
Improvements in outdoor recreation equipment for persons with disabilities.	3.68	0.6
Increased emphasis on professional training for high skill areas (e.g., behavior modification, peer acceptance/social inclusion, support strategies, etc.).	3.65	0.5

Source: Austin, Lee, & Geta, 2003.

recreation experiences for persons who have disabilities. Among its programs, Bradford Woods offers extensive camping and outdoor adventure activities for persons with disabilities. In addition, many training opportunities are provided through Bradford Woods. These include internships and an annual institute on innovations in outdoor recreation programming for persons with disabilities. Programs like Wilderness Inquiry, C. W. Hog, Northeast Passage, and POINT continue to provide challenging outdoor experiences for persons who have disabilities.

Summer Camps

A growing number of summer camps are being developed for children with disabilities. An example is Camp I-Thonka-Chi for children ages 6 to 18 who have burn injuries. This camp is sponsored by Parkland Health and Hospital System in Dallas, Texas. Another example is Camp Optimism, in Prince William County, Virginia, that serves children from 4 to 14 with cancer, juvenile diabetes, hearing impairments, or mental retardation. Still another is the Hole in the Wall Gang Camp, in northeastern Connecticut, founded by actor Paul Newman. It provides programs for children with cancer, sickle-cell anemia, or other blood diseases. Some camps involve computer technology. One computer camp in Virginia serves children with disabilities such as cerebral palsy, autism, Attention Deficit Hyperactivity Disorder (ADHD), muscular dystrophy, and mental retardation (Coale, 1999). Other camps are unique in their camper populations. Indiana University's Bradford Woods, mentioned previously, has camps specifically for campers with disabilities and inclusive camps that serve both children with and without disabilities. Lekotek of Georgia's computer camp serves both children with disabilities and their friends or siblings (Deavours, 1997). The Birch Family Camp, located in Putnam Valley, New York, is for families and children with AIDS. It is anticipated that more camps will include both children with and without disabilities and families of children with disabilities. An emerging trend that extends the idea of

family camping is a growing focus on family leisure of all types among families with children with disabilities (Zabriskie & Heyne, 2003).

An important source of information on inclusive camps is *Including Youth with Disabilities in Outdoor Programs* by Brannan, Fullerton, Arick, Robb, and Bender (2003). Within this book, highly successful inclusive camping programs at Girl Scout, Camp Fire, and CYO camps in Illinois, Indiana, Texas, and Washington are featured. The book also provides research evidence from a national study stating that "campers and students with and without disabilities enjoyed and profited from personal, social, and skill development as a result of their participation together in inclusive outdoor programs" (Brannan & Fullerton, 2003, p. 237).

Sports and Fitness

Competitive athletics continue to thrive under the auspices of traditional organizations such as the National Wheelchair Basketball Association, American Blind Bowlers Association, and Special Olympics.

Interest in such sports organizations has continued to expand. For example, the United States Cerebral Palsy Athletic Association was formed to fill the need for sports experiences for people with cerebral palsy who could not find equitable competition through other organizations. The USCPAA offers competition in a broad range of team and individual sports. Additional organizations have been formed for, among others, wheelchair road racers, downhill mountain wheelchair racers, wheelchair marathoners, wheelchair rugby players, wheelchair softball and tennis players, wheelchair curling teams, and skiers with disabilities. Inclusive sports are also developing, such as competitive fishing tournaments sponsored by the Veterans Administration in cooperation with local fishing clubs.

Community-based adapted sports for youth and adults have been promoted by the U.S. Disabled Athletes Fund Incorporated through its BlazeSports program. This competitive sports and physical fitness program for athletes with physical disabilities has been directed toward park and recreation departments across the United States. BlazeSports has provided training on the coaching and management of sports and fitness programs for persons with physical disabilities (McKenzie, 2000, 2002).

Although many of the athletic programs initially instituted were competitive sports for children and young adults, noncompetitive opportunities are beginning to develop for both children and adults. Many persons do not want competition but seek health and fitness through sports and exercise. One leader in this effort is Disabled Sports USA (DSUSA) (formerly National Handicapped Sports). Originally devoted exclusively to snow skiing, DSUSA has expanded to include a variety of sports rehabilitation programs for anyone with a permanent physical disability. The Rehabilitation Institute of Chicago (RIC) has instituted a fitness program for persons with disabilities. In addition, the University of Illinois at Chicago has collaborated with RIC and the National Center on Accessibility (NCA) to establish the National Center on Physical Activity and Disability (NCPAD). The mission of NCPAD is to promote the substantial health benefits that can be gained from participation in regular physical activity.

Aerobic dance, karate, weight lifting, and yoga are also activities demanded by those in inclusive and special recreation programs. Still others desire to learn lifetime sports through adult leisure education classes. For example, in Indianapolis, bowling instruction is being provided to adults with disabilities under a program modeled after the President's Council on Physical Fitness and Sport.

Golf

Contacts with the National Alliance for Accessible Golf and the National Center on Accessibility indicate a growing interest in golf by persons with disabilities. Research by the National Center on Accessibility and Clemson University has revealed that 10% of persons with disabilities already play golf. Another 35% indicated a desire to become a golfer (Robb, 1997). There are any number of happenings that display there is a trend to develop golf for persons with disabilities. Among these is sup-

port given by the United States Golf Association (USGA), the PGA, and the Golf Course Superintendents Association of America. The USGA has published *A Modification of the Rules of Golf for Golfers with Disabilities,* which has been approved by The Royal and Ancient Golf Club of St. Andrews, Scotland. Golf courses have been designed to be accessible to persons with disabilities. Fox Hollow and Saddlerock in Colorado and Clemson University Golf Course in South Carolina are examples. PGA and Ladies' Professional Golf Association (LPGA) professionals are taking teaching clinics on teaching persons with disabilities and are providing instruction for golfers with disabilities. Assistive devices, such as single-rider golf carts equipped for persons with disabilities, are commercially available. Finally, golf equipment manufacturers are producing equipment with the needs of golfers with disabilities in mind (Robb, 1997).

The emergence of an expanding interest in golfers with disabilities was reflected by the formation of the National Alliance for Accessible Golf in 2001 by leaders of the golf industry and representatives of organizations serving people with disabilities. Among other organizations, members of the Alliance include the Golf Course Superintendents of America, the United States Golf Association, the Ladies Professional Golf Association, and the PGA of America. With the mission of increasing participation of people with disabilities in the game of golf, the Alliance is housed at Indiana University's National Center on Accessibility in Bloomington, Indiana.

Another step forward in golf for persons with disabilities occurred in 2003 with the publication of ADA Accessibility Guidelines (ADAAG) for golf courses. These guidelines were published by the Access Board, an independent federal agency committed to accessible design for persons with disabilities, and appear on the Access Board website at www.accessgolf.org.

Travel Programs

Travel programs that have a primary concern for travelers with disabilities are growing in popularity.

Many golf equipment manufacturers are producing products to meet the needs of golfers who have disabilities.
(Courtesy of *Sports 'n Spokes*/Paralyzed Veterans of America)

In recent years the travel and tourism industry for persons with disabilities has made significant advances. There are three major membership organizations that provide services for travelers with disabilities. Mobility International (MI) is one of these organizations. MI, which has offices in more than 25 countries throughout the world, was founded in London to include persons with disabilities in international educational exchange and travel programs. The United States office (MIUSA, P.O. Box 10767, Eugene, OR 97440; [541] 343-1284; e-mail: miusa@ige.apc.org; website: http://www.miusa.org/index.htm) is a nonprofit agency, directed by a person with a disability, which has organized successful exchanges to many countries, including China and Germany. Another membership organization is Travelin' Talk (P.O. Box 1796, Wheat Ridge, CO, 80034;

[303] 232-2979; e-mail: info@travelintalk.net; website: http://www.travelintalk.net). Travelin' Talk is an international membership network of people that refers travelers with disabilities to other members in destination cities for advise and assistance. A third membership organization is the Society for the Advancement of Travel for the Handicapped (SATH). SATH (347 Fifth Avenue, Suite 610, New York, NY 10016; [212] 447-7284; e-mail: sathtravel@aol.com; website: http://www.sath.org/) has been representing the interests of travelers with disabilities since 1975. SATH provides literature, brief specific answers on travel for persons with disabilities, and extended help to its members.

The publication *Directory of Travel Agencies for the Disabled* by Helen Hecker lists more than 350 agencies worldwide that specialize in travel arrangements for persons with disabilities. Among a number of successful agencies has been The Guided Tour (7900 Old York Road, Suite 114B, Elkins Park, PA 19027-2339; [215] 782-1370; e-mail: gtour400@aol.com; website: http://www.guidedtour.com) founded by a social worker, Irv Segal, in 1972. It specializes in providing travel experiences for individuals with developmental disabilities. Another agency is Accessible Journeys (35 W. Sellers Avenue, Ridley Park, PA 19078; [800] 846-4537; website: http://www.disabilitytravel.com) that offers worldwide tours for travelers with mobility impairments and assists persons to find travel companions. Still another source for travel and touring in Wilderness Inquiry (1313 Fifth Street SE, Box 84, Minneapolis, MN 55414; [800] 728-0719; website: http://www.wildernessinquiry.org/). Wilderness Inquiry is a nonprofit organization that started in 1978 by conducting canoe trips to the Boundary Waters in Minnesota. The aim of the organization is to get people from all ages, backgrounds, and abilities to experience nature. It is best known for conducting multiday adventures such as: canoeing in the Boundary Waters, the Yukon, Ontario, and Alaska; sea kayaking on Lake Superior; and rafting in the Grand Canyon.

There is a trend toward greater travel and tourism opportunities for persons with disabilities. It is likely that ADA requirements will even further enhance the popularity of travel by persons with disabilities.

Leisure Education in Schools

Children with disabilities too often do not have the same opportunities as other children to learn about leisure. A developing trend is toward using leisure education to help build leisure skills and attitudes. For example, the Northeast DuPage Special Recreation Association near Chicago has designed curricula to help teachers provide leisure education to children with disabilities. These curriculum materials have been eagerly accepted and widely used by teachers. Among national leaders in leisure education for children with disabilities have been

Dr. Stuart Schleien of the University of North Carolina Greensboro and Dr. Charles Bullock of the University of Nevada, Reno. Schleien, Meyer, Heyne, and Brandt (1995) have authored the book, *Lifelong Leisure Skills and Lifestyles for Persons with Developmental Disabilities.* Bullock, writing with Mahon (2000), has written on leisure education in the book, *Introduction to Recreation Services for People with Disabilities: A Person-Centered Approach.*

With the implementation of the Individuals with Disabilities Education Act (PL 101-476), known as IDEA, recreation is not viewed by educators as simply a means to improve functional domains but as an important lifetime skill area in and of itself. This federal legislation recognizes that students with disabilities need therapeutic recreation services to develop leisure lifestyles for enhancing their quality of life. As a result of this legislation, it is anticipated that leisure education will continue to be an expanding area in the public schools.

Leisure Counseling

As inclusive and special recreation programs grow, greater numbers of individuals and families will require leisure counseling. Professionals competently prepared with counseling skills and a knowledge of leisure will advance the field of leisure counseling far beyond the relatively simple level of today's leisure counseling programs. Leisure services agencies offering leisure counseling services for people with disabilities will be at the forefront of this effort. Advances will include higher levels of counseling skills and innovations in the use of computers in leisure counseling programs. A computerized resource center is being used by the Northeast DuPage Special Recreation Association to match client interests with available community leisure resources. The computer will play a larger and larger role in leisure counseling and leisure education as computer programs are developed to teach people about leisure opportunities, to assess interests, and to catalog leisure resources.

Programs for Individuals in Group Homes

There is a continuing trend to provide community living situations for individuals who have been hospitalized or institutionalized or who need an alternative to living at home. Group homes have been established by both private and public agencies for persons with disabilities who need living situations that approximate, as closely as possible, living experiences of other people. Group homes offer supervised community living in houses located in the residential neighborhoods of towns and cities.

With the advances of physical medicine, there is a growing population of persons with spinal cord injuries, head injuries, and developmental disabilities who require the community living opportunities offered by group homes. Some group homes are for individuals with disabilities who will reside in the homes on a temporary basis while building their independent living skills. An example of this type of service is ReMed Recovery Care Centers in Pennsylvania. These centers offer community-based services to individuals who have head (brain) injuries, and they focus on practical concerns of daily life. Individual recreation plans, designed by therapeutic recreation specialists, guide the person toward increased leisure independence within the community. As noted by David Strauss, ReMed's Clinical Director, "If an individual is learning to live in the community, then the community must be the classroom." Other homes provide more long-term living arrangements for adults who, while having mental retardation or another disabling condition, can function relatively independently but who may need some amount of assistance. A U.S. Supreme Court ruling on the ADA, which calls for the provision of more community-based services for individuals who are mentally disabled, will likely accelerate the movement of these persons from institutions into community settings (Hinnefeld, 1999).

Some individuals residing in group homes need motor skill development. More common is the need to develop competencies related to social and leisure skills. Many special recreation programs have been created to help those living in group homes to develop motor skills and to have positive social and leisure experiences. Often these programs take place in the evening because participants usually are employed in the community, in a sheltered workshop, or in the group home. Some programs are conducted in the group homes, while others are offered in community recreation centers or human service agencies.

APPROACHES TO PROGRAMS AND SERVICES

Inclusion

Inclusion is the term adopted to describe the process by which persons both with and without disabilities are being served in one environment. Inclusive recreation reflects a program philosophy directed not only to the physical integration of groups of people but to embracing the needs of all within one environment. Inclusive recreation implies that persons with disabilities are actively involved with others and that there is an interaction pattern that leads people toward normative roles and relationships.

In 1997, the National Therapeutic Recreation Society published a position statement on inclusion that, in part, states:

> Inclusive leisure experiences encourage and enhance opportunities for people with varying abilities to participate and interact in life's activities together with dignity. It also provides an environment that promotes and fosters physical, social, and psychological inclusion of people with diverse experiences and skill levels. Inclusion enhances individuals' potential for full and active participation in leisure activities and experiences.

Programs designed to facilitate inclusive recreation, such as the Mainstreaming Initiative in Montgomery County, Maryland (see chapter 8), are becoming integral parts of community recreation programs. Such opportunities have been shown to increase positive social interactions between participants with and without disabilities (Edwards &

Smith, 1989). Yet, research has revealed the process of inclusion may be difficult. Findings from a study of persons with mental retardation indicated that these individuals typically engaged in activities at home and tended not to broaden their social networks to include persons without disabilities (Hayden, Soulen, Schleien, & Tabourne, 1996). Also, while leisure interactions between persons with and without disabilities have been found to produce positive outcomes, such interactions do hold the potential for strain to develop as a result of participants displaying inadequate social skills or self-consciousness (Wilhite, Devine, & Golderberg, 1999). To foster the trend toward inclusion, it will therefore be important that strategies are developed to enhance inclusion. For instance, both participants with and without disabilities may need prior preparation to encourage inclusive interactions. Leaders may need to employ strategies to set a positive tone during inclusive interactions.

The ADA will likely play a large role in the development of inclusive recreation in America. Reynolds (1993) has stated that "the ADA may well result in a new era of leisure service provision, an era in which *all* Americans can work and *play* together" (pp. 231–232). First, more recreation facilities will become accessible to persons with disabilities. Not only public park and recreation areas but private sector theaters, museums, stadiums, hotels, and restaurants will become accessible to persons with disabilities. Private enterprise, including the travel and tourism industry, should be remarkably changed.

In addition to expansion in accessible recreation and leisure opportunities, the range of persons with disabilities served will greatly increase because ADA extends beyond individuals with visual or physical disabilities. Persons with mental impairments (e.g., individuals with mental retardation or chronic mental illness) are covered so that *programmatic accessibility* will have to be considered along with physical accessibility. It is also likely that greater programmatic and physical accessibility will encourage expanded family

recreation. As more public and private facilities are made accessible, other family members will have increased opportunities to take part in recreation with family members with disabilities (Reynolds, 1993; Schleien, Rynders, Heyne, & Tabourne, 1995; Zabriskie & Heyne, 2003).

Levels of Programming

There exists a definite trend to establish several levels of programs within community services for persons with disabilities. For example, the Cincinnati Recreation Commission has a four-level system encompassing teaching sensory-motor and self-help skills (Level I), instructing basic activity and socialization skills (Level II), developing advanced recreation and socialization skills (Level III), and providing relatively independent participation where staff act as facilitators, trainers, consultants, liaison persons, and advocates (Level IV). Following these levels of programming, participants may become integrated into ongoing programs of the department (see chapter 8). Another illustration is a model proposed by Hunter (1981). This model has five levels: (1) institutional and homebound one-to-one visitations, (2) developmental skill programming focusing on the acquisition of skills transferable to community recreation participation, (3) special interest groups where segregation is by choice for a particular activity such as wheelchair basketball, (4) integration with support (e.g., transportation, emotional support) to promote community involvement, and (5) direct independent participation in community leisure experiences. Throughout the five levels, leisure counseling and leisure education services may be provided to facilitate the participants' involvement. Still another model has been presented by Schleien, Ray, and Green (1997) that contains three levels: segregated, integrated, and inclusive. Segregated programs, or special recreation programs, are stepping-stones in which to develop prerequisite skills to prepare for integrated experiences. Integrated programs offer persons with disabilities general community recreation experiences alongside participants without disabilities. People with "mixed abilities" are brought together so that they may learn from one another and prepare for inclusive interactions. Inclusive programs are the ultimate goal for organized recreational programs. Participants are able to experience leisure free from intrinsic constraints (e.g., skill limitations, characteristics of disability) or extrinsic constraints (e.g., transportation, barriers of omission).

Approaches to Including Persons with Disabilities

Schleien, Green, and Stone (2003) have suggested three approaches to including persons with disabilities in community recreation. One is *facilitating the integration of an individual* with a disability into an existing, age-appropriate community recreation program. This involves an inclusion specialist attempting to remove or lessen any gap between the individual's capabilities and the requirements of the activity so the individual may participate in the program. The second approach is *reverse mainstreaming*. This involves integrating persons without disabilities into programs traditionally designed for persons with disabilities. For example, formally segregated programs, such as camps or after-school activities for children with disabilities, are opened to children without disabilities. The third approach is *zero exclusion*. These are programs that, from the beginning, are aimed at aggressively recruiting a variety of participants with varying abilities so that they contain persons both with and without disabilities.

Therapeutic Programs

Closely related to the trend to offer various levels of programs is a trend toward the provision of therapeutically oriented programs. Community-based therapeutic recreation specialists are offering purposeful interventions for clients needing goal-directed programming. The therapeutic recreation process (assessment, planning, implementation,

and evaluation) is being employed by skilled therapeutic recreation specialists to reach specified client outcomes. While the primary thrust of community-based special recreation programs will remain recreation participation, more therapeutically oriented programs will develop as therapeutic recreation specialists are employed by community leisure service agencies and public schools.

Campus Recreation Programs

A growing area of programming is found on college and university campuses throughout the United States and Canada. Students who have disabilities have made their needs for recreation services known to campus administrators, who have begun to respond with a variety of leisure services. These services have included wheelchair user and nonwheelchair-user sports, outdoor recreation offerings, lectures, special events, and leisure counseling. Leisure services for students are sometimes administered by an office for disabled student services but are more often found in traditional campus recreational service systems, such as departments of recreational sports.

Assistive Technology

Technology is the application of science into any purposeful use (Brennan, 1999). What then is assistive technology? Assistive technology is any item or piece of equipment used to maintain or enhance the functional capabilities of people with disabilities (Lekotek, 1998). Assistive technologies can be powerful tools to enable millions of individuals with disabilities to do things that they otherwise could not accomplish. It also makes good business sense to advance technology in the form of assistive devices. In the United States alone, there are nearly 50 million adults with disabilities who collectively have $175 billion in discretionary incomes (Jordan, 2001).

Assistive technology includes an expansive range of technologies, which are increasingly computer-based. The following quote from Brett

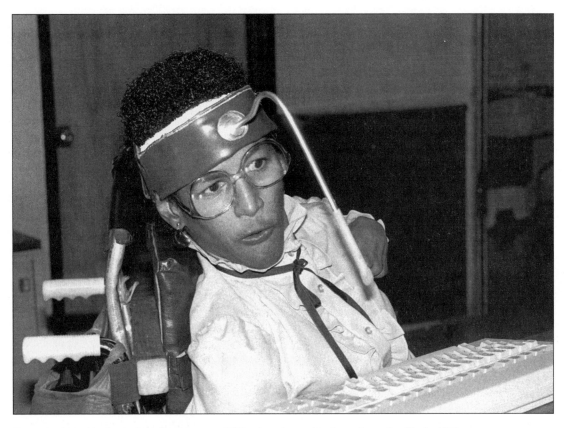

Computer-based technologies offer many possibilities to enhance the lives of people with disabilities.
(Photo Courtesy of The League: Serving People with Physical Disabilities, Inc., Baltimore, MD)

and Provenzo (1995) captures the potential impact of computers on the lives of persons with disabilities:

> Scanning systems allow an individual who is blind to take a printed text and have it read back to him or hear aloud. Individuals who have cerebral palsy can use their head movements to guide an electronic beam across a special keyboard in order to communicate. A gifted student who is also learning disabled, and who has great difficulty reading, can use a talking word processor to write stories and improve her reading. An adult with little or no control over his body movements, but who can still speak, can control his environment by talking into a computer that can recognize spoken commands. An individual who can move only his eyes can type messages on a computer using his eye movements. (pp. 3–4)

Computer-based technologies offer many possibilities to enhance the lives of people with disabilities. For example, computer programs can enlarge text and graphics on the monitor's screen for easier viewing for persons with visual impairments. A computer product for people with visual impairments, the reading machine, can scan newspapers, books, and other printed materials by reading it aloud through a voice synthesizer, allowing it to be read in a large print, or converting it into braille. Another means to magnify printed materials, or other things, is by closed-circuit television, sometimes referred to as CCTV. This product uses a small camera to shoot the book or other object with the enlarged image appearing on a screen. A new product for persons who are visually impaired is a portable head-mounted display that will allow a person wearing it to watch television from across the room or sporting events from the stands (Goodrich, 1997).

Assistive devices for people with hearing impairments are helpful in using the telephone, listening to television, and in other everyday activities. A wide variety of amplified telephones are available. There is also a telecommunication device for the deaf (TDD), sometimes referred to as the teletype (TTY). The TDD has a keyboard, display, and a means of connecting to a telephone. Some newer TDDs communicate with computer terminals. Such devices are useless, however, if the person receiving the telephone call does not know the telephone is ringing. Therefore, a variety of telephone alerting devices have become available. Special devices for listening to television allow the TV signal to be transmitted to a headset that amplifies the sound. Devices that assist persons with hearing impairments in their everyday lives include smoke alarms with strobe lights and vibrating or flashing alarm clocks (McFadyen, 1996). Closed caption features are required on all television sets manufactured and many TV shows include closed captions for viewers who wish to see them.

For persons with physical disabilities, assistive technology comes in many forms. An example is a computer hardware device, the Head Master from Prentke Romich Company, which functions as a mouse emulator. By turning their heads, users can position the cursor in the desired location on their computer screens. Then, through use of either an external switch or "puff" (mouth-activated) switch, a selection can be made. Another device, the FreeWheel, allows individuals who are paralyzed to wear a small passive reflector and use only slight head movements to operate a computer. The Aurora computer enhancement program allows an individual to produce typed works through a number of means, such as small head movements or the blink of an eye. AccessDOS permits persons who have difficulty pressing more

than one key at a time to operate a keyboard with only one finger. Additionally, there are speech recognition systems for personal computers through which the user talks and the computer does the typing (Brett & Provenzo, 1995; Spede, 1993). Finally, a great deal of progress has been made in developing communication aids for individuals who are nonverbal. Devices, such as the Alphtalker or Speakeasy, allow messages to be stored in a computer. The person who is nonverbal then uses a communication device with a keyboard or switch to "speak" a message (Lekotek, 1998).

Finally, text-to-speech (TTS) synthesis can be used to translate normal text into speech so that persons who are nonverbal can communicate by voice. This technology also allows persons who are blind or visually impaired to hear the contents of databases (e.g., phone books) by voice or to hear e-mail messages (Vitale, 1996).

Computers can also provide recreational opportunities for persons with disabilities. Computer software allows students with severe physical disabilities to create music by movements such as squeezing air in a bulb or tapping a finger. Berklee College of Music graduate Jon Adams developed the program called Super Switch Ensemble that "allows students to play 128 instruments, along with various beats, vocals, and chords, by hitting a switch set up to take advantage of whatever movement they can best control" (Linsday, 2003, p. E4). Interactive computer games exist that are stimulating for children and adults and may be played by almost anyone, including persons with severe physical disabilities. For example, flight simulator games allow players to land (or crash!) at dozens of airports across the United States. Games are not the only type of recreational computer technology available to persons with disabilities. Word processing, musical composition, and artistic endeavors are a few examples of software available to enhance the leisure functioning of people with disabilities. Computers also allow indoor virtual golf simulators to operate so that golfers who have had to give up outdoor golf for health reasons can play courses such as Pebble Beach, Pinehurst, and Torrey Pines by hitting into a screen that portrays each hole in high-resolution graphic detail (Duncan, 1998). Another recreational use of computers is that we may employ them to simulate real life through the technology of virtual reality (VR). VR uses a combination of visual, audio, and kinetic effects to create the virtual reality of going caving, hiking through the Grand Canyon, or any number of exciting recreational endeavors (Caneday, 1992). Caneday has suggested that people with disabilities will be able to use VR "to enter an artificial universe and interact with other people, giving no hint as to their handicap" (p. 50).

One space-age technological invention has been a wheelchair-type device called the Ibot. This all-terrain mobility device employs sensors and gyroscopes similar to those used to stabilize spacecraft. It permits persons using it to go literally anywhere, including up and down stairs, and to stand on the back wheels in order to elevate themselves to the eye level of others. Ibot's inventor, Dean Kamen, has been quoted as saying: "The most extraordinary thing about that machine is that it lets people [with disabilities] do ordinary things" (Chandler, 2000, p. A18).

Today's assistive devices, and others in the planning stage, hold great potential to enhance the lives of persons with disabilities, particularly those with severe disabilities. President King Jordan (2001) of Gallaudet University has predicted that, due to the rapid pace of technology, in the future "more marvels of accessibility will emerge and further blur the distinctions between those with and without disabilities" (p. B15).

Changing Views toward Sexuality

Traditionally, individuals with disabilities and older persons have not been perceived by many human service professionals to have sexual feelings or sexual activity. The traditional view has been that these individuals are asexual. However, professionals have been undergoing substantial changes in their views toward the sexuality of both groups. Perhaps the "sexual revolution" has

inspired a healthier view. It may be that society is finally beginning to perceive people with disabilities as persons with feelings and desires similar to those of others. Whatever the reason for the change, it seems there is a definite trend toward perceiving persons with disabilities and individuals who are older as sexual beings who need to express their sexuality.

A handbook on sexuality and persons with disabilities (Cornelius, Chipouras, Makas, & Daniels, 1982) states that "sexuality can be defined as an integration of physical, emotional, intellectual, and social aspects of an individual's personality which expresses maleness or femaleness" (p. 1). Cornelius and colleagues later state:

> People do not express their maleness or femaleness only in the bedroom. Sexuality is a part of all the activities in which a person engages: work, socialization, decoration of one's home, telephone conversations, political discussions, expressions of affection, arguments, eating a meal, child rearing, walking down the street, watching a movie, etc. Sexuality, then, is an expression of one's personality and is evident in everyday interactions. (p. 1)

Recreation professionals are recognizing that persons with disabilities and individuals who are older should be free to express their sexuality like anyone else. For example, progressive recreation professionals do not treat adults with mental retardation like children who are to be protected from sexuality. Instead, these adults are offered opportunities for learning and practicing social skills necessary to deal with their sexuality in appropriate ways. Such learning opportunities include education about the responsibilities that one accepts when he or she becomes sexually active. Responsible sexual behavior is especially important in an era overshadowed by the AIDS epidemic.

Progressive professionals offer opportunities for single adults and teenagers who have disabilities to mix with others in inclusive recreation activities such as dances, parties, and corecreational sports. Through such healthy recreation, *all* participants can express their sexuality. Similarly, progressive professionals provide older persons recreational opportunities through which they may express their sexuality in social interactions with others with whom they share common interests.

In sum, there exists a trend for human service professionals, including recreation professionals, to accept the sexuality of persons who are older or have disabilities. These professionals provide opportunities within their programs for the normal expression of sexuality.

Outreach Workers

Outreach workers are being used by more than one agency to identify those who are homebound or for other reasons have not had the opportunity to become aware of programs and services for people with special needs. Outreach workers also develop referral systems with local hospitals and nursing homes that are returning clients to the community. Finally, these staff workers help refer those who contact the agency to appropriate programs and services. In short, it is the responsibility of the outreach worker to contact persons who are newly disabled and those not traditionally served so that they may have the benefit of inclusive recreation programs and services. This may involve not only contacting and referring participants but also assisting clients to initially take part in existing programs. Outreach workers will become more widely used as agencies learn of their value.

Playgrounds

Traditional playgrounds have not been constructed to accommodate the needs of all children. Often barriers have excluded children with disabilities from playgrounds, creating feelings of social isolation. There is a trend, however, toward playgrounds that employ universal design to meet the needs of all children, including those with disabilities. Advancements in playground design are discussed in detail in chapter 6. Far more will occur in playground design as knowledge becomes

more widely disseminated and playground apparatus manufacturers include design features for children with disabilities.

Innovations with Equipment

Two types of trends have occurred related to equipment. One is the advent of equipment rental programs, such as the one run by Northeast Passage in New England (Sable & Gravink, 1997). These rental programs rent adapted recreational equipment that is often prohibitively expensive for individuals to purchase. For example, Northeast Passage lists sit-skis, biskis and monoskis among equipment items for 10 different sports. The second trend is the tremendous growth in the types and numbers of adapted equipment commercially available. Examples of catalogues with such equipment include: Don Krebs' *Access to Recreation,* which contains a variety of pieces of exercise equipment, ramps, pool lifts, fishing aids, bowling equipment, and gloves and cuffs; *Enabling Devices,* a catalog featuring communication devices and toys for children; *Fun and Achievement* with many unique recreational items for children and adults; and *Sportime Abilitations* with many movement related items. Even a standard *L.L. Bean* catalog has featured a backpack designed to be used on a wheelchair.

TRENDS IN COMMUNITY RELATIONS

Community and Hospital Linkages

Community leisure service departments are building linkages between themselves and hospitals, institutions, and behavioral health centers. In doing so, networks are being developed to enhance the programs of all agencies involved. For example, the Cincinnati Recreation Commission has worked with state institutions to facilitate the transition of clients to the community. The arrangement allows Recreation Commission staff to meet individuals before they are released from the institution. The need for a close working relationship between institutions and community programs is

A preschool developmental play center in Tampa, Florida, designed to meet the needs of children with disabilities.
(Design by Dr. Louis Bowers, University of South Florida; Photo by David R. Austin)

likely to grow as institutions place more clients into alternative community living situations.

Volunteer Programs

Volunteers are extremely important to the success of special recreation programs. For this reason, the Cincinnati Recreation Commission has developed an awards program to formally recognize volunteers. Volunteers who give 50 hours of service are awarded an "I'm a TRiffic Volunteer" T-shirt. Other appropriate awards are given for all levels of service. Another trend is using special recreation programs participants as volunteers. In so doing, participants not only help the program but gain a sense of giving as well as receiving. The concept of using volunteers with disabilities has been termed inclusive volunteering. Inclusive volunteering is occurring in both Canada and the United States (Phoenix, Miller, & Schleien, 2002). Finally, strong advisory councils and parents'

groups have become essential to establishing and maintaining high-quality special recreation programs. The involvement of citizens is particularly necessary to securing appropriate community support and funding. It is likely that the trend toward expanded use of volunteers in many roles will continue and enlarge.

Cooperative Arrangements among Leisure Service Agencies

The trend toward two or more leisure service agencies cooperating to meet the leisure needs of constituents with disabilities grew out of the frustrations of several progressive park districts and municipalities in Illinois during the late 1960s. Although efforts to serve persons with disabilities had been made in the form of summer camps and special events, the park districts and municipal recreation departments realized the limited nature of their programs and that they served only a small fraction of people with disabilities living in their geographic areas. Although recreation and parks personnel wanted to enlarge their services for persons with disabilities, their efforts were hampered by financial restrictions, low incidences of some disabilities in given districts, and a lack of trained professionals to design programs. Out of this situation arose the concept of pooling resources to establish special recreation cooperatives, each to be supported by several park districts and municipal recreation departments (Robb, 1976).

In 1970, the Northern Suburban Special Recreation Association (NSSRA) was formed by eight local park districts and community recreation departments in Cook and Lake counties. From the beginning, it was clear that the NSSRA was setting a trend for Illinois and the nation. The special recreation cooperatives in the Chicago area remain a vital part of each of their member districts and municipalities. This sentiment is expressed in the NSSRA *Policy Manual,* which states: "Rather than a separate program, the N.S.S.R.A. is an extension of its member agencies whose specific responsibility is to provide for the special population a program of recreation comparable to that which is offered the general public." Thus the cooperative associations are not "add-on" programs, but are a means for each park district and community to provide a comprehensive recreation program for its entire population.

NSSRA began the trend toward cooperative ventures by park and recreation jurisdictions to establish special recreation services. From these pioneering efforts have come a concept and a model for cooperation that we hope will continue to grow throughout the nation.

Other Cooperative Arrangements

Cooperative arrangements of many types are expanding inclusive and special recreation services. In Chicago, the Chicago Park District is participating with the Chicago Public Schools in a number of programs. A full spectrum of services is provided. These range from school-based prescribed programs of basic leisure skills to

community-based inclusive recreation activities (e.g., inclusive sled hockey, inclusive beep baseball) to independently chosen socially integrated programs in the community (McPike, 1999). In Knoxville, Tennessee, Camp Koinonia staff involve public schools, universities, 4-H organizations, and agricultural extension services in facility arrangements and staff and camper recruitment. In addition, civic, religious, and business organizations contribute financially to the camp (Hayes, 1999). In New York City, colleges and universities are working with organizations for persons with disabilities to provide fitness programs for individuals with physical disabilities (Kunstler, 1999). Park and recreation authority Michal Anne Lord (1999) has exclaimed that today's world is full of "partnerships" and "partnering" to provide increasing numbers of leisure opportunities for persons with disabilities.

FINANCIAL TRENDS

Fees and Charges

There exists a general trend within leisure service agencies to levy fees and charges for services. This trend is being followed within special recreation programs. Usually, fees charged for special recreation programs are comparable to those charged the general public. It is the feeling of administrators of special recreation programs that they should not place an unfair burden on their participants by charging them disproportionately higher fees than other citizens, even though special recreation programming is often more expensive to conduct. This trend is anticipated to persist as long as leisure service agencies continue to depend on the collection of fees and charges.

Fund-Raising

Fund-raising efforts have become widespread among special recreation programs. Approaches to fund-raising are varied. Illustrative of fund-raising projects are those of the Cincinnati Recreation Commission, which has developed a gift catalog, sponsored various 10K runs, and raffled tickets for a hot air balloon ride with a local celebrity. The Northeast DuPage Special Recreation Association has established the Cabin Foundation to help support the Cabin Nature Program Center, which offers integrated nature programs. Corporate sponsorship of major activities is also becoming a popular means of financing expensive events that include persons with disabilities.

These fund-raising projects are all positive efforts. Questionable fund-raising practices, such as promoting feelings of pity for children with disabilities, are on the decline. Positive, innovative means to fund-raising will be important for some time as a means to supplement tax funds.

PROFESSIONAL TRENDS

Continuing Education

Continuing education is an area that is growing tremendously today and will become even larger in the future. All types of leisure service providers will need to receive information on inclusive and special recreation services. Among topics covered will be attitudes toward serving persons with disabilities, issues surrounding the inclusion of persons with disabilities in ongoing programs, and the design of accessible areas and facilities.

Those concerned with continuing education have already developed many new alternatives to educate staff on inclusive recreation. The National Institute on Recreation Inclusion (NIRI) had its inception in September 2000 in Deerfield, Illinois, near Chicago. Sponsored by the National Recreation and Park Association, the NIRI has been held every year since with hundreds of park, recreation, and tourism professionals in attendance. Other innovative approaches to continuing education typically have involved the use of technology. The National Center on Accessibility (NCA), at Indiana University, has been an early adopter of modern educational technology. For example, the NCA has provided educational programs via interactive television and over the World Wide Web to a variety of professionals in the National Park Service, the U.S. Forest Service, and municipal park and recreation departments, as well as to leisure service professionals from the private sector.

Field-Based Research and Evaluation

Local leisure service agencies are beginning to enter into joint efforts with universities to answer applied research questions and to evaluate programs systematically (Bocarro & Barcelona, 2003). Both faculty and graduate students with research and evaluation skills are being called upon by agencies to conduct studies important to the agencies. For example, a graduate student in therapeutic recreation has conducted a study of a pilot program of the West Suburban Special Recreation Association near Chicago. Another therapeutic recreation graduate student investigated the efficacy of one of the Mainstreaming Initiative programs of Montgomery County, Maryland. As inclusive and special recreation programs multiply and grow in sophistication, it will become established practice to conduct cooperative agency-university research and evaluation studies.

Further Definition of Inclusive Recreators and Therapeutic Recreation Specialists

There is a trend toward an identified area of professional specialization in inclusive and special recreation separate from therapeutic recreation (Hamilton & Austin, 1992). Individuals are beginning to become recognized for their expertise in providing inclusive and special recreation experiences for people with disabilities. While some of these professionals have credentials in therapeutic recreation, others come from leisure service professions. The characteristics that set apart those who assume this new role is that they function in the community to enhance the leisure lifestyles of persons with disabilities and they are nonclinical in their approach.

Thus, there is a movement toward a separation of inclusive recreation from therapeutic recreation because the focus of inclusive and special recreation is on the provision of leisure experiences, not therapy. Professor Carla Tabourne, of the University of Minnesota (1999), has succinctly written this about the place of special and inclusive recreation: "Neither special recreation nor inclusive recreation is a concentration nor branch of the therapeutic recreation profession. Both special recreation and inclusive recreation may be (perceived to be) branches of the field(s) of recreation and parks."

Schleien et al. (1997) have called for recreation agencies, advocacy groups, and public schools to create new professional staff positions titled community leisure planners (CLP) or community leisure facilitators (CLF). The chief function of CLPs, or CLFs, would be ensuring persons with disabilities are appropriately included in community recreation programs and settings through the provision of inclusive and special recreation services.

Ramifications of this trend will be: (1) the establishment of at least one professional organization devoted to the concerns of inclusive and special recreation; and (2) the development of university professional preparation opportunities specifically designed for students desiring careers in inclusive and special recreation. Hamilton and Austin (1992) have suggested that perhaps a branch of the National Recreation and Park Association, the National Therapeutic Recreation Society (NTRS), will evolve as the professional organization that has as its primary mission championing the cause of inclusive recreation. The publication of NTRS's strong position statement on inclusion in 1997 may be perceived as a sign of the organization's growing interest in inclusive recreation.

Advocacy

To advocate is to make an argument to gain something from persons of power (Austin, 2004). The term *advocacy* comes from the Latin term *ad vocare*, or being "inspired, dedicated, and noble" (Locke, Myers, & Herr, 2001, p. 92). A noble trend seen today is advocacy to organize communities toward the provision of inclusive recreation. Brannan and his colleagues (2003) have written

that "inclusive programs are relatively new, so continued advocacy is important if persons with varying abilities are to be included in the mainstream of society" (p. xiii).

One means of advocating for inclusive recreation is providing materials to elected and appointed officials and other policy makers to interpret the need for such programs. In particular, brochures and Web programs are being developed that provide persuasive arguments for the need for communities to make their programs and facilities fully accessible to persons with disabilities. There also exists a growing trend for recreation and park professionals to advocate the need for inclusive recreation to colleagues at professional conferences.

National Park Service

During the early 1980s, the National Park Service (NPS) initiated a concerted effort to improve accessibility to its facilities and programs for visitors with disabilities. A Special Programs and Populations Branch was established, under the direction of David Park, to facilitate NPS accessibility efforts. This division was given the responsibility of working closely with all units of the Park Service to identify and eliminate barriers to accessibility. Toward this end, the NPS has continued its efforts to correct accessibility problems, and many actions within the park system are clear signs of a trend toward making all of our national parks accessible to visitors who have disabilities. It is our opinion that the positive stance taken by the National Park Service will serve as a model to enhance accessibility efforts at state and local levels as well. NPS policies will positively affect accessibility in parks throughout America.

Greater Acceptance of Inclusive Recreation by Leisure Service Providers

There exists an ever increasing acceptance of inclusive recreation in both Canada and the United States. This movement has been due in large measure to a variety of individuals and organizations that have advocated for inclusive recreation. We, as the authors of this book, hope that we have assisted this movement by actively advocating for inclusive recreation. One of the most convincing cases for inclusive recreation has been presented by Sylvester, Voelkl, and Ellis (2001). These authors have perceived recreation inclusion as a quality of life issue. Like people without disabilities, people with disabilities need access to the same leisure opportunities that offer all of us chances to enjoy personal well-being. Without opportunities for recreation inclusion, people with disabilities are cheated from having self-determined leisure experiences. When normal leisure experiences are absent, people, including those with disabilities, are excluded from needed human social interactions in which they may gain feelings of self-confidence and self-esteem. As Sylvester, Voelkl, and Ellis have indicated, it would truly be a shame if persons with disabilities were denied access to leisure opportunities, because studies of inclusive recreation programs have documented outcomes including increased social interaction, improved decision making, and enhanced confidence and self-esteem for people with disabilities.

Another compelling argument made by Sylvester, Voelkl, and Ellis is that recreation inclusion should exist for the sake of the community. Providing for recreation inclusion signals that a sense of community exists that allows no group, including those with disabilities, to be left behind. Disenfranchising any group of citizens is not an option for vital communities. Thus such communities, by their nature, provide all citizens with the ability to participate in the life of the community.

The National Recreation and Park Association (NRPA) is a leader in the advocacy movement in the United States. The chair of NRPA advocated for recreation inclusion in an editorial in the Association's magazine, *Parks & Recreation*. He wrote:

> Disabilities affect one-fifth of all Americans. That's an incredible number of people—in fact, half of the seniors 65 and older have some kind of disability. What's more, this statistic can only be expected to increase as the baby boomer generation ages. Parks and recreation can play a vital role in maintaining the quality of life for people with all kinds of disabilities—and I'm pleased to say that NRPA is working on new initiatives to serve this important population even better. (Lose, 2002, p. 2)

In addition to advocacy, another major force behind the inclusive recreation movement has been legislation. This has been particularly true in the United States where the Americans with Disabilities Act (ADA) has forever changed the face of leisure services. As both public and private leisure services and facilities have become more programmatically and physically accessible due to the ADA, there has been a growing realization by service providers of the necessity to enlarge their roles to include the provision of services to persons with disabilities.

As a result of the twin forces of legislation and advocacy, in both the United States and Canada there is today a growing recognition by leisure service providers that adopting the concept of inclusive recreation is clearly the right thing to do. Leisure service providers in both the public and private sectors have begun to embrace the role of ensuring the rights of persons with disabilities to full inclusion into the leisure mainstream.

SUMMARY

We strongly endorse the trend toward the provision of inclusive recreation services for those with disabilities. Persons with disabilities have the right to the same recreation and leisure activities that are available to the rest of the community.

The present period promises to be an exciting one in the history of community leisure service delivery systems in the United States and Canada. Progressive systems have already gone beyond the philosophical question of "Should we provide services for persons with disabilities?" to the question "How can we best serve the needs of persons who have disabilities?"

SUGGESTED LEARNING ACTIVITIES

1. In a small group, discuss the statement: "Few activities cannot be entered into by persons with disabilities. Therefore, programs for people with special needs are likely to follow societal trends." Agree or disagree with the statement. List reasons for your position. Then discuss these with the entire class.

2. Pick one type of activity listed in the chapter in which you have not previously taken part. Arrange to participate in this activity with persons who have disabilities. Write a one- to two-page paper on this experience or give a report in class.

3. Survey several community parks and recreation departments or park districts to determine the type and extent of leisure education and leisure counseling programs serving persons with disabilities. Prepare a report on your findings.

4. Interview several persons with disabilities about trends they see in programming. Then interview program directors or other recreation administrators from the same community. Compare the responses of the consumers and professionals. Report your findings in class.

5. Invite a therapeutic recreation specialist from a state institution into class to discuss the institution's community linkages. Question the specialist as to what would be ideal in community linkages with leisure service delivery systems.

6. Debate the question in class as to whether participants in special recreation programs should pay fees equal to other citizens, even though special recreation programming is often more expensive to conduct.

7. Invite a therapeutic recreation specialist and an inclusive recreator to class to discuss their roles and what they see as future directions for inclusive recreation.

8. Search the Web for information on accessible golf, wheelchair rugby, or other sports for persons with disabilities of interest to you. Report your findings in class.

9. Discuss inclusive recreation with family members of children with disabilities. Inquire as to whether their community provides adequate inclusive recreation services and their attitude toward their community recreation agencies. Prepare a written report on your discussion.

REFERENCES

Austin, D. R. *Therapeutic Recreation Processes and Techniques* (5th ed.). Champaign, IL: Sagamore Publishing Inc., 2004.

Austin, D. R., Y. Lee, & D. Getz. *Trends in Inclusive Recreation: A Delphi Study.* Bloomington, IN: Indiana University, 2003.

Bocarro, J., & B. Barcelona. Come together: Unlocking the potential of collaboration between universities and park and recreation agencies. *Parks & Recreation, 38*(10), 50–55, October 2003.

Brannan, S., & A. Fullerton. Epilogue. In S. Brannan, A. Fullerton, J. R. Arick, G. M. Robb, & M. Bender. *Including Youth with Disabilities in Outdoor Programs: Best Practices, Outcomes, and Resources.* Champaign, IL: Sagamore Publishing Inc., 2003, pp. 237–239.

Brannan, S., A. Fullerton, J. R. Arick, G. M. Robb, & M. Bender. *Including Youth with Disabilities in*

Outdoor Programs: Best Practices, Outcomes, and Resources. Champaign, IL: Sagamore Publishing Inc., 2003.

Brennan, P. F. Harnessing innovative technologies: What can you do with a shoe? *Nursing Outlook, 47*(3), 128–132, 1999.

Brett, A., & E. F. Provenzo. *Adaptive Technology for Special Human Needs.* Albany: State University of New York Press, 1995.

Bullock, C. C., & M. J. Mahon. *Introduction to Recreation Services for People with Disabilities: A Person-Centered Approach* (2nd ed.). Champaign, IL: Sagamore Publishing, 2000.

Caneday, L. Outdoor recreation: A virtual reality. *Parks & Recreation, 27*(8), 48–51, 1992.

Chandler, D. L. Finally, eye to eye: "Ibot" may revolutionize life in wheelchair. *The Boston Globe,* pp. A1, A18, November 18, 2000.

Coale, P. J. Greetings from Camp Technology. *Parks & Recreation, 34*(5), 79–81, 1999.

Cornelius, D. A., S. Chipouras, E. Makas, & S. Daniels. *Who Cares? A Handbook on Sex Education and Counseling Services for Disabled People* (2nd ed.). Baltimore: University Park Press, 1982.

Deavours, M. N. A summer computer camp for children with disabilities and their friends. *Therapeutic Recreation: Innovative Programs in Community Recreation.* Arlington, VA: National Recreation and Park Association, pp. 12–21, 1997.

Duncan, D. No problem—state-of-the-art Indy indoor golf could be the answer. *Hoosier Health, Fitness & Sports, 1*(1), 14, 15, 1998.

Edwards, D., & R. Smith. Social interaction in an integrated day camp setting. *Therapeutic Recreation Journal, 23*(3), 71–78, 1989.

Galambos, L., & B. Williams. Times are changing, are you ready? *Therapeutic Recreation: Innovative Programs in Community Recreation.* Arlington, VA: National Recreation and Park Association, pp. 26–30, 1997.

Galvin, J. C., & M. J. Scherer. *Evaluating, Selecting, and Using Appropriate Assistive Technology.* Gaithersburg, MD: Aspen Publishers, Inc., 1996.

Godbey, G. C. *The Future of Leisure Services: Thriving on Change.* State College, PA: Venture Publishing, 1989.

Goodrich, G. L. Information access—from newspapers to the Internet. *Aging & Vision News, 9*(1), 1, 2, 1997.

Hamilton, E. J., & D. R. Austin. Future perspectives of therapeutic recreation. *Annual in Therapeutic Recreation, 3,* 72–79, 1992.

Hayden, M. F., T. Soulen, S. J. Schleien & C. E. S. Tabourne. A matched, comparative study of the recreation integration of adults with mental retardation who moved into the community and those who remained at the institution. *Therapeutic Recreation Journal, 30*(1), 41–63, 1996.

Hayes, G. Personal communication. April 1999.

Hinnefeld, S. Local advocates welcome court ruling. *The Herald-Times,* Bloomington, IN, *123*(36): 1, 7, July 23, 1999.

Hunter, J. C. Leisure education: Its role in the recreation integration process. *Recreation Canada,* Special Issue, 76–81, 1981.

Jordan, I. K. Colleges can do even more for people with disabilities. *The Chronicle of Higher Education,* section 3, pp. B14, B15, June 15, 2001.

Kunstler, R. Personal communication. March 1999.

Lekotek. *Re-creating Recreation for Inclusion.* Evanston, IL: The National Lekotek Center, 1998.

Linsday, J. Technology allows disabled to make music. *Hoosier Times,* p. E4, January 26, 2003.

Locke, D. C., J. E. Myers, & E. L. Herr. *The Handbook of Counseling.* Thousand Oaks: Sage Publications, 2001.

Lord, M. A. Personal communication. April 1999.

Lose, D. O. NRPA works to create access for people with disabilities. *Parks & Recreation, 37*(6), 2, June 2002.

McFadyen, G. M. Aids for hearing impairment and deafness. In J. C. Galvin & M. J. Scherer, Eds. *Evaluating, Selecting, and Using Appropriate Assistive Technology.* Gaithersburg, MD: Aspen Publishers, Inc., 1996, pp. 144–161.

McKenzie, K. B. BlazeSports: A model program for community-based adapted sports. *Parks & Recreation, 35*(10), 76–82, October 2000.

McKenzie, K. B. BlazeSports: Grassroots sports for physically disabled becoming a reality. *Parks & Recreation, 37*(3), 60–65, March 2002.

McPike, T. Personal communication, April 1999.

Phoenix, T., K. Miller, & S. Schleien. Better to give than receive. *Parks & Recreation, 37*(10), 26–33, 2002.

Reynolds, R. Recreation and leisure lifestyle changes. In P. Wehman, Ed. *The ADA Mandate for Social Change.* Baltimore: Paul H. Brookes, 1993.

Robb, G. Golfers with disabilities: Business or bust for professional clubmakers? *The Professional Clubmakers' Society Journal,* 19–21, September/October 1997.

Robb, G. M., Ed. *Guidelines for the Formation and Development of Special Recreation Cooperatives in the State of Illinois.* University of Illinois at Urbana-Champaign: Office of Recreation and Park Resources, Department of Leisure Studies and the Cooperative Extension Service, 1976.

Sable, J., & J. Gravink. Northeast Passage: An innovative model for community-based service delivery. In S. J. Schleien, M. T. Ray, & F. P. Green, Eds. *Community Recreation and People with*

Disabilities (2nd ed.). Baltimore: Paul H. Brookes Publishing Co., 1997, pp. 194–198.

Schleien, S. J., F. P. Green, & C. F. Stone. Making friends within inclusive community recreation programs. *American Journal of Recreation Therapy, 2*(1), 7–16, 2003.

Schleien, S. J., S. Meyer, L. Heyne, & B. Brandt. *Lifelong Leisure Skills and Lifestyles for Persons with Developmental Disabilities.* Baltimore: Paul H. Brookes Publishing Co., 1995.

Schleien, S. J., M. T. Ray, & F. P. Green. *Community Recreation and People with Disabilities* (2nd ed.). Baltimore: Paul H. Brookes Publishing Co., 1997.

Schleien, S. J., J. E. Rynders, L. A. Heyne, & C. E. S. Tabourne. *Powerful Partnerships: Parents and Professionals Building Inclusive Recreation Programs Together.* Minneapolis: University of Minnesota, 1995.

Schuler, D. *New Community Networks: Wired for Change.* New York: Addison-Wesley Publishing Company, 1996.

Spede, J. F. Computers that make life possible. [Indiana] *University Computing Times,* 14, 15, January–February 1993.

Sylvester, C., J. E. Voelkl, & G. D. Ellis. *Therapeutic Recreation Programming: Theory and Practice.* State College, PA: Venture Publishing, Inc., 2001.

Tabourne, C. Personal communication. May 1999.

Vitale, A. J. Interactive technologies. In J. C. Galvin & M. J. Scherer, Eds. *Evaluating, Selecting, and Using Appropriate Assistive Technology.* Gaithersburg, MD: Aspen Publishers, Inc., 1996, pp. 277–299.

Wilhite, B., M. A. Devine, & L. Golderberg. Perceptions of youth with and without disabilities: Implications for inclusive leisure programs and services. *Therapeutic Recreation Journal, 33*(1), 15–28, 1999.

Zabriskie, R. B., & L. A. Heyne. A refocus on family. *Therapeutic Recreation Journal, 37*(1), 15–17, 2003.

APPENDIX A

Selected Organizations Concerning Persons with Disabilities

Adaptive Environments
(www.adaptenv.org)
374 Congress Street
Suite 301
Boston, MA 02210
Phone: (617) 695-1225

AIDS Action Council
(www.aidsaction.org)
1906 Sunderland Place NW
Washington, DC 20036
Phone: (202) 530-8030
Toll-Free: 800-644-AIDS

American Amputee Foundation
P.O. Box 250218, Hillcrest Sta.
Little Rock, AR 72225
Phone: (501) 666-2523

American Association on Mental Retardation
(www.aamr.org)
444 N. Capital St. NW, Ste. 846
Washington, DC 20001
Phone: (202) 387-1968
Toll-Free: 800-424-3688

American Association of Retired Persons
(www.aarp.org)
601 E St. NW
Washington, DC 20049
Phone: (202) 434-2277
Toll-Free: 800-424-3410

American Council of the Blind
(www.acb.org)
1155 15th Street, NW, Suite 1004
Washington, DC 20005
Toll-Free: 800-424-8666

American Diabetes Association
(www.diabetes.org)
ATTN: National Call Center
1701 North Beauregard St.
Alexandria, VA 22311
Toll-Free: 800-342-2383

American Foundation for the Blind
(www.afb.org)
11 Penn Plaza, Suite 300
New York, NY 10011
Phone: (212) 502-7600
Toll-Free: 800-AFB-line

American Psychiatric Association
(www.psych.org)
1000 Wilson Blvd., Ste. 1825
Arlington, VA 22209
Phone: (703) 907-7300

American Spinal Injury Association
(www.asia-spinalinjury.org)
Rehabilitation Institute of Chicago
345 East Superior Street, Room 1436
Chicago, IL 60611
Phone: (312) 238-6207

**American Therapeutic
Recreation Association**
(www.atra-tr.org)
1414 Prince Street, Suite 204
Alexandria, VA 22314
Phone: (703) 683-9420

Arthritis Foundation
(www.arthritis.org)
P.O. Box 7669
Atlanta, GA 30357
Toll-Free: 800-283-7800

**Association of Rehabilitation Programs in
Computer Technology**
(www.arpct.org)
503 South York St.
Denver, CO 80209
Phone: (303) 733-2111

Autism Society of America
(www.autism-society.org/)
7910 Woodmont Ave., Ste. 300
Bethesda, MD 20814
Phone: (301) 657-0881
Toll-Free: 800-3AUTISM

Brain Injury Association
(www.biausa.org)
8201 Greensboro Dr., Ste. 611
McLean, VA 22102
Phone: (703) 761-0750

**Canadian Down Syndrome
Society**
(www.cdss.ca)
811 14th St. NW
Calgary, AB, Canada T2N 2A4
Phone (403) 270-8500
Toll-Free: 800-883-5608

Center on Human Policy
(soeweb.syr.edu/thechp/)
805 S. Crouse Ave.
Syracuse, NY 13244
Phone: (315) 443-3851
Toll-Free: 800-894-0826

**Disability Rights Education
and Defense Fund**
(www.dredf.org)
2212 Sixth St.
Berkeley, CA 94710
Phone: (510) 644-2555

**Epilepsy Foundation of
America**
(www.efa.org)
4351 Garden City Dr.
Landover, MD 20785
Toll-Free: 800-332-1000

**Helen Keller National Center for
Deaf/Blind Youths and Adults**
(www.helenkeller.org)
111 Middle Neck Road
Sands Point, NY 11050
Phone: (516) 944-8900

**Learning Disabilities Association of
America**
(www.ldanatl.org)
4156 Library Road
Pittsburgh, PA 15234
Phone: (412) 341-1515

Muscular Dystrophy Association
(www.mdausa.org)
3300 Sunrise Dr.
Tucson AZ 85718
Toll-Free: 800-572-1717

**National Association
of the Deaf**
(www.nad.org)
814 Thayer Ave.
Silver Spring, MD 20910
Phone: (301) 587-1788

**National Attention Deficit Disorder
Association (ADDA)**
(www.add.org)
P.O. Box 543
Pottstown, PA 19464
Phone: (484) 945-2101

National Center for Learning Disabilities (NCLD)
(www.ncld.org)
381 Park Avenue South, Ste. 1401
New York, NY 10016
Phone: (212) 545-7510
Toll-Free: (888) 575-7373

National Center on Accessibility
(www.indiana.edu/~nca)
2805 East 10th St., Ste. 190
Bloomington, IN 47408
Phone: (812) 856-4422

National Center on Physical Activity and Disability (NCPAD)
(www.ncpad.org)
1640 W. Roosevelt Road
Chicago, IL 60608
Toll-Free: 800-900-8086

National Easter Seal Society
(www.easter-seals.org)
230 W. Monroe, Ste. 1800
Chicago, IL 60606
Phone: (312) 726-6200
Toll-Free: 800-221-6827

National Institute of Diabetes and Digestive and Kidney Diseases (NIDDK)
(www.niddk.nih.gov)
National Institute of Health, Office
of Communications and Public Liaison
Building 31, Rm. 9A04
Center Drive, MSC 2560
Bethesda, MD 20892

National Multiple Sclerosis Society
(www.nmss.org)
733 3rd Ave.
New York, NY 10017
Phone: (212) 986-3240
Toll-Free: 800-fight-ms

National Organization on Disability
(www.nod.org)
910 16th St. NW
Suite 600
Washington, DC 20006
Phone: (202) 293-5960

National Spinal Cord Injury Association
(www.spinalcord.org)
6701 Democracy Blvd., Ste. 300-9
Bethesda, MD 20817
Phone: (301) 881-9817
Toll-Free: 800-962-9629

National Therapeutic Recreation Society
(www.nrpa.org/index.cfm?publicationid=21)
22377 Belmont Ridge Road
Ashburn, VA 20148
Phone: (703) 858-0784

Spina Bifida Association of America
(www.sbaa.org)
4590 MacArthur Blvd., NW, Suite 250
Washington, DC 20007
Phone: (202) 944-3285
Toll-Free: 800-621-3141

The Arc of the United States
(www.TheArc.org)
1010 Wayne Ave., Ste. 650
Silver Spring, MD 20910
Phone: (301) 565-3842

United Cerebral Palsy
(www.ucpa.org)
1660 L St., NW, Suite 700
Washington, DC 20036
Phone: (202) 776-0406
Toll-Free: 800-USA-5UCP

U.S. Access Board
(www.access-board.gov)
1331 F St., NW, Ste. 1000
Washington, DC 20004
Phone: (202) 272-0080
Toll-Free: 800-872-2253

APPENDIX B

Athletic and Recreation Organizations for Persons with Disabilities

Access to Sailing
(www.accesstosailing.org)
6475 East Pacific Coast Highway
Long Beach, CA 90803
Phone: (562) 437-0548

American Blind Bowling Association
411 Sheriff St.
Mercer, PA 16137
Phone: (412) 662-5748

American Wheelchair Bowling Association
(www.awba.org)
2912 Country Woods Lane
Palm Harbor, FL 34683
Phone/Fax: (727) 734-0023

American Wheelchair Table Tennis Association
23 Parker St.
Port Chester, NY 10573
Phone: (914) 937-3932

Association of Disabled American Golfers
P.O. Box 280649
Lakewood, CO 80228-0649
Phone: 303-922-5228

Blind Outdoor Leisure Development (BOLD)
533 E. Main
Aspen, CO 81661
Phone: (970) 925-9511

British Columbia Wheelchair Sports Association
(www.bcwheelchairsports.com)
224-1367 W. Broadway
Vancouver, BC, Canada V6H 4A9
Phone: (604) 737-3090

Canadian Amputee Sport Association
(www.interlog.com/~ampsport/can_amputee.html)
217 Holmes Avenue
Willowdale, ON   M2N 4M9
Phone: (416) 222-8625
E-mail: ampsport@interlog.com

Canadian Association for Disabled Skiing
(www.canuck.com/cads)
Suite 200, 505-8th Avenue S.W.
Calgary, Alberta, Canada T2P 1G2
Phone: (403) 777-3200

Canadian Blind Sports Association
(http://www.canadianblindsports.org)
7 Mill St., Lower Level
Almonte, ON   K0A 1A0
Phone: (613) 256-7792

Canadian Cerebral Palsy Sports Association
(www.ccpsa.ca)
305-1376 Bank Street
Ottawa, Ontario K1H 7Y3
Phone: (613) 748-1430

Canadian Deaf Sports Association
(www.assc-cdsa.com)
4545 Ave. Pierre-De Coubertin
C.P. 1000, Succ. M
Montreal, Quebec Canada H1V 3R2
Phone: (514) 252-3069
Toll-Free: (800) 855-0511

Canadian Special Olympics
(www.cso.on.ca)
60 St. Clair Avenue East, Suite 700
Toronto, Ontario Canada M4T 2N5
Phone: (416) 927-9050

Canadian Therapeutic Riding Association
(www.cantra.ca)
P.O. Box 24009
550 Imperial Rd. North
Guelph, ON, Canada N1E 6V8
Phone: (519) 767-0700

**Canadian Wheelchair
Basketball Association**
(www.cwba.ca)
Suite B2, 2211 Riverside Drive
Ottawa, ON, Canada K1H 7X5
Phone: (613) 260-1296

**Cooperative Wilderness Handicapped
Outdoor Group**
(www.isu.edu/departments/cwhog)
Idaho State University
P.O. Box 8128
Pocatella, ID 83209
Phone: (208) 282-3912

**Diabetes Exercise and Sports
Association (DESA)**
(www.diabetes-exercise.org)
8001 Montcastle Dr.
Nashville, TN 37221
Toll-Free: (800) 898-4322

Disabled Sports USA
(www.dsusa.org)
451 Hungerford Dr. Suite 100
Rockville, MD 20850
Phone: (301) 217-0960

Dwarf Athletic Association of America
(www.daaa.org)
418 Willow Way
Lewisville, TX 75077
Phone: (972) 317-8299

Handicapped Scuba Association
(www.hsascuba.com)
1104 El Prado
San Clemente, CA 92672
Phone: (949) 498-4540

International Wheelchair Aviators
(www.wheelchairaviators.org)
P.O. Box 1126
Big Bear Lake, CA 92315
Phone: (909) 585-9663

Mobility International USA
(www.miusa.org)
P.O. Box 10767
Eugene, OR 97440
Phone: (541) 343-1284

National Amputee Golf Association
(www.nagagolf.org)
11 Walnut Hill Road
Amherst, NH 03031
Toll-Free: (800) 633-6242

National Beep Baseball Association
(www.nbba.org)
5568 Boulder Crest Street
Columbus, OH 43235
Phone: (614) 442-1444

**National Disability Sports Alliance
(formerly United States Cerebral Palsy
Athletic Association)**
(www.ndsaonline.org)
25 W. Independence Way
Kingston, RI 02881
Phone: (401) 792-7130

National Foundation of Wheelchair Tennis
940 Calle Amanecer, Ste. B
San Clemente, CA 92673
Phone: (714) 361-3663

National Handicap Motorcyclist Association
404 Maple Ave.
Upper Nyack, NY 10960
Phone: (914) 353-0747

National Ocean Access Project
451 Hungerford Dr., Ste. 100
Rockville, MD 20850
Phone: (301) 217-0960

National Sports Center for the Disabled
(www.nscd.org)
P.O. Box 1290
Winter Park, CO 80482
Phone: (970) 726-1540

National Wheelchair Basketball Association
(www.nwba.org)
8245 Charles Crawford Drive
Charlotte, NC 28269
Phone: (704) 593-1721

National Wheelchair Poolplayers Association
(http://nwpainc.com)
30872 Puritan
Livonia, MI 48154
Phone: (734) 422-2124

National Wheelchair Racquetball Association
C/O American Amateur Racquetball Association
815 North Weber
Colorado Springs, CO 80903
Phone: (719) 635-5396

National Wheelchair Softball Association
1616 Todd Court
Hastings, MN 55033
Phone: (612) 437-1792

North American Riding for the Handicapped Association, Inc.
(www.narha.org)
P.O. Box 33150
Denver, CO 80233
Toll-Free: 800-369-ride

Ski for Light
(www.sfl.org)
1455 West Lake Street
Minneapolis, MN 55408
Phone: (612) 827-3232

Special Olympics International
(www.specialolympics.org)
1325 G St., NW, Ste. 500
Washington, DC 20005
Phone: (202) 628-3630

Turning P.O.I.N.T.
(www.turningpointtexas.org)
403 Pacific Ave.
Terrell, TX 75160
Voice/Fax: (972) 551-4231

U.S. Association for Blind Athletes
(www.usaba.org)
33 N. Institute St.
Colorado Springs, CO 80903
Phone: (719) 630-0422

U.S. Handcycling Federation
(www.ushf.org)
P.O. Box 2245
Evergreen, CO 80437
Phone: (303) 679-2770

U.S. Les Autres Sports Association
(www.americasathletes.org/uslasa.html)
9207 Baber Drive
Houston, TX 77095
Phone: (281) 855-7422

U.S. Wheelchair Swimming, Inc.
c/o Wheelchair Sports, USA
3595 E. Fountain Blvd., Ste L-1
Colorado Springs, CO 80910
Phone: (719) 574-1150

U.S.A. Deaf Sports Federation (USADSF)
(www.usadsf.org)
1052 Darling Street
Ogden, UT 84403
Fax: (801) 334-8711

United States Quad Rugby Association
(www.quadrugby.com)
5861 White Cypress Drive
Lake Worth, FL 33467
Phone: (561) 964-1712

**United States Wheelchair
Weightlifting Federation**
39 Michael Pl.
Levittown, PA 19057
Phone: (215) 945-1964

Universal Wheelchair Football Association
U.C. Raymond Walters College
Disability Services Office
9555 Plainfield Road
Cincinnati, OH 45236
Phone: (513) 792-8625

Wheelchair Archery USA
c/o Wheelchair Sports, USA
3595 E. Fountain Blvd, Suite L-1
Colorado Springs, CO 80910
Phone: (719) 574-1150

Wheelchair Sports, USA
(www.wsusa.org)
10 Lake Circle, Ste. G19
Colorado Springs, CO 80906
Phone: (719) 574-1150

Wilderness Inquiry
(www.wildernessinquiry.org)
808 14th Ave SE
Minneapolis, MN 55414
Phone: (612) 676-9400
Toll-Free: 800-728-0719

INDEX

Access aisles, for parking, 102
Access Board, 43, 83, 98, 107,
    112, 116, 124, 274, 294
AccessDOS, 281
Accessibility. *See also* ADAAG
    checklist for park and
        recreation facilities,
        113–115
    definition of, 25, 97
    international symbol, 101
    overcoming of barriers, 88–89
    playgrounds, 116–118
Accessibility Checklist, The
    (Goltsman et al., 1993),
    116, 118
Accessible Journeys
    (Pennsylvania), 276
Access to Recreation (Krebs), 283
Acquired Immunodeficiency
    Syndrome (AIDS), 66–67
Active Living Alliance for
    Canadians with a Disability,
    166–167, 169, 175
Activities. *See also* Major life
    activities
    definition of, 21
    selecting and modifying,
        139–141
    structuring to promote
        inclusion, 141–142
ADA. *See* Americans with
    Disabilities Act
ADAAG (ADA Accessibility
    Guidelines), 98, 274
Adams, Jon, 281
Adams, Michael, 49
Adaptations. *See also* Assistive
    technology devices
    equipment for community
        programs, 262–263
    implementation of planning
        process, 139–141
    playground equipment,
        123–124
Addams, Jane, 5
Adventure playgrounds, 123
Advocacy
    definition of, 25–26
    future trends, 287
Age, and essential eligibility, 42
Aging, and special recreation,
    63–64

AIDS.ORG, 67
Air Carrier Access Act of 1986
    (ACAA), 84
Ajzen, I., 31–32, 33
Alexander, Jane, 206
Alexander Graham Bell
    Association for the Deaf and
    Hard of Hearing, 60
Allen, L. R., 148
Alphtalker, 281
Alternative equipment, 263
Amabile, Teresa, 200–201
American Alliance for Health,
    Physical Education,
    Recreation and Dance
    (AAHPERD), 259
American Association of Mental
    Retardation, 61, 62, 292
American Blind Bowling
    Association, 259, 295
American Camping Association
    (ACA), 181, 184
American Foundation for AIDS
    Research, 67
American Foundation for the
    Blind, 58, 259, 292
American Park & Recreation
    Society (APRS), 160
American Psychological
    Association, 65
American Recreation Society
    (ARS), 6–7, 10
American Society for Testing and
    Materials (ASTM), 119
Americans with Disabilities Act
    (ADA). *See also* ADAAG
    architectural barriers, 83, 98
    arts programs, 200, 207, 220
    camping opportunities, 181
    definition of disability, 20, 40
    future of inclusive recreation,
        271, 278, 288
    history of inclusive and special
        recreation, 7–10
    leadership responsibility in
        community recreation, 15
    persons with disabilities and
        awareness of, 78
    playgrounds, 115–116
    providers of recreation and
        parks services, 42–44
    purpose of, 39

requirements of businesses and
    organizations, 40–41
rules and regulations
    barriers, 86
titles of and compliance
    with, 40
transportation, 84
Universal Design, 125
American Therapeutic Recreation
    Association (ATRA),
    10, 293
American Youth Soccer
    Organization, 228–229
Anderson, L., 22, 25, 195
Animals. *See* Guide dogs
Animal therapy, and autism, 71
Apathetic behaviors, 81, 82
Apparatus, and playgrounds,
    119–120
Appell, M. J., 204
Architectural barriers, 43,
    82–83, 210
Architectural Barriers Act of
    1968 (PL 90–480),
    98, 261
Architectural and Transportation
    Barriers Compliance Board
    (A&TBCB), 44–45
Arick, J. R., 183
Artistic, Cultural, and
    Entertainment Program
    (California State
    University), 204
Art programs. *See also* Music
    autism, 71
    benefits, 201–207
    definition of "the arts,"
        200–201
    disability culture, 207–208
    examples of participation,
        210–220
    leadership, 209–210
Arts in Education Project,
    204–205
Art & Soul Festival (Los
    Angeles), 207
Assessment tools, for program
    evaluation, 150–152
Assistive technology devices
    (ATDs), 97–98, 274,
    279–282
Associated Press, 43

Association of Mouth and Foot
    Painting Artists (AMFPA)
    (London, England), 220
Association for Retarded
    Citizens, 62
Associations for Community
    Living (Canada), 173
Attention deficit hyperactive
    disorder (ADHD), 69–70
Attitudes
    arts programs, 210
    barriers to participation, 81–82
    competencies, 13
    importance of negative, 29
    inclusion, 136
    language, 26–29
    means to change, 29–31,
        32–33
Audiotapes, 58
Auditory impairments, and
    facility design, 100. *See also*
    Deafness
Aurora computer enhancement
    program, 281
Austin, D. R., 11, 13–14, 287
Autism spectrum disorder (ASD),
    70–71
AXIS Dance Company (Oakland,
    CA), 219

Bacon, Natalie, 224
Baer, B., 201–202
Balance, and hearing loss, 59
Barnes, C., 208
Barrie Integrated Baseball
    Association, 230, 242–244
Barriers. *See also* Architectural
    barriers
    communication barriers, 86–88
    environmental barriers, 80–86
    intrinsic barriers, 77–80
    overcoming, 88–92
Barriers to Community
    Involvement scale, 90
Baseball, 242–244
Basketball, 140, 230–233, *235*
Beaches, and facility design, 106
Beaver, D., 229
Bedini, L. A., 132, 189, 255–256
Behavior
    attention deficit hyperactive
        disorder (ADHD), 69–70

Behavior (*continued*)
    attitudes and prediction of,
        31–32, 33
    autism, 70–71
    brain injury, 65–66
    implementation of programs,
        143–144
    mental retardation and learning
        impairments, 61
    youth-at-risk, 68
Behavioral disorders, 64–65.
        See also Attention deficit
        hyperactive disorder
Behavior management
    techniques, 65, 66, 143
Beliefs, and attitudes, 32–33
Benches, for picnic areas, 106
Beneficial Designs, Inc.,
    104–105
Benefits-based management
    (BBM), 148
Bicycling, 227, *263*
Birch Family Camp
    (New York), 273
Bishop, K. D., 151
BlazeSports program, 273–274
Blinde, E. M., 236
Blindness, 57–58. *See also* Visual
    impairments
Boat docks, 107
Bocce, 230, 244–246
Body Silent, The (Murphy,
    1987), 82
Boston Marathon, 224
Boston Sand Gardens, 5
Botschner, J. V., 91
Bowe, F., 79, 84
Bowers, L., 118
Braddock, D., 85
Bradford Woods Outdoor
    Education, Recreation,
    and Camping Center
    (Indiana University), 188,
    271, 273
Braille, 58
Brain injury, 65–66
Brain Injury Association of
    America, 66, 293
Brain Injury Resource
    Center, 66
Brannan, S., 183, 287
Brasile, F. M., 226
Bregha, F. J., 80
Brett, A., 279–80
Bridge to My Thoughts, A
    (Fowler), 213
British Columbia, examples of
    community services,
    168–171, 173–174
Brown, Christy, 22, 202, 205
Brown, Jon, 234
Brown, S. E., 207, 208
Bruck, L., 83
Buildings. *See* Recreation
    buildings
Bulletin boards, 58
Bullock, C. C., 11, 24, 38, 56–57,
    62, 65, 264, 276
Burlington (Canada) Parks and
    Recreation Department, 132

Cabin Foundation and Cabin
    Nature Program Center, 286
Caesar, B., 120, 122, 123

California. *See also* RCH, Inc.;
        Theatre Unlimited
    examples of arts programs,
        207, 210, 213–217, 219
    examples of community
        services, 164–165, 171–173
California State University, 204
Camping Magazine, 181
Camp I-Thonka-Chi (Texas), 273
Camp Koinonia (Tennessee), 285
Camp Optimism (Virginia), 273
Camps and camping programs,
    181–189
Campus recreation programs, 279
Canada. *See also* British
        Columbia; Ontario
    examples of arts programs,
        219–220
    examples of community
        services, 166–171, 173–174
    health problems as barrier to
        physical activity, 79
    history of leisure for persons
        with disabilities, 9
    legislation, 49–50
    national policy on
        transportation of persons
        with disabilities, 84
    population with hearing
        loss, 59
    population of persons with
        disabilities, 9
    wheelchair basketball, 233
Canadian Charter of Rights and
    Freedoms (Constitution Act
    of 1982), 50
Canadian Rehabilitation Council
    for the Disabled, 137
Canoe trips, 194, 195, 276
Caplan, J., 80
Caroleo, O., 67
Car pooling, 264
Carter, M. J., 5, 7, 11
Catalogues, for equipment, 283
Categorizing, and labeling, 55
Centers for Disease Control and
    Prevention, 67, 70
Central route, to persuasive
    communication, 29
Cerebral palsy, 63, 229–230,
    236, 273
Certified Therapeutic Recreation
    Specialist (CTRS), 11, 257
Challenge by Choice, and Project
    Adventure, 192
Challenging environments, for
    playgrounds, 120–122
Chamberlin, J., 91
Chanias, A. K., 240
Character, of community, 267
Chicago Park District, 237
Children. *See also* Youth
    attention deficit hyperactive
        disorder (ADHD), 69–70
    autism, 70
    deafness and hearing loss, 59
    fishing piers, 107
    mental retardation, 61, 62
    motor impairments, 62
    playgrounds, 112, 115–124
    RCH, Inc., 165
    wheelchairs, 99
Children, Youth and Families at-
    Risk Program (CYFAR), 69

Choice, factors providing
    framework for, 77
Cincinnati Recreation
    Commission (CRC),
    160–161, 174, 278, 283,
    284, 285–286
Citizenship, and conditions for
    inclusion, 39
Civil rights, 8, 38
Class. *See* Socioeconomic status
Classification systems
    athletes with disabilities,
        227–228, 232–233, 234
    Special Olympics, 239–240
    trails, 104
Clemson University, 274
Closed-circuit television (CCTV),
    280–281
Coalition of Provincial
    Organizations of the
    Handicapped (COPOH), 84
Cody, Ann, 228
Cognitive functioning, and
    learning impairments, 61
Cohen, D. J., 241
Colleges and universities. *See also*
        specific institutions
    campus recreation
        programs, 279
    continuing education, 259
    field-based research and
        evaluation, 286
    students and professional field
        experiences, 257–258
    students as volunteers, 254
Communication. *See also*
        Language; Speech
        recognition systems
    Americans with Disabilities
        Act and barriers to, 43–44
    arts programs, 202–203
    attitudes toward persons with
        disabilities and persuasive,
        29–30
    autism, 70, 71
    barriers to participation, 86–88,
        90–91
    deafness and hearing loss,
        59–60
Community and community
    recreation
    definition of, 253
    examples of community
        services, 160–175
    facility and equipment
        resources, 261–264
    financial resources, 259–261
    future trends, 283–285
    history of, 5, 6
    human resources, 253–258
    inclusion and models of, 39
    importance of, 253
    informational resources,
        258–259
    leadership responsibility, 14–15
    needs assessment, 131–132
    person-centered planning, 133
    planning process and
        development, 130
    sociocultural variables, 264–267
    Special Olympics and
        partnerships, 240
    sports programs, 228–229
    transportation resources, 264

Community Brokerage Services
    Society (Canada), 173
*Community and Community
    Development* (Edwards and
    Jones, 1976), 264
Community leisure planner (CLP)
    or community leisure
    facilitator (CLF), 257, 287
*Community Recreation and
    People with Disabilities*
    (Schleien et al., 1997), 258
Competencies, for work with
    persons with disabilities,
    13–14
Competition, and inclusion, 142.
        See also Sports
Computer-based assistive
    technologies, 280–282
Computer camps, 273
Computers. *See* Computer-based
        assistive technologies;
        Web sites
Condor, B., 79
Conferences, and continuing
    education, 259
Connolly, K., 134
Constitution Act of 1982
    (Canadian Charter of Rights
    and Freedoms), 50
Consultants and consultation
    services, 256, 258
Consumer Product Safety
    Commission (CPSC),
    119–120
Contextual factors, in disabilities
    or activity limitations, 21
Continuing education, 259
Continuous play, 122
Contracting, and community
    recreation
    financial resources, 260
    human resources, 258
    transportation resources, 264
Coomaraswamy, Ananda, 210
Cooperation
    climate of, 142, *143*
    leisure service agencies,
        284–285
    wilderness-adventure
        programs, 191
Cornelius, D. A., 282
Corporate sponsorship, 286
Corty, J., 195
Council on Quality and
    Leadership, 146
Counseling, and leisure, 276
Counselors, and camping
    programs, 186, *187*
Craft, D. H., 237
Crase, C., 228
Crawford, D., 86
Creativity, and arts programs,
    200–201, *203*, 209
Creator, of artwork, 201
Csikszentmihalyi, M., 80
Curb ramps, 102, *103*, 109
Curling, 271
Curtis, K. A., 234
Curtiss, Charlene, 206
C. W. Hog (Idaho), 189, 192, 273

Dallmeijer, A. J., 236
Dance, and arts programs,
    211, 219

Dattilo, J., 27, 28, 61, 65, 79, 80, 138, 191, 193
Deafness. *See also* Auditory impairments
  communication barriers, 88
  selected facts, 59
  tips and techniques for recreation, 59–60
DeGraff, D., 183
Deinstitutionalization, and normalization, 25
Delinquency, and youth-at-risk, 68
Delwaide, Sonya, 219
Dementia, and AIDS, 67
Demographics. *See* Population
Demonstrations
  blindness and low vision, 58
  deafness and hearing loss, 59
  mental retardation and learning impairments, 61
Dendy, Elizabeth, 245–246
Department of Defense, 45
Department of Health and Human Services (HHS), 45
Department of Housing and Urban Development, 45
DePauw, K. P., 225
Dependency, physical and psychological, 79–80
Design. *See* Facility design
Developmental disabilities, and legislation, 47–49
Developmental Disabilities Assistance and Bill of Rights Act of 1990 (DDA), 49
Developmental Disabilities and Facilities Construction Act of 1970, 47–49
Developmental Disabilities Services and Facilities Construction Act of 1971, 261, 264
Developmentally Disabled Assistance Bill of Rights Act of 1975, 48
Devine, M. A., 12–13, 24, 193, 229
Diabetes, and visual impairments, 58
Diagnostic and Statistical Manual of Mental Disorders, fourth edition (DSM-IV), 64, 69
Diamondstein, G., 200, 202
Dickerson, F. B., 91
Dimensional requirements, and facility design, 98–100, 126
Directed experience, and organized camping, 181
Directions, and brain injury, 66. *See also* Instructions
Directory of Travel Agencies for the Disabled (Hecker), 275–276
Disabled Sports USA, 229, 274, 296
Disability. *See also* Developmental disabilities; Persons with disabilities
  characteristics of specific conditions, 57–71
  definitions of, 20, 21, 40
  labeling, 55–57
Disability Rag, The (Johnson, 1989), 26–27

Disability and Sport (DePauw & Jones, 2001), 225
Discrimination, in recreation programs and services, 38–39
Dogs. *See* Animal therapy; Guide dogs
Dominated or restricted power community, 265
Donaldson, J., 30
Down All the Days (Brown), 202
Down syndrome, 61, 62
Draheim, C. C., 240
Drinking fountains, 106
Drugs. *See also* Substance abuse
  abnormal behavior, 64, 65
  AIDS and side effects, 67
Dummer, G. M., 227
Dupuy, Diane, 220
Dwarf Athletic Association of America, 229, 296
Dykens, E. M., 241
Dynamic social activity, 91

Eareckson, Joni, 205
Ecological barriers, 83
Economic barriers, 84–86, 89
Education. *See also* Colleges and universities; Continuing education; Prevention education; Schools; Training
  legislation, 46–47
  leisure for children with disabilities, 276
  youth-at-risk, 68
Education for All Handicapped Children Act of 1975, 46–47
Edwards, A. D., 264, 266–267
Elderly. *See* Aging
Elevated areas, and playgrounds, 118
Elevators, and recreation buildings, 109–10, *114–115*
Elites, and community, 265
Ellis, G. D., 25, 288
Employment, and economic barriers, 84
Empowerment. *See also* Power
  affirmative versus negative language, 28
  attitudes toward persons with disabilities, 31
  overcoming barriers, 91–92
Enabling Devices (catalog), 283
England. *See* Association of Mouth and Foot Painting Artists
Environics, 49
Environmental adaptations, 141
Environmental barriers, 21–22, 80–86
Epilepsy Foundation, 259, 293
Epstein, R. S., 49
Equipment. *See also* Assistive technology devices
  adaptations for playgrounds, 141
  community resources and adaptive devices, 262–263
  future innovations, 283
Equitable use, and Universal Design, 125
Error, and Universal Design, 125–126

Ervin, M., 81
Essential eligibility, and Americans with Disabilities Act, 42
Evaluation
  field-based research and, 286
  planning process, 144–52
Everest, Mt., 193
Expectations, and stereotypes, 55
Exposure, and changing of attitudes, 30
Expressive blocks, to communication, 87
Exterior circulation and entrances, of recreation buildings, 108–110

Facilities, and resources for communities, 261–263. *See also* Facility design
Facility design
  assistive technology devices (ATDs), 97–98
  competencies, 13, 14
  general guidelines, 98–100
  legislation, 98
  parks and outdoor recreation areas, 100–106
  playfields, 107–108
  playgrounds, 112, 115–124
  recreation buildings, 108–112
  terminology, 97
  Universal Design, 124–126
  water-related areas, 106–107
Factional or conflict-dissipated power community, 265
Fahnestock, M. F., 138, 142
Family. *See also* Parents
  camping, 273
  social support, 91
Famous People Players (Toronto, Canada), 219–220
Farley, E. M., 185
Federal-Aid Highway Act of 1973, 264
Federal/Provincial/Territorial (FPT) working group, 50
Federal Register, 44, 45, 112
Feeley, Jeanne, 182
Fees and charges, 260, 285
Ferrel, M., 85
Ferris, B. F., 79
Field-based research and evaluation, 286
Financial resources. *See also* Economic barriers; Fees and charges; Grants
  community recreation, 259–261
  economic barriers, 86
  future trends, 285–286
Finger spelling, 59
Fire and Ice: The United States, Canada and the Myth of Converging Values (Adams, 2003), 49
Fiscus, E., 57
Fishing piers, 107, *108*
Flared ramp, 102, *103*
Flexibility in use, and Universal Design, 125
Florida, 8, 161–162
Focus groups, and needs assessment, 132

Forest, M., 136
Form in Art (Pennsylvania), 218–219
Fowler, Claudia, 210, 211–213, 214
Fragile X syndrome, 60
Free appropriate public education (FAPE), 46
FreeWheel (computer assistive device), 281
Frieden, L., 230
Frogley, M., 229
Frost, J. L., 120, 122
Frost, Robert, 191
Fullerton, A., 183, 186, 187
Full Value Contract, and Project Adventure, 192
Fun and Achievement (catalog), 283
Functional classification, of athletes with disabilities, 227
Fund-raising, 260, 285–286
Furnishings, of outdoor recreation areas, 106

Galambos, L., 271
Games, and computers, 281
Gavron, S. J., 225
General Services Administration, 45
Genetics, and attention deficit hyperactivity disorder, 69
Gentle Teaching Approach, 144
Gilbert, A., 101
Gill, C., 207
Girl Scouts of the USA, 259
Goals. *See also* Objectives
  arts programs, 209
  fund-raising, 260
  planning process, 130–131, 135
  sports participation, 225
Godbey, G. C., 136, 271
Goldenberg, L., 24
Golf, 9, 43, 86, 274, 281–282
Gradients, for walks and trails, 103–104
Graefe, A., 189
Grants
  community resources, 260–261, *262*
  Rehabilitation Act of 1973, 45
Gravink, J., 91
Gray, D. E., 5
Green, F. P., 39, 81, 257, 278, 279
Grossman, A. H., 67
Group homes, 277
Guadagnolo, F. B., 148
Guerin, N., 61
Guide to Designing Accessible Outdoor Recreation Facilities, A (U.S. Department of the Interior, 1980), 104, 118
Guide dogs, 58, 82
Guided Tour, The (Pennsylvania), 276

Hahn, H., 82
Hallways and corridors, of recreation buildings, 111
Hamilton, E. J., 287

Handholds, and playgrounds, 118
Handicap, definition of, 20–21
Handrails, and swimming
   pools, 107
Hardin, B. & M., 224
Hardman, M. L., 240, 241–242
Harkin, Tom, 43
Harlan, J. E., 210
Harris, J., 183
Hart, R., 123
Hass, Jay, 86
Havens, M. D., 183
Hawkins, B. A., 64
Hawkins, D. E., 185
Hayman, d'A., 200
Head Master (computer hardware
   device), 281
Health
   intrinsic barriers, 79
   Special Olympics, 241
Hearing. *See* Auditory
   impairments; Deafness
Hecker, H., 275–276
Hedrick, B. N., 236
Height, of playground
   equipment, 120
Hemiplegia, 62
Hendershot, G., 77, 91
Henderson, K. A., 132, 255–257
Henderson, W., 118, 119
Herbert, J. T., 191, 194
Heyne, L. A., 82, 132
Hiepe, Richard, 220
Hillman, W. A., 25
History, of recreation for persons
   with disabilities, 5–7, 9
Hole in the Wall Gang Camp
   (Connecticut), 273
Holland, Eileen, 208
Homeland Neighborhood
   Cultural Center
   (California), 219
Hooker, S. P., 235
Hoover, M. L., 240
Hopman, M. T. E., 236
Horseback riding, 71, *241*
Hospitals
   community linkages,
      283–284
   recreation workers, 6
Hull, J. E., 204
Human Immunodeficiency Virus
   (HIV), 66–67
Human intervention, 141
Human resources, and
   community recreation,
   253–258. *See also* Staff and
   staff training programs;
   Volunteers
Human Resources Development
   Canada, 170
Hutchison, P., 55–56, 78, 90,
   91, 92

Ibot, 282
Ice picking, 271
Idaho. *See* C. W. Hog
Iera, R., 88
Illich, I., 80
Illinois. *See also* Chicago Park
   District; Northern Suburban
   Special Recreation
   Association; Special Music
   by Special People

cooperative arrangements
   among leisure service
   agencies, 284–285
special taxes to fund
   community recreation, 260
Impairment, definition of, 20, 21
Imperial Counties Self-
   Determination Project
   (California), 171–173, 175
Implementation, and planning
   process, 135–144
Importance-performance (I-P)
   analysis, 148–150
*Including Youth with Disabilities
   in Outdoor Programs*
   (Brannan, Fullerton, Arick,
   Robb, and Bender,
   2003), 273
Inclusion. *See also* Barriers;
   Inclusive recreation
   attitudes, 136
   camping programs, 183–184
   competitive sports, 225–226
   definition of, *23*
   future trends, 277–283
   legislation and barriers, 39
   mainstreaming, 24
   preparing foundation for,
      136–139
   Special Olympics, 240
   structuring activities to
      promote, 141–142
   survey of parks and recreation
      agencies, 160
   wilderness adventure
      programs, 194–195
*Inclusion: Including People with
   Disabilities in Parks and
   Recreation Opportunities*
   (Anderson and Kress,
   2003), 258
Inclusion specialists, 160
Inclusive leisure services, 49
Inclusive programming, 22
Inclusive recreation. *See also*
   Inclusion
   definition of, 22–23
   therapeutic recreation and
      polarity between, 12
Inclusive volunteering, 255
Independent Living
   Movement, 207
Indiana University, 188, 271,
   273, 274
Individual differences, of persons
   with disabilities, 56–57
Individual Education Program
   (IEP), 47
Individual program plan
   (IEP), 133
Individuals, and needs
   assessment, 132–133
Individuals with Disabilities
   Education Act (IDEA), 47,
   181, 276
Inert or power-avoidance
   community, 266
Informational resources, for
   communities, 258–259
In-service training programs, 210
Instructions. *See also* Directions
   deafness and hearing loss, 59
   mental retardation and learning
      impairments, 62

Integrated options, 23
Integrated Recreation Services
   (Canada), 169
Integration Project (Ontario,
   Canada), 227
Integration specialist, 137–138
Interactive computer games, 281
Interesting and challenging
   environments, for
   playgrounds, 120–122
Internalized oppression, 80
International City Management
   Association, 6
International Classification of
   Functioning and Disability
   (WHO, 2001), 21
International Festival of
   Wheelchair Dance, 219
Internet. *See* Web sites
Interns, and community
   recreation, 257–258
Intrinsic barriers, 77–80
*Introduction to Recreation
   Services for People with
   Disabilities* (Bullock and
   Mahon, 2000), 258, 276
In Unison
   (Federal/Provincial/Territori
   al Ministers Responsible
   for Social Services,
   1998), 50
Inventory approach, to program
   evaluation, 147–148
Iso-Ahola, S. E., 189
Iverson, M., 121–122

Jacobs, C., 203, 208
Jacobson, L., 55
Jasper Talks symposium
   (1986), 166
Jeffrey, A. J., 207
Jewell, D. L., 265–266
John, J. A., 207
Johnson, D. W., 142
Johnson, Mary, 26–27
Johnson, R. T., 142
Jones, D. B., 132
Jones, D. G., 264, 266–267
Jones, J. A., 193, 225, 227, 230
Jordan, I. K., 282
Journal of Leisurability, 9, 258
Jubala, K. A., 151
Junior National Wheelchair
   Games, 234

Kamen, Dean, 282
Kelley, J. D., 5, 7, 11
Kelly, C., 84
Kelly, J. B., 224
Kelly, J. D., 230
Kemp, John, 203
Kendrick, M., 144–145
Kennedy Foundation, 237
Kentucky, and Americans with
   Disabilities Act, 41
Keung, J. L. W., 183
Key Bridge Foundation, 41
Kimball, R. O., 186, 191
Klein, B. L., 120, 122
Knowledge, and intrinsic
   barriers, 78
Kraus, R., 5
Krebs, Don, 283
Kuntsler, R., 68

Labanowich, S., 226, 237
Labeling, and disabling
   conditions, 55–57
Ladies' Professional Golf
   Association (LPGA), 274
Lais, G., 193, 194–195
LaMere, T., 237
Landscape Structures, Inc.,
   118, 119
Language, and attitudes, 26–29.
   See also Labeling; Sign
   language
LaVerde, D., 189
Law, M., 134
Leadership. *See also* Supervision
   arts programs, 209–210
   brain injury, 66
   camp programs, 186
   competencies, 13–14
   training needs, 12–13
   wilderness-adventure
      programs, 191–192
Learning disabilities, and mental
   retardation, 61
Learning impairments, 60–62
Least restrictive environment, 23
Leasure, Judy, 202
Legal definition, of blindness, 57
Legislation. *See also* Americans
   with Disabilities Act (ADA)
   architectural barriers, 83
   Canadian, 49–50
   developmental disabilities,
      47–49
   education, 46–47
   facility design, 98
   hopes and limitations of,
      38–39
   rehabilitation acts and
      amendments, 44–46
Leisure
   cooperative arrangements
      among service agencies,
      284–285
   counseling, 276
   education on in schools, 276
   volunteering as, 256
Leisure on Wheels program, 162
Lekotek (Georgia), 273
Letter board, *87*
*Lifelong Leisure Skills and
   Lifestyles for Persons with
   Developmental Disabilities*
   (Bullock and Mahon,
   2000), 276
Lighthouse International, 58
Lighting conditions, and visual
   impairment, 57, 58
Light Motion dance company
   (Washington), 206
Likert scales, 149
Lipton, Ben, 233
Little League, 42–43
Living Skills Club, 151
L. L. Bean (catalog), 283
Longmore, P. K., 82
Loose parts, and playground
   equipment, 122–123
Lord, J., 20, 55
Lord, Michal Anne, 285
Lose, D. O., 288
Louis Harris and Associates, 9
Low physical effort, and
   Universal Design, 126

Low vision, 57, 58
Lundegren, H., 188
Lusher, R. H., 124
Lyle, Betty, 181
Lyons, R., 132, 134

Mace, R. I., 124
Macular disease, 58
Mahon, M. J., 11, 24, 38, 56–57, 62, 65, 264
Mainstreaming, 14, 23–24
Mainstreaming Activities for Youth (MAY) project (YMCA), 259
Mainstreaming Initiative (Maryland), 277, 286
Major life activities, 9. *See also* Activities
Mandates, and planning process, 134, 135
Managing Municipal Leisure Services (Lutzin, 1980), 6
Mandell, C. J., 57
Mangiacasale, A., 206
Maps, of walks and trails, 104
Martin, Casey, 9, 43, 86
Maryland, and bocce tournaments, *245,* 246. *See also* Montgomery County Mainstreaming Initiative
Massachusetts, and Education for All Handicapped Children Act, 47. *See also* Boston Marathon; Boston Sand Gardens
Matlin, Marlee, 205
McAvoy, L. H., 82, 191–192, 193, 194, 195
McCann, Caibre, 228
McClung, L. R., 236
McCormick, B., 188
McCubbin, J. A., 240
McGee, J., 144
McGhee, V. L., 64
McGill, J., 9, 55–56, 91, 92, 137
McGovern, J. N., 39, 42, 49
McGovern, T. D., 148
McGuire, F. A., 188
McKnight, J., 80
McNeil, J. M., 86
Medical classification, of athletes with disabilities, 227
Memory deficits, and brain injury, 66
Mental health professionals, 65
Mental retardation
    camping programs, 188
    selected facts, 60–61
    Special Olympics, 237, 238, 239
    tips and techniques for recreation, 61–62
Mentors, and youth-at-risk, 69
Mercer, G., 208
Miami Department of Recreation, 161–162, 174–175
Microboards, and community services, 173–174
Millar, Brett, 243
Miller, Bob, 231
Miller, K., 255
Miller, Laura, 227
Ministry for Children and Families (Canada), 170

Ministry of Social Services (Canada), 174
Minnesota. *See* Wilderness Inquiry
Mobility International (MI), 275, 296
Modification, of activities for inclusion, 140–141
Modification of the Rules of Golf for Golfers with Disabilities, A (USGA), 274
Molloy, L., 206
Monoplegia, 62
Montgomery County (Maryland) Mainstreaming Initiative, 138
Moon, M. S., 49, 132, 134
Moore, G. T., 120, 122–123
Moore, R. L., 80, 193
Motivation, and wheelchair sports programs, 236
Motor impairments, 62–63
Mountain climbing, *190,* 193, 195
Movie theaters, and Americans with Disabilities Act, 41
Multiple pyramid system, and social stratification, 265
Multiple skill levels, and playgrounds, 120
Murphy, Robert, 82, 83
Murphy, W. D., 191
Murray, George, 237
Muscular Dystrophy Association, 63, 293
Music. *See also* Arts programs
    autism, 71
    computers and assistive technology, 281
Mustonen, T., 206
Mutual interdependence, 30–31
Mutuality, and communication, 87
My Left Foot (Brown), 202

National Alliance for Accessible Golf, 274
National Association for the Deaf, 60, 293
National Association on Mental Illness, 65
National Association of Recreational Therapists (NART), 6–7, 10
National Center on Accessibility (NCA), *48,* 107, 112, 274, 286
National Center for Learning Disabilities, 62, 294
National Center on Physical Activity and Disability (NCPAD), 246, 274, 294
National Center for Traumatic Brain Injury, 66
National Cerebral Palsy Games, 236
National Collegiate Athletic Association (NCAA), 8–9, 230, 231–232
National Easter Seal Society (NESS), 27, 28, 182, 259, 294
National Endowment for the Arts (NEA), 204
National Federation for the Blind, 58

National Inclusive Camp Practices (NICP) Project, 183
National Institute for Deafness and Other Communication Disorders, 60
National Institute on Disability and Rehabilitation Research, 125, 200–201
National Institute on Recreation Inclusion (NRPA), 259, 286
National Institutes of Mental Health, 65
National Network for Child Care, 69
National Organization on Disability, 9, 77, 78, 294
National Park Service, 286, 287
National Playground Safety Institute (NPSI), 120
National Recreation and Park Association (NRPA), 10, 12, 148, 160, 259, 288
National Spinal Cord Injury Association, 63, 294
National Strategy for the Integration of Persons with Disabilities, 84
National Therapeutic Recreation Society (NTRS), 10, 12, *15,* 43, 160, 277, 294
National Wheelchair Basketball Association, 140, 230–233, 259, 297
Naugle, Mike, 246
Needs assessment, and planning process, 131–133
Negative attitudes, 29, 81
Newman, Paul, 273
New York. *See* Theatre Access Project
Noninvolvement, and continuum of services, 23
Normalization, definition of, 24–25
Normative structure, of community, 266–267
North American Free Trade Agreement (NAFTA), 49
Northeast DuPage Special Recreation Association, 276, 286
Northeast Passage, 273, 283
Northern Suburban Special Recreation Association (NSSRA), 163, *164,* 175, 285
Notice Kit, and Americans with Disabilities Act, 43

Objectives. *See also* Goals
    camping programs, 184–185
    planning process, 135
O'Connor, E. O., 236
Official NWBA Rules and Case Book, 232
Ohio. *See* Cincinnati Recreation Commission; Shaker Lakes Regional Nature Center
Oliva, G., 89
Oliver, M., 207, 208
Olympic Games, 226–227. *See also* Special Olympics

Omission, and environmental barriers, 86
Ontario
    integrated sports organizations, 227, 242–244
    Ontario Disabilities Act (ODA), 49, 50
    Ontario Ministry of Tourism and Recreation, 137
    Reach for the Rainbow, 167–168
    Theatre Ashbury, 206
Oppression, and negative attitudes, 81
Oregon School Activities Association, 229
Oregon State Track and Field Championships, 229
Orelove, F. P., 87
Organizations
    information resources for communities, 259
    web sites and addresses of selected, 292–298
Organized camping, 181
Orientation
    blindness and low vision, 58
    for volunteers, 255
Outdoor Environmental Education Program (California), 165
Outdoor recreation programs
    facility design, 100–106
    future trends, 271, 273
Outreach workers, 283
Outward Bound, 189, 191

Paciorek, M. J., 193, 225, 227, 230
Page, S. J., 236
Palaestra (journal), 258
Pantzer, B. D., 185
Paralympic Games, 225, 228, 230, 236, 244, 245–246
Paraplegia, 62
Parents. *See also* Family
    attention deficit hyperactive disorder (ADHD), 70
    autism spectrum disorder (ASD), 71
    behavior management, 144
Park, D. C., 44, 82–83
Parking, accommodations for persons with disabilities, 101–102, *113*
Parkland Health and Hospital System (Texas), 273
Parks
    checklist for accessibility, *113–115*
    facility design, 100–106
    survey on inclusion, 160
Parks & Recreation magazine, 258, 288
Participation. *See also* Barriers; Inclusion
    arts programs, 201–207
    definition of, 21
    goals of sports, 225
Participatory Action Research (PAR), 134, 146
Passenger loading zones, 102

Paternalism
    attitudinal barriers, 81–82
    language and attitudes toward
        persons with disabilities, 28
Paths, and playgrounds, 116–117.
    See also Walks and trails
Patyrala, L., 202
Pearpoint, J., 136
Peer Acceptance Survey, 151–152
Peers. *See also* Social interaction
    attention deficit hyperactive
        disorder (ADHD), 70
    youth-at-risk, 68
Pennsylvania, 41. *See also* Form
    in Art
Perceived behavioral control, 33
Perceiver, of artwork, 201
Perceptible information, and
    Universal Design, 125
Perception, and skill/challenge
    gap, 80
Performance, and Theatre
    Unlimited, 216–217
Performer, of artwork, 201
Peripheral route, to persuasive
    communication, 29
Perlman, Itzhak, 205
Perrin, A. & B., 131–132
Personal factors, in disabilities or
    activity limitations, 21
Person-centered planning,
    132–133
Personnel. *See* Human resources;
    Professional development;
    Staff and staff training
    programs; Volunteers
Persons with disabilities. *See also*
    Attitudes; Disability
    ADA definition of, 9
    camping programs, 181–189
    competitive sports, 224–230
    numbers of in U.S. and
        Canada, 9
    parking accommodations,
        101–102
    use of term, 56
    as volunteers, 255, 284
    web sites and addresses of
        selected organizations,
        292–294
Persuasive communication, 29–30
Peters, S., 207–208
Peterson, C., 227, 228
Philadephia Museum of Art, 218
Phoenix, T., 255
Physical accessibility, 25, 97
Physical dependency, 79–80
Picnic areas, and facility design,
    106, *113–114*
Pierce, J. T., 56
Pittsburgh Architects Workshop,
    123, 124
PLAE, Inc., 97–98, 118
Planned behavior, theory of,
    31–32, 33
Planning process, for programs.
    See also Service and facility
    planning
    evaluation, 144–152
    goals of, 130–31, 135
    implementation, 135–144
    mandates, policies, and
        objectives, 133–135

needs assessment, 131–133
persons with HIV or AIDS, 67
youth-at-risk, 68
Plath, Sylvia, 205
Playfields, and facility design,
    107–108
Playground for All Children, A
    (U.S. Government Printing
    Office, 1978), 118
Playgrounds
    Americans with Disabilities
        Act, 43
    facility design, 112, 115–124
    future trends, 283
"PlayTurf," 119
Pluralistic or accordant power
    community, 265–266
Poetry, and arts programs, 208,
    212, 213, 214
Poitevin, J., 201
Policy
    planning process, 134–135
    transportation for persons with
        disabilities, 84
Pomeroy, Janet, 165, 254
Population
    aging, 63
    deafness and hearing loss, 59
    mental retardation, 60
    persons with disabilities, 9, 57
    psychological disorders, 64
Positive reinforcement, and
    behavior management,
    143–144
Powell, L. G., 13–14
Power, and social structure of
    community, 265–266.
    See also Empowerment
Prentke Romich Company, 281
Presentations, and changing
    attitudes, 30
President's Committee on
    Employment of People with
    Disabilities, 26
Prevalence, of autism, 70
Prevent Blindness American, 57
Prevention education, and
    AIDS, 67
Priorities, and overcoming
    barriers, 89–90
Procedural/operational
    adaptations, 141
Professional Crisis Management
    Association, 144
Professional development,
    286–288. *See also* Staff and
    staff training programs
Professional field experiences, for
    college students, 257–258
Professional Golf Association
    (PGA), 9, 43, 86, 274
Program accessibility, 25, 278.
    See also Recreation
    programs
Project Adventure, 192
Project CARE (Continuum of
    Adapted Recreation
    Education), 162
Project LIFE (Life Is For
    Everyone), 255
Project STAR (Staff Training for
    Adapted Recreation),
    161–162

Props, for play, 122
Protective factors, and
    youth-at-risk, 68
Provenzo, E. F., 280
Psychological dependency, 79–80
Psychological disorders, 64–65
Psychosocial benefits, of
    wheelchair sports, 236
Public awareness
    arts programs, 205–206
    wheelchair sports
        programs, 236
Publicity, and accessibility of
    programs, 89
Public recreation and parks
    departments, 6. *See also*
    Community recreation
Public transportation, 264
Punishment, and behavior
    management, 144

Quadriplegia, 62
Quigley, M., 84

Railings, and playgrounds, 118
Ramps
    parking areas, 102, *103*
    playgrounds, 117
    recreation buildings, 109, *114*
Ray, M. T., 39, 81, 146, 147,
    257, 278
RCH, Inc. (California), 164–165,
    175, 254
Reach for the Rainbow (Ontario),
    167–168, 175
Reaching, from wheelchair, 100
Reading, and low vision, 58
Receptive blocks, to
    communication, 87
Recognition, of volunteers,
    255, 256
Recreation, inclusive and special.
    See Community and
    community recreation;
    Inclusive recreation;
    Leisure; Recreation
    buildings; Recreation
    programs; Recreation
    services; Recreation
    therapists; Service and
    facility planning; Special
    recreation; Therapeutic
    recreation
"Recreation Ability Burlington"
    (Canada), 132
Recreation Access
    Advisory Committee
    (Access Board), 98
Recreation buildings, and facility
    design, 108–112, *114*
Recreation Integration Victoria
    (British Columbia),
    168–171, 175
Recreation Inventory for
    Inclusive Participation
    (RIPP), 147–148
*Recreation Programming
    for Visually Impaired
    Children and Youth*
    (Kelley, 1981), 259
Recreation programs
    arts, 201–220
    camps and camping, 181–189

competitive sports, 224–246
future approaches to services
    and, 277–279
future trends, 271–277
planning process, 67, 68,
    130–152
wilderness-adventure
    programs, 189–195
Recreation services, and
    therapeutic recreation, 11
*Recreation and Special
    Populations* (Stein &
    Sessoms, 1977), 12
Recreation therapists, 6–7.
    See also Therapeutic
    recreation specialists
Reeve, Christopher, 91
Refreshments, and dietary
    requirements of persons with
    AIDS, 67
Rehabilitation Act of 1973,
    44–45, 48, 98, 261
Rehabilitation Act of 1978, 46
Rehabilitation Act Amendment of
    1974, 45
Rehabilitation acts and
    amendments, 44–46
Rehabilitation Comprehensive
    Services and Developmental
    Disabilities Amendments, 48
Rehabilitation Institute of
    Chicago (RIC), 274
Rehabilitation Services
    Administration (RSA), 44
Rehearsal, and Theatre
    Unlimited, 215–216
Reid, G., 240
Relative skills, and essential
    eligibility, 42
ReMed Recovery Care Centers
    (Pennsylvania), 277
Rental programs, for
    equipment, 283
Residency, and essential
    eligibility, 42
Resiliency, and youth-at-risk, 68
Resources, definition of, 253.
    See also Community and
    community recreation
Rest rooms, and recreation
    buildings, 111–112, *115*
Retinitis pigmentosa, 58
Returned curb, 102, *103*
Reverse integration, and
    competitive sports, 226
Reverse mainstreaming,
    23, 279
Reynolds, R., 278
Right to leisure, and NTRS
    Position Statement
    (1997), *15*
Rimmer, J. H., 84–85
Ripp, Christina, 224
Robb, G. M., 11–12, 188
Robinson, F. M., 184
Roche, David, 208
Roehner, B. G., 200, 209
Role playing
    attitude change, 29–30
    staff training, 187–188
Rosenhan, D. L., 56
Rosenthal, R., 55
Ross, M., 209

Royal and Ancient Golf Club of St. Andrews, Scotland, 274
Rubin, S. S., 85
Rules and regulations barriers, 86
Rynders, J. E., 22, 132, 138, 142, 194, 206

Sable, J., 91, 137, 183
Safety
    deafness and hearing loss, 59
    essential eligibility, 42
    playgrounds, 118–120
St. Peter, S., 138
Sand, and beaches, 106
Sandhu, J. S., 124
San Francisco Recreation and Park Department, 164–165
Scenarios, and staff training, 187
Schaefer, S., 220
Schleien, S. J., 22, 23, 29, 39, 81, 82, 132, 146, 147, 151, 194, 195, 206, 255, 257, 264, 276, 278, 279, 287
Schools. See also Colleges and universities; Education
    leisure education in, 276
    Special Olympics and partnerships with, 240
Schurke, P., 194–195
Seating areas
    playfields, 108
    playgrounds, 118–119
Segregation and segregated programs
    camping, 182–183
    competitive sports, 225–226
    wilderness adventure programs, 195
Self-advocacy, 25–26
Self-concept. See also Self-esteem
    arts programs, 203–204
    camping programs, 188–189
    labeling, 56
    social ineffectiveness, 79
Self-determination, and community services, 172–173
Self-discovery, and arts programs, 202
Self-esteem, and youth-at-risk, 68. See also Self-concept
Self-fulfilling prophecy, and labeling, 55–56
Seligmann, D., 195
Senate Committee on Human Resources, 46
Sensory stimulation, and playgrounds, 120–121
Service broker, and self-determination, 172–173
Service and facility planning barriers, 77–92
    design of accessible and usable environments, 97–126
    examples of community services, 160–175
    planning process, 130–152
Sessoms, H. D., 12, 253, 265
Sessoms, H. G., 5
Setlow, Pete & Barbara, 212–213
Settlement-house movement, 5

Sexuality, changing views toward, 282–283
Shaiken, H., 80
Shaker Lakes Regional Nature Center (Ohio), 105
Shapiro, D. R., 241
Shaw, R., 210
Shepley, S. G., 188
Shock absorbency, of playground surfacing, 119
Showers, and rest rooms in recreation buildings, 112
Shriver, Eunice Kennedy, 237–238, 240
Sick roles, and negative attitudes, 29
Sighted guides, 58
Signage
    park and outdoor recreation areas, 101
    recreation buildings, 110
Sign language, 59
Silverberg, K., 256–257
Simonson, A., 89
Simple and intuitive use, and Universal Design, 125
Siperstein, G. N., 240, 241–242
Size and space for approach and use, and Universal Design, 126
Skiing, 139, 140
Skill/challenge gap, and intrinsic barriers, 80
Skills
    arts program and development of, 204–205
    playgrounds and multiple levels, 120
Skinner, S. S., 184
Sledge hockey, 271
Slides, and playgrounds, 123–124
Smith, Jean Kennedy, 217
Smith, R. W., 22, 27, 28, 115, 120, 226
Sobsey, D., 87
Social accessibility, of programs, 89
Social capital, and volunteering, 256–257
Social groups, and communities, 264–265
Social ineffectiveness, as intrinsic barrier, 79
Social interaction. See also Peers
    aging, 64
    arts programs, 206–207
    autism, 70
Social norms
    abnormal behavior, 64
    attitudes toward persons with disabilities, 31
Social Rehabilitation Act, 261
Social Security Act for Aid to Families with Dependent Children, 261
Social services agencies, and transportation, 264
Social skills
    attention deficit hyperactive disorder (ADHD), 70
    brain injury, 65
    intrinsic barriers, 79
    mental retardation, 62

Social support
    approaches to building, 139
    overcoming barriers, 91–92
Social welfare subsystem, of community, 266
Society for the Advancement of Travel for the Handicapped (SATH), 275
Sociocultural variables, of communities, 264–267
Socioeconomic status
    community structure, 264–267
    learning impairments, 61
    youth-at-risk, 68
Sociogram Evaluation Graphing Form, 151
Soft Contained Play Equipment (SCPE), 121–122
Soli, P., 22
Space requirements, and facility design, 98–100, 126
Speakeasy, 281
Special Music by Special People All Star Band (Illinois), 206
Special needs coordinator, 137–138
Special Olympics International, 229, 297
Special Olympics, 225, 237–242, 259
Special populations, definition of, 22
Special Programs and Populations Branch, of National Park Service, 287
Special recreation. See also Recreation, inclusive and special
    definition of, 22
    relationship of therapeutic recreation to, 10–12
    use of term, 12
Speck, G., 219–220
Speech recognition systems, 281
Sport for Disabled–Ontario (SDO), 227
Sportime Abilitations (catalog), 283
Sports. See also Paralympic Games; Special Olympics
    bocce, 244–246
    classification of athletes with disabilities, 227–228
    community recreation, 228–229
    competitive programs, 229–230
    contact information for selected organizations, 295–298
    future program trends, 273–274
    goals of participation, 225
    history of programs for persons with disabilities, 224–225
    segregation vs. inclusion, 225–226
    vertical integration, 226–227
    wheelchairs, 230–237, 246
Sports and Recreation for the Disabled: A Resource Handbook (Paciorek & Jones, 2001), 225

Sports 'n Spokes (journal), 258
Staff and staff training programs. See also Supervision; Volunteers
    arts programs, 210
    camping programs, 186–188
    community services, 168, 170–171, 257
    future trends, 286–288
    inclusion, 137
    volunteers, 256
Stainback, S. & W., 151
Stairs, and recreation buildings, 109, 114–115. See also Steps
Statement on Inclusion (NTRS, 1997), 10, 15
Steadward, R. D., 227, 228, 236, 237
Stein, T. A., 12
Steinfeld, E., 124–125
Steps, and swimming pools, 107. See also Stairs
Stereotypes
    labeling, 55
    older persons, 63
Stevenson, J. L., 5
Stone, C. F., 279
Strategy identification, and staff training, 188
Strauss, D., 277
Subjective norms, and beliefs, 33
Substance abuse, 64, 68
Subsystems, of community, 266
Sumerian civilization (3000–1500 B.C.), 224
Summer camps, 273
Summers, Laureen, 204
Sun exposure, and playgrounds, 119
Super Switch Ensemble, 281
Supervision. See also Leadership; Staff and staff training programs
    brain injury, 66
    leadership competencies, 14
    mental retardation and learning impairments, 62
Surfacing, of playgrounds, 119
Swift, Dixie, 219
Swimming pools, and facility design, 106–107
Swings, and playgrounds, 120, 124
Sygall, Susan, 86
Sylvester, C., 25, 288
Sylvestre, J. C., 91
Szychowski, E., 79

TAB (temporarily able-bodied), 28
Tabourne, C. E. S., 132, 287
Tactile warning signals, and stairs, 109
Taxes and taxation, and financial resources for communities, 260
Taylor, A. R., 91
Teague, M. L., 64
Technology, and wheelchair sports, 237
Telecommunication device for the deaf (TDD), 281

Telephones
  checklist for accessibility, *114*
  deafness and hearing loss,
    59–60
  outdoor recreation areas,
    106, *114*
Ten percent (10%) rule, and
  Special Olympics,
  239–240
Texas. *See* Turning POINT
Text-to-speech (TTS)
  synthesis, 281
Textured Life, A (Pedlar et al.,
  1999), 173
Theatre Access Project (TAP)
  (New York), 220
Theatre Ashbury (Ontario), 206
Theatre Unlimited (California),
  165, 210, 213–217
Therapeutic recreation
  future trends, 279, 286–287
  history of, 6–7
  relationship of special
    recreation to, 10–12
Therapeutic Recreation
  Directory, 152
*Therapeutic Recreation
  Journal*, 258
Therapeutic Recreation
  Specialists, 163. *See also*
  Recreation therapists
Thiboutot, A., 226
Thompson, D., 118
Ticket booths, and playfields,
  107–108
Timber slides, 123–124
Time-out procedures, 144
Today Show, The (television), 225
Tolerance for error, and Universal
  Design, 125–126
Tomlinson, R., 202–203
Touch the Top of the World
  (Weihenmayer, 2002), 193
Training, of staff. *See also*
  Education
  arts programs, 210
  camping programs, 186–188
  community services, 168,
    170–171
  inclusion, 137
  volunteers, 255–256
Transfer platforms, and
  playgrounds, 117–118
Transient lodging, and facility
  design, 110–11, *115*
Transitional Training Program
  (Miami), 162
Transportation. *See also* Parking
  barriers, 83–84
  community resources, 264
Travelin' Talk, 275
Travel programs, 274–76
TREATS (camping program),
  183–184
Trowbridge, J., 245

Trust, and wilderness-adventure
  programs, 191
Turning platforms, of ramps, 109
Turning POINT (Texas), 189,
  192, 195, 273, 297
Tweedy, S. M., 228

Undue burden or hardship, and
  Americans with Disabilities
  Act, 43, 44
Unified Sports program, of
  Special Olympics, 240
United Cerebral Palsy, 63, 294
United Nations, Universal
  Declaration of Human
  Rights, 200
United States. *See individual
  states and agencies*;
  legislation
U.S. Access Board. *See* Access
  Board
U. S. Association for Blind
  Athletes, 229, 297
U. S. Cerebral Palsy Athletic
  Association, 229, 230,
  236, 273
U. S. Deaf Sports Federation,
  229, 297
U.S. Department of Justice, 41
U.S. Department of
  Transportation, 83, 84
U.S. Disabled Athletes Fund
  Incorporated, 273–274
U.S. Disabled Cycling, 227
U.S. Forest Service, 286
U.S. Golf Association
  (USGA), 274
U.S. Olympic Committee
  (USOC), 230
U.S. Postal Service, 45
Universal accessibility, 25, 97
Universal Declaration of Human
  Rights (United Nations), 201
Universal Design, 124–126
*Universal Playground: A
  Planning Guide, The*
  (Province of British
  Columbia, 1990), 112
Universal Program Participation
  Model (UPPM), 194–195
Universal Trail Assessment and
  Mapping Process
  (UTAP), 104–105
Universities. *See* Colleges and
  universities
University of Illinois, 30
University of Indiana, 188
University of North Carolina, 255
Usability, definition of, 97
USA Cycling Team, 227

van As, H. H. J., 236
van der Woude, L. H. V., 236
Variety, and playgrounds,
  122–123

Vaughan, J. L., 259–60, 264
Vela Housing Society (British
  Columbia), 173–174
Vela Microboard Association
  (British Columbia), 174, 175
Vertical integration, and
  competitive sports, 226–27
Victoria Integration Society
  (British Columbia), 169
Vinton, D. A., 185
Virtual reality (VR), 282
Visual acuity and visual field, 57
Visual impairments. *See also*
  Blindness
  facility design, 100, 101, 104
  signage, 101
  walks and trails, 104
Voelkl, J. E., 25, 288
Voeltz, L. M., 151
*Volunteer Connections: Creating
  an Accessible and Inclusive
  Environment* (Volunteer
  Canada, 2001), 255
Volunteers. *See also* Staff and
  staff training programs
  community resources, 254–257
  future trends, 284
  inclusion, 138–139
  Reach for the Rainbow
    program, 168
VSA arts, 202, 204, 207,
  210–211, 217–218

Wakefield, D., 82
Walker-McConnell Assessment,
  150–151
Walks and trails, and facility
  design, 102–105, *113*.
  See also Paths
Walsh, C., 236
Walt Disney Company, 8
Washington. *See* Light Motion
  Dance Company
Water-related areas, and facility
  design, 106–107, *114*
Weaving, and arts programs, 204
Web sites
  Access Board, 98, 112, 124
  AIDS and HIV, 67
  arts programs, 219, 220
  behavior problems, 144
  blindness and low vision, 58
  brain injury, 66
  community services, 174–175
  contact information for
    selected, 292–298
  deafness and hearing loss, 60
  mental retardation and learning
    impairments, 62
  motor impairments, 63
  psychological disorders and
    behavioral disorders, 65
  Special Olympics, 237
  sports programs, 230, 233
  youth-at-risk, 69

Weihenmayer, Erik, 193
Wellman, Mark, 193
Wells, C. L., 235
WeMedia, Inc., 237
West Suburban Special
  Recreation Association
  (Chicago), 286
Wheelchairs
  basketball, 140, 230–233, *235*
  bocce, 246
  dimensional requirements for
    facility design, 98–100
  Ibot assistive device, 282
  playgrounds, 117–118
  seating areas of playfields, 108
  sports programs, 230–237, 246
  walks and trails, 103–104
Wheelchair Sports USA, 230,
  233–37, 298
"When You Meet a Handicapped
  Person," 90
White, C., 188
White House Conference on
  Handicapped Individuals
  (1977), 45
Whittaker, Tom, 193
Wiele, K., 131–132
Wilder, S., 131–132
Wilderness-Adventure programs,
  189–195
Wilderness Inquiry (Minnesota),
  189, 193, 194, 273,
  276, 298
Wilhite, B., 24
Wilkinson, R. E., 184
Williams, B., 263, 271
Williams, D. P., 240
Winslow, R., 259–260, 264
Winter Paralympic Games, 224
Wolfensberger, W., 24
Women, and wheelchair
  basketball programs, 233
Wonder, Stevie, 205
Workshops, and Theatre
  Unlimited, 217
World Bank, 256
World Health Organization
  (WHO), 20–22
Wright, B. A., 79

YMCA, 259
Yost, E. J., 206
Youth. *See also* Children
  wheelchair sports programs,
    233, 234, 236
  recreation programs for youth-
    at-risk, 67–69

Zajonc, R. B., 30
Zeigler, Earle, 224
Zero-depth entry, and swimming
  pools, 107
Zero exclusion, 279
Zola, I. K., 80